Press Reports:

Ronayne writes with the confidence of a man who
The revelations given by the statements in this bool
be rational and self evident. Or is this also an illusic

If you didn't know the difference between a Derri.
Bowie knife, then you will find this magician will conjure up an image that an assassin can strike with an invisible illusion and still hit his target.

Jane's Fighting Weapons

This American Civil War Epic, even if it doesn't add up, will still set your pants on Fire. I 'wuz' gutted.

The Sum

This fine writer has opened our minds to the possibility of an alternative explanation as to how and why President Lincoln was assassinated and even dares to suggest it was not John Wilkes Booth. This is bound to raise some fierce debate from legitimate American historians. Will they counter his thrusts and parries successfully? Or will they lunge, in a counter attack?

The Gardian

This forceful author seems to create his own illusions within a parody of delusions. The biggest illusion is time itself, in this magical journey through relativity, that frequently upsets history with a big bang. Then, a coincidental disturbance on the event horizon, causes Alice in the Looking Glass, to disappear through a galactic black hole.

The Old Scientist

We are all magicians behind the retina of our eyes when we are forced to look and see the illusions. This genie show's us how it's done, multiplying our images in his journey through time.

The Time's Times

John Wilkes Booth created an image in the mirror of a devil inspired. This magical and reflective writer reflects this image back to the public turning him into a saint. Is this another Catholic plot? Or just another refractive shimmer in the mirage?

The Mirrror

Nothing but tripe from beginning to end. There were too many twists and turns. I was led astray after the seventh chapter and lost all sense of the plot. And I would have preferred to find out how America beat the British in their War of Independence in 1776, than just another endless tale of the American Civil War, 89 years later.

The Independence

If it were a crossword I could complete it in my coffee break. There were that many signals, it was easy to solve. And it so happens you don't even have to learn the Morse Code.

The Telegraph

If you ever get the feeling your being programmed and watched all the time , then don't worry your not being paranoid, we all are.

The Watchmen

It takes half a second for an assassin to fall 11 feet according to Newton but if you missed it, it never happened, because it was only a relative instant in time, according to Einstein.

Time Clock Magazine

This is a must for all peoples if they can grasp its significance.

Venus The Morning and Evening Star

This book implies that all Scotsmen belong to a clan. It fails to impress any of our rights, north of the border.

The Scotsmen

This book is not for the feint hearted but neither is it for the dedicated psycho-path.

The Male on Sunday

Observation and Deduction is what this book is all about but even Sherlock Holmes did not have any where near as many enemies. And the fiendish Professor Moriarty is not a patch on the treacherous General Baker.

The Observers

It would seem that the biggest lesson from this adventure in illusion is not only to look well, but to listen well for correct English.

The Listeners

After reading the true account about the missing '18' pages you will laugh your socks off in the cinema next year, and in your cab on the way home.

The Chromicle

If you want to know how John Wilkes Booth made a pile of money without losing his head then read this book and become a rich man.

The Finical Times

The problem with this historical account is one becomes confused as to who is writing it. Is it J.K.R., L.B., Phinias Camp Headley or perhaps even John Milton?

The Book Cub

Written with the passion of the man who inspired it, the passion of John Wilkes Booth.

The People's Republic

You will need to be more than a spectator in this gripping drama you will need to be the stage hand, the actor, the theatre audience as well as the Greek Chorus. And who said traitors were illiterate?

The Spectrator

If your hard up, don't play the lottery, take a gamble on this book.

The Economy

I was doing alright until I got to Edgar Allen Poe and his ciphers and thought puzzles, which led me right up the garden path. So I got frustrated and watched a film called 'The Pit and the Pendulum' starring Vincent Price instead, which was far more graphic. At least Poe was a genuine Victorian poet and author, but sadly died a pauper.

The Illustrate

If George Orwell had left wing sympathies, but created works of fiction and still had Militant Intelligence worried, what are they to do with an author who recreates history, according to the facts? Banish him to Lilliputia, Narnia or Never, Never land or string him up as an example for Democracy? Let him rest assured we will defend him.

Daily Expresss

This prattle faced, self seeking, sanctimonious, new kid on the block, self styled impresario and so called writer seems to imply that the North carried out a systematic whole-sale slaughter on the South, going around plundering cotton and tobacco, and burning down all of their Capitols and committing national fratricide at will, in order to suit the ends of some mythical figment of his acerbic and mordant imagination. Why doesn't he grow up and leave politics to those who know what is best for the people and the world?

The New Amsterdam Times

Written with style and flair although he's a bit out of date in his knowledge of Washington.

The Washinton Post

Mr. Ronayne should leave his sucking up to black people alone, we are a much stronger political force than he thinks and we can defend are own corner, and fire a rifle more accurate than he. One quarter of our military boys are black and proud to fly the banner at all times. We are darned sure to God, it was Mr. Lincoln who formed our first 'coloured' regiment. What has Ronayne done for his country? Shoot his mouth off?

Dallass Times

I was only a little surprised to learn that John Wilkes Booth was a great actor with passion and love, and not just a so called anti - black crazed 'assassin' come stunt man. This writer strongly implies that his real purpose in trying to kidnap the President was to seek an exchange of prisoners, who were starving and dying of hunger and disease, in both the North and the South. And that it was so much unnecessary suffering on a Global scale, and that it would have made no difference to the outcome of the war, since we would have won anyway.

The Chicago Tribute

Nightmare on Elm Street in the Land of the Un-dead. Yes, the illuminati control us all now with their splints for legs and chips for brains. And next stop Iran - for more dead wood.

Woody Woodpecker's Song

This pseudo-surreal existentialist seems to imply, in this Hans Christian Anderson fairy tale book of his, that the real killer of President Lincoln was the Supposed Assassin of the Supposed Assassin of Lincoln, except he was not a Marylander, but an Englishman. This is so bizarre he must think America sells oil to Arabia.

The Cincinnati Herold

I wanted to learn about the American Civil War and who shot the President, but I had to wade through the abstract poetry of John Milton, the fairy tales of Hans Christian Anderson and the cryptic puzzles of Edgar Allen Poe to get there.

The St. Louis Blues

Now we have another so called Englishman who thinks America is a playground for his artistic whims and outmoded imaginations. May we respectfully remind him that our country is a target for easy criticism, yet millions of people have flocked to our shores to improve their standard of life, and to seek freedom for all their endeavours. And no country can match our 'Know How' and our Advanced Technology. If he dare's to come over here again we'll clip his wings and plant a Silicon chip in his brain, so that he will know what real Democracy is all about.

The Los Angels Times

What little you know about geography will be updated in this round the world tour. Except you will need an army compass, field glasses and an ordinance survey map to navigate, plus a bottle of bourbon in case you fall from your horse. And throw in two carbines and seven revolvers in case you get accosted by the army.

Views of the World

The speed of a bullet moves at near hyper-velocity. You will have to move faster than this to keep up with the time frames in this exciting re-run of the old classic 'I Shot The Sheriff', sung by Bob Marley and Eric Clapton. Indeed, Wild Bill Hickock was a pussycat compared to Johnny Corbett. And Jim Bowie had nothing on Wilkes Booth.

Ballistics Magazine

We all trust our doctors and surgeons to heal our weaknesses and injuries. You will think twice before your next operation having read about the skills of the Surgeon General.

The Medicine Journal

This gentleman has written a book which condemns Victorian values and ridicules Northern morality, yet favours the South's culture. Perhaps he ought to spend some time in the deep South and learn what real life is all about. He will find his English won't match the ready repartee of straight talking Southerners, who will bite his head off, if he mentions a word about our American way of life.

Live Magazine

Grant was a 'brilliant General' and put on the back of the Federal dollar. Lincoln printed US greenbacks and saved the Union but they put a hole in the back of him.

Fed-Up Reserve

It's time this chap got things straight. He should stick to his own subject and put his mind where is mouth is. Einstein rode on a light beam from Switzerland to America and proved he could return here any time, without getting any older. Perhaps this chap could do the same but be fortunate enough to get bent into a black hole, before he gets here. Then, this flying Peter Pan won't get any younger, as there just ain't any politics or history to worry about in a black hole.

The Fourth Dimension Magazine

I was surprised to learn that John Wilkes never had a diary, let alone him having lost '18 missing pages,' which are in fact 28 missing pages.

The Baltimore Echo

If you read this book you will have a totally new concept of the fairy tale ballet of Hans Christian Anderson. You will find out not only why the vain and bold young girl put on the fairy's red shoes and couldn't stop dancing, until she chopped her feet off. Indeed you will see that 'Red Shoes' got very cold feet and never put them on at all, but was rewarded anyway by being plain and wise, and by spinning a good yarn instead.

The Copenhagen Legend

In 1993 Clint Eastwood made a film that simulated a re-run of a modern day assassination using an assassin with the code name of John Booth (John Malkovich) and he drew up his psychological profile. The scenario was exactly the same, one lone assassin against the combined intelligence of Washington, the FBI and the ZIA. They all ran rings around each other and stumbling until they accidentally cottoned on, but the assassin of course had the 'brains and military genius of Booth' outwitting them easily from behind every lamp post. The paranoia matches the 'brilliance of Booth' and reinforces the image of the lone assassin, reinforcing the mythology of the illuminati, by the image of singular genius - the threat from without, appearing to outwit the combined legions of chaos, and thus side-lining the real threat from within. In any other culture it would be a comedy - of errors. Even the actors (except Malkovich) were laughing with straight faces, at the expense of a late great fellow actor- John Wilkes Booth.

Psychological Mysteries in the Wiring Line

I 'waz' totally 'gob smacked.'

Punch and Judy Magazine

If the average American could only stop and wait for the moment of truth, to wipe the hype, then they could become what they truly feel in their innermost hearts, in an instant, a real winner. The same goes for all of us, at any decent level.

Anon

It will take a century for the message to penetrate the mystery and mythology of our culture, if there are many left to read or understand correct English.

Nostradamus.

Our American Hero

A Tale of The

American Civil War

by

JK Ronayne

For
Anil
A Splendid fellow
in Recruitment
Best Wishes
Jack Ronayne

FOUNTAIN
MUSIC UK

First Published in Great Britain
by Fountain Music UK in 2007

Copyright © JK Ronayne 2007

All Rights Reserved.
This book is sold subject to the
copyright act to date 2007 and should not be reproduced
in any other format subject to these rules
without the Author's permission.

jkron@hotmail.co.uk

Mobile: Text to 07895040604

A CIP catalogue record for this book
is available from The British Library.
Also available from the Library of Congress,
Trinity College, Dublin
Birmingham, Oxford, Cambridge & Harvard Universities.
University of Richmond, Virginia
The Open University
And Birmingham Public Library

ISBN
978-0-9557522-0-9 Our American Hero paperback
978-0-9557522-1-6 Our American Hero hardback

Printed in England by ADVEK
47, Lower Tower St.,
Newtown
Birmingham
England.

To:

Anna Mae

And

In loving Memory

Of Kathleen

Contents

		Page
Forward		6
Prologue		7
Introduction		10
Chapter 1	Facts and the Meaning of History	12
Chapter 2	Abraham Lincoln and his Faith	18
Chapter 3	John Wilkes Booth and His Letters	27
Chapter 4	Dr. Samuel Alexander Mudd and his Valour	57
Chapter 5	John Surratt and his Lectures	68
Chapter 6	Lewis Payne, his Bravery and his Defence	78
Chapter 7	The Master's of Illusion	91
Chapter 8	A Scenario of Strange Circumstances	114
Chapter 9	Events in the Theatre	135
Chapter 10	Probability v Illusion	154
Chapter 11	The Real Scenario	171
Chapter 12	Pandemonium and More Illusions	174
Chapter 13	The Great Escape	176
Chapter 14	The Journey	182
Chapter 15	The Crossing of the Potomac and Rappahannock Rivers	187

Chapter 16 Ruggles Encounters Boyd at The River 190

Chapter 17 The Siege at Garrett's Barn 197

Chapter 18 The Autopsy on the Montauk 216

Chapter 19 The Macabre Burial in the Arsenal 222

Chapter 20 The Final Trail 226

Chapter 21 Booth's Second Death and his Resurrection 233

Chapter 22 The Strange Case of David E. Herold & the Confederate 237

Epilogue Andrew Johnson 249

Appendix I The Prosecution and Defence of Edward Spangler 250

Appendix II The Hanging of Mary Surratt 257

Appendix III References and Bibliography 258

Acknowledgements 259

About the Author 260

Illustrations

Alexander the Great 6

Adam Weishaupt 8

Master's of Illusion 8

The Dying President's Assault Course 17

President Lincoln 18

A Speech outside the White House 26

John Wilkes Booth 27

The Farm at Belair 29

John's Letter to Asia 33

Baker's Handiwork 38

The Writing of Wilkes Booth 40

Edwin Booth and Edwina 48

William Tell and Son 56

Matthew Henson First Man to Reach the North Pole 56

Doctor of Healing 57

Dr. Mudd's House 59

Straight from the Horses Mouth 60

This Man from Pennsylvania 62

The Wound is already Mortal 63

Edman Spangler saved Dr. Mudd 65

Friend of John Surratt 67

He Ventured Much but Lost His Mother's Heart 68

Captain William E. Doster 77

He Was their Bravest Soldier 78

Red Shoes. 80
Seward - Kenai Peninsula Alaska. Seward's wife Frances

The Froth Rises To the Top 91

Her Faith in God did not Falter 93

My English was not Perfect 97

The Hanging of an Innocent Woman 99

A Man of Few Words 107

Stanton's Version of the News 113

Judge Holt Master of War 117

Seward 1861.
Seward's House and Judge Elijah Miller's House 120

A Tall Man Ran Across the Stage 139

The 'Assassin' and His Twin Pursuer 140

The Beautiful Picture in Mary's House 147

The Navy Bridge that Tyson Crossed 153

Ford Theatre circa 1868 and its Location on Tenth Street near The White House 153

The Girl with The Golden Eye 156

The Supposed Route of Booth 157

Boston's Dug Out 165

Boston - Forever Amber 167

The Talented Laura Keene 173

General Ulysses S Grant 175

The Dummy Escape Route 184

The Two Decoy Detectives cross the Potomac in Mr. Jones' Boat 187

Sunset on the Beautiful Rappahannock River 191

Buffalo Bill a Man of Action 196

Baker Circles a Ten Mile Dragnet 198

War Department 20th April - No Mention of a Lame Booth 200

The Troopers Comfort Their Dying Rebel Brother 206

Stanton's Account to the New York Times 213

Jim Bowie and his Knife 215

Surgeon General Barnes Probes the Unknown Soldier's Brain 219

The Return on the Montauk 221

The Macabre Burial of the Unknown Soldier 223

At the Start of the Victorian Period and the Argand Oil Lamp 225

Updated Wanted Posters from Baker 227

'Herold' prior to Hanging 232

Brilliant Izola L. Forrester and Dastardly Finus L. Bates with his Mummy 236

Samuel Arnold - A Man of Principle and Honour 237

Herold - First and Second Take 238

The Extra Man and the Thin Blue Line 239

Herold's Weeping Sisters 240

Unidentified Man on the Saugus and Michael O'Laughlin 242

Tragic Mary and Brave Lewis 243

Andrew Johnson 249

FORWARD

If the book becomes a challenge it is because of the amount of mystery and mythology you will have to penetrate

However if you persevere you will find that

If you can eliminate the improbable then what is left becomes probable

Then you will find there is no mystery at all, just infinite chaos resolved

If sometimes you find tragic irony, you will experience the same sense of loss and helplessness in providence that we all do

But the reward is given in the objective truth

Enlightenment is the dawning of man's conscious mind

356- 323 BC. Alexander the Great in Battle against Persia.

Prologue

There has been a lot of interest lately in the year of our lord 2007 concerning the assassination of Abraham Lincoln 14th April 1865. Indeed, some sites on the internet have hit the 10 million mark, it shows how passionate people are and many are totally baffled by the events surrounding his death. This book through a process of logical reproductions intends to recreate the probable circumstances, using the essential facts and then proceed to certain unavoidable conclusions starting from the witnesses and trial statements, the lectures of John Surratt, Booth's letters, the diary, names and places, site visits, internet and library research, location, events, insight and finally by observation and deduction to work out the method of assassination and its true perpetrators.

The strongest peace of evidence giving me the real key to what actually happened on stage that terrible night, was given to me through the statement by the stage hand Ed Spangler. It was written in his own hand for his own defence, and found in his toolbox months after his death by Dr. Mudd. This statement gave one vital clue which made the truth suddenly unfold before me, and the rest followed as a logical consequence.

In this book I make frequent reference to the name of an 18th century mystical sect founded in Bavaria by a Jesuit trained novice called Adam Weishaupt. It stemmed from the Alumbrados of Spain and included Moorish and Jewish converts but was a practising secret sect in fear of the Inquisition, where even the very wealthy could be deprived or imprisoned by the Church. The Illuminati based its philosophy very loosely around the concept and deeds of Lucifer the fallen angel, as a counterpoint. Lucifer is aptly described in biblical literature and in John Milton's poem of 'Paradise Lost' and indeed is probably the very re-incarnation of Satan. Lucifer is construed as having certain powers of light to illuminate the way for those mortals on earth who choose to follow his path. Although this light is feeble compared to God's, it is strong enough for these erstwhile 'Master's of Illusion' and can grow even more powerful, when tapped by those deviant masters who find out the secret of its source.

The problem is that God can extinguish this light whenever he chooses but allows it to continue, in order to provide total freedom of thought, to all his higher beings such as in his gifted angels and man. It is in his God however, that Lucifer had struck on the idea of an apparent weakness such that it was possible to gain more freedom by choosing a different path. Hence the profit or son of God, Jesus in Christian literature, had to say 'I am the way, the truth and the light' in order to lead the true way to the father and not the path to evil. It seemed from this in a Christian sense that the supreme creator did find it necessary to allow another path; in order to provide total freedom of creativity and thought, in his creatures; so they could evolve further in his all embracing light, than in his less mentally well endowed animals. This in a sense is to show that God was able to create a perfect universe though seemingly flawed, where all things are possible even chaos, which can lead to evil, from which he created it.

Johann Adam Weishaupt

1748 - 1830

Master's of Illusion

The Symbolic expression of Secret Power in the Light and all Seeing Eye of Esoteric meaning and of Masonic and Mystical Egyptian Origins

Lucifer's light is very strange however in that it appears to give its followers much more craft and power than God's own true believers, such that indeed Lucifer seems to have greater powers on earth than God, at least in the short term. However if Lucifer's powers within the evil one, are undone by anyone of God's creatures, then they will become cast down under a great moral destruction, as God's foot crushes upon the serpents head, and they are miserably cast down to their own hell on earth; where they are suddenly confronted with the guilt and abject horror of all there past deeds, buried in their souls. And without the spirit of God's will, all is seemingly lost. However if we try to interpret the practical or pragmatical sense of purpose and meaning of this historical sect called the illuminati, it does appear that it was propagated like many other breakaway sects to gain independence and influence over other peoples lives, perhaps in reaction to the Church.
This sect probably did have a secret agenda, which was to gain access to the hidden powers behind the nation, and may have been successful. Even today similar network(s) or cabal(s) of rich and powerful people do in fact control to some degree many western or indeed world governments, often through high ranking members of various disciplined financial and secret societies. This power becomes stronger or weaker depending on the inner strengths or weaknesses of the political parties and leaders in power, of the powerful nations at the time. For example, Lincoln in his day was a strong advocate of justice but in his strength there was also a weakness, like the mighty oak, he was struck down in his prime when he had all but achieved abolition.
The outward symbol of this hidden power is quite obvious, in its control of the official media which always seems to repeat between them, the same messages over and over again with blatant variations of validity and accuracy, or often adjusting the stories to suit the circumstances and in a patronising manner. It rarely asks an obvious or intelligent question but beams out the micro-second sound bites of the official line. In fact sometimes on TV, the film will show the lie to the story, if people are smart enough to observe the small details in the film. Only a very few gifted journalists and reporters are able to break outside this cabal at the risk of the wrath of their editors and peers who might easily throw them to the wolves.
To get back to the illuminati, it is to try to explain to whom I am referring to. The word is being used in this book as a generic term referring to a now long defunct secret sect but has no real connection to it, either good or bad, except that it is being used here as an allegorical term referring to almost any practising secret sect that is powerful enough to effect the workings of government, at any given time. At that time there was a powerful, extreme right wing, radical Republican cabal behind Lincoln's assassination, of which no one person can be exclusively implicated, and the plot took an extreme amount of planning, cunning, lateral thinking, imagination, arrogance and supreme confidence with a lot of money and utter ruthlessness to carry it out. The number of people behind it or directly involved in it must have literally run into scores, particularly if you think of the financial profits that were undoubtedly to be gained from it.

Introduction

This book is written in the Honour of Abraham Lincoln, Mary Lincoln and Dr. Samuel Alexander Mudd and to the memory of John Wilkes Booth with the explicit intention to enlighten the public as to the true nature and otherwise real intentions of this man, and to elucidate as much as possible of the true facts relating to the events of the assassination of Abraham Lincoln. It is also written in the memory of Mary Surratt, Edman Spangler, Lewis Payne, the Confederate Boyd and his friend the Unknown Soldier. It is specially written however in regards to the heroic suffering of Dr. Mudd who managed to save many lives from the diseased ridden prison in the Dry Tortugas island off Key West. During their four years incarceration Ed had selflessly helped to save Dr. Mudd himself, when he finally succumbed to yellow fever. And thirdly to look more favourably upon the other questionable victims including Samuel Arnold, George Adzerodt and Michael O'Laughlin caught up in the miss happenings of that time. It also intends to categorically prove that Booth did not kill Lincoln although he did indeed plan to kidnap him, and for this Booth paid the price; and no doubt was the prime cause of the sufferings of his friends of which he would not, or sadly could not try to circumvent in the aftermath.

This kidnap plan he felt necessary perhaps misguidedly in order to gain considerable bargaining power for an exchange of prisoners between the North and South. Whatever his inner feelings, (that were personally favourable towards abolition), with regards to the use of slavery in the South cannot be truly understood in terms of the general ills of Victorian values, no more than can that of the feelings of the average white person at the time which perhaps has only marginally improved today, in some parts of the world. And Booth treated all men as equals, but did not like over familiarity with his workers on the farm, in as much that he would eat with them but did not like his sisters to do so. It is has to be surely measured in terms of his passionate concern about his chosen countrymen, be they black or white, being kept in military prisons under abominable conditions. The exchange of prisoners would have been a humane act and could not have effected the balance of the war to any great degree. After all enlisted men are not generals, as generals are not politicians, so they cannot change the direction of the war if the balance of numbers is maintained. Except the Union had far greater man power and could afford to keep their men suffering in Confederate prisons with their more unlimited resources, but the balance of power rested more with their industrial resources and capital, rather than excessive numbers of men.

There are of course many examples in history where smaller countries have repelled or resisted overwhelming force but the circumstance like geographical terrain, indigenous culture, solidarity of purpose, hearts and minds and many other factors have overcome the odds. Examples being Finland v Russia, Vietnam v France, Vietnam v America, America v England (the War of Independence), Switzerland v Austria, Afghanistan against Edwardian England, Afghanistan v Russia, Ireland v England (the Easter

Rebellion), Korea v America (stale-mate), Cuba v America (Bay of Pigs fiasco), Carthage against Rome, Macedonian Greece against the Eastern Empire of Persia, because of Alexander the Great. Perhaps there was a certain paranoia in the mind of the Union's secretary of war Stanton that any concession of this kind would be a sign of weakness. Stanton was the kind of man who would sack a general but never promote one. In other words break a man before he breaks you. His clear intentions, mainly stemming from a radical Republican cabal, was to utterly break the South and take it over as likened to a foreign country with all spoils to the victor. However Lincoln would never have allowed this to happen even though he gave Stanton the lead in running the war.

Yet Stanton wanted to gain as much control over Lincoln as he possibly could even if it meant prolonging the war. And keeping prisoners would definitely prolong the hatred on both sides and propagate or rekindle the war till no honourable peace terms could be achieved. Whether Booth realised that a fanatical right wing republican cabal of industrialists and bankers, were using Stanton, to put pressure on Lincoln is not clear but of course the ruthlessness of a government at war knows no bounds and the President is always the obvious target and in this case the final sacrifice. This sacrifice however was not to keep the peace with honour but to rekindle the war, until the South was totally subjugated, and dispossessed of its lands and property and dependent on the North, and being subject to military law for as long as possible. Although politically the war was over just before his assassination, Lincoln still had to negotiate the terms of peace through congress and with Jefferson Davis, with the goal of finishing all hostilities, abolishing slavery and providing a just and honourable peace. The musical theme for this book is from Bob Marley:

Mmmm.........mmmm, mmmm........mmmm
One love, one heart
Let's get together and feel all right
Hear the children crying ....One love
Hear the children crying ....One heart
Sayin',
Give thanks and praise to the Lord and I will feel all right.
Sayin', "Let's get together and feel all right."
Whoa, whoa, whoa, whoa

Let them all pass all their dirty remarks ....One love
There is one question I'd really love to ask ...One heart
Is there a place for the hopeless sinner
Who has hurt all mankind just to save his own?
Believe me

One love, one heart
Let's get together and feel all right
As it was in the beginning ....One love
So shall it be in the end ....One heart
Alright,
"Give thanks and praise to the Lord and I will feel all right."
"Let's get together and feel all right." One more thing

Lets get together to fight this Holy Armageddon......One Love
So when the man comes there will be no, no doom....One song
Have pity on those whose chances grow thinner
There ain't no hiding place from the Father of Creation
Sayin',
"One, one heart "Lets get together and feel alright."

I'm pleading to mankind.................................One Love
Oh, Lord...One Heart, Whoa
Give thanks and pray to the lord and I will feel alright...Repeat

Chapter 1

Facts and the Meaning of History

Once upon a time as a young man the writer took the opportunity to visit Washington and visited the Abe Lincoln Museum and learned a little about Abe Lincoln and of his assassination by John Wilkes Booth. The most vivid recollection that impressed him was that a small third rate actor, in the Ford theatre, had shot the President and leapt from a balcony onto the stage and damaged his leg, causing him to become lame and then escaped. At first he imagined that the theatre must have been nearly empty for him to get away with it. And he also had a picture of Booth as being not a real actor but some kind of out of work villainous stunt man, even a ruffian, with no credentials whatsoever. Whatever it seemed a very odd affair that didn't seem to make sense, particularly if he had done it in a crowded theatre and took a serious injury, yet had somehow managed to limp across the stage and get away. Yet consciously he must have accepted the account as a true event mainly because Lincoln had been shot in public and there was a description of the assassin, an actor with a moustache who had become lame by the deed. He left the museum simply accepting that it was history and thought no more about it accept what a strange event and why would a stuntman want to do such a thing unless he was insane, or indeed a dangerous psychopath with near super-human powers of strength and acrobatic ability. On reflection in the mirror, the devil himself could not have been more talented as indeed Booth was so portrayed.

Henry Ford once said history was a load of bunk perhaps because he felt that history can have no effect on the future and those people who labour at it are non-productive members of any society. To an extent this could be conceived as true in terms of a nation just requiring productive labour and simply reading the newspaper, however even in more primitive societies history is vitally important. Even today certain tribes carry their history from their elders religiously and the decades marked on sticks or in stone and most importantly by word of mouth. Indeed our stone age ancestors have shown us graphic descriptions of their history in vivid artistic re-creations of animals they had most often hunted and killed, sealed forever into their imaginations and so inspired by their daily struggles for survival, these animals have elevated man's mind, from or in extension to, the primitive passion of killing, to the resplendent beauty of art and form of the hunted animal, yet rarely depicted this art of themselves, beyond body paint.

In tribal culture even today most of the details are lost but it is the power of the spoken word, rhythm, dance and music which really holds them together. It is in the wealth and poetry of the spoken, if not also in the written word, that gives it its beauty, its power and its spirit to the descendants whether the elder is the grandfather or chieftain or witch-doctor or warlock or medicine man. Indeed often it is the elder women who are most gifted in language and memory to pass on the stories of the living and dead generations. Without it the spirit of the tribe would be broken or dead and indeed the tribe would be weakened, without the spirit of their ancestors, along with their spiritual embodiment of their gods and the supernatural. It is as essential as language itself because language has created it and is an inseparable part of it. It is that which truly separates us from other primates that sadly can have little or no concept of history.

So although Ford had a point of view which in a throw away line he condemned history there was method at work here. That is the reading of books in general could be considered history and a waste of time for most young people, who should be working hard at earning money instead, in order to pull their weight in society. Naturally this remark would enrage all educated people whatever their station but they would simply disregard as nonsense words from a profit making oligarch. Nevertheless how many young impressionable young people would be affected by this remark and justify it in not continuing their studies, but instead rushing into the factory for ready manual work with ready cash.

However, the top and bottom of it is although we need history, does it really matter how accurate it is and do we in fact change the facts, to make history suit our feelings of well being. Or more to the point do governments, partly through schools and universities, control the teaching of history in order to reinforce their political dogmas or agendas, which may or may not fall in line with the majority of its citizens? For example a nation goes to war and the outcome is a stale mate. This nation will teach history so that it favours or even suggests that it won the war. It is a natural consequence of wanting to feel good about itself in order to engender self love and satisfaction and self confidence, which indeed are all forms of patriotism at any level. But at the highest level it is simply propaganda, to circumvent any sign of apparent weakness, in order to assert itself against any further or future threats. That is it comes full circle and behaves like any other pack animal or indeed, even the lone and ravaging tiger.

This account is not historical in the sense of being intentionally or overtly politically biased, nor is it based on the hearsay of legends to any measured degree. It does however contain many passages where political or at least democratic feelings of moral right and wrong have influenced the author to make certain evaluations, as to the political motivations of the characters and regions North or South, at the end of the American Civil War. However plenty of information has been available and easily obtained, as to the real people concerned or connected to the legends associated with these people. In this way one can relate the various events and times and places, such that it is possible to then ascertain certain facts, and then disregard many of some of the more political, imaginative and florid accounts but holding onto the essential truths. It is also intended to be accurate because it is based on observation, logical reasoning and deduction according as much as possible to the known or established facts. As an example of this method one starts from known facts and then questions the non-established facts as much as possible. Thus, what are the known facts and what are the non-facts of this case:

Fact: Lincoln was assassinated in the Ford theatre. Evidence his sudden public death there and his public funeral.

There is no public evidence that Booth was killed. The Latin dictum Habeas Corpus was not made open to the public. In fact only a very select few even knew where he was buried in a concrete cell, in the navy fort in the prison arsenal along the Potomac River, buried in total secrecy by two men called Baker and Baker.

Fact: General Grant had been invited but failed to attend the performance of 'Our American Cousin'.

There is no evidence that Booth had plotted to kill the President and General Grant that night, except for a forged, purloined diary.

Fact: Booth was either in or outside the theatre that day according to many sources on both sides including Harry Clay Ford, James Ford, Thomas J Raybold, Ed Spangler, James Maddox, Joseph Burroughs, John F. Sleichman, Mr. Taltavul and the questionable Colonel Joseph Stewart. At least one female witness said he was at the front of the theatre before 10 pm with Lucy Hale, but the front doorman John Buckingham said he was walking in an out checking the time, with two other men. This also tallied with a police sergeant Joseph M. Dye out front, who said Booth was walking about with two other men, one of which looked like a 'ruffian', and they separated at about 10 pm when Booth went into the Star tavern. The strongest witness was Ed Spangler because he looked after Booth's horse as he had often done before, and James Gifford the theatre manager had said 'Spangler was always a drudge for Booth.'

The is no satisfactory evidence that Booth jumped from the President's box catching his foot in the union flag that must certainly have caused a turning or rotating force. Only a cat could survive this athletic feat according to the laws of vector forces and angular momentum, particularly acting on a non-spherical body. The catching of his foot would lever the body and cause it to twist or turn from a vertical fall. He would then hit the stage at a certain angle of spin, that is unless he was a trained acrobat and did a full somersault to pull out of this wayward spin in full flight, otherwise he would have required the instinctive agility of a cat. Major Rathbone vividly described the assassin's leap, after being wounded by him, he nearly grabbed him from his fall whilst shouting 'Stop that man'. He said Booth, knife in hand, had jumped over the parapet to land on the stage. Nobody did stop him except the giant Stewart, only two feet away, did chase and try to catch the injured man recovering from a 20 mph fall onto a hard stage. It takes only an instant to fall 11 feet that is in fact 0.6 seconds. It is an event in which certainly many of the audience would have seen had it occurred.
However if you were one of the audience who did not see this fall how would you know

for certain it had happened AT THAT MOMENT IN TIME! And this observation of probability can be applied to each and every person in the audience. If someone tells you later that an event happened but you did not actually see it you would have the choice of believing them or not since you did not see it for yourself, and seeing is believing. This is especially true when you learn about it in the paper a day or two later. This equally applies to the observations of Clara Harris and Mary Todd Lincoln who witnessed a fictitious fight with an assassin, which they could only have learned or read about later. Mary was taken to her bed for a month and did not attend the funeral. Later she was admitted to a rest hospital by her son Robert, and Clara was eventually murdered.

Fact: Someone ran across the stage after a shot rang out at about 10.15 pm. This was confirmed by Harry Hawk, Jake Ritterspaugh, Ed Spangler, James Maddox, J. Ferguson, Captain Theodore McGowan, Colonel Stewart, Mr. Taltavul and also witnessed by the audience and William Willard the band leader in the orchestra and Laura Keene the famous actress who was on stage at the time with Harry Hawk. And J. Sleichman the assistant prompts man at right stage stated that he saw this man, whom he thought was Booth standing by the Prompters place behind the wings at this juncture, whilst he himself was exiting the first entrance from the wings.

Spangler did not recognise this man as Booth and he knew him well, but he said a man did run across the stage immediately after the shot rang out. Colonel Stewart however stated that it was Booth under oath. Years later as a solicitor, Stewart made another sworn statement in a legal letter which was proved to be false by a Senate committee. But Stewart himself wearing a dark moustache, did run across the stage according to his own statement and from almost the same position as Booth's supposed landing.

Fact: Ten days later two men were apprehended in Confederate uniforms, one possibly lame, near Bowling Green, Virginia and both cornered in Garrett's barn. One was killed by a gun shot wound to the head and the other eventually hung. Evidence is gained from the local newspaper reports and the full army report of Lieutenant Doherty officer in charge of the 16th New York cavalry detachment detailed to capture these men. Also prior to this three mounted cavalry Confederate officers had met these two men and took a ferry ride with them across the Rappahannock river, from Port Conway to Port Royal and then rode with them about three miles or so, to Garrett's farm near Bowling Green, Virginia.

Neither of these men were publicly proven to be Booth and Herold. The dead man was wrapped in an army blanket and taken back in a rented wagon to a boat on the Potomac, thence to Washington. The other man was escorted back as a prisoner and supposedly put on trial. At the military trial, the public were restricted and a photograph of this man, preparing to be hung on the gallows, clearly shows a full face whose features had been blanked out. Later his body was dug up and his head decapitated, according to various sources. However, a courtroom likeness was commissioned and an artistic drawing of this man was allowed (but see Chapter 22). A drawing is not proof of exact identification because its likeness depends on accuracy and artistic license, except this drawing did resemble Herold a little, without a hood on. His grave in the Congressional Cemetery is still marked today with a header stone, yet it was never visited by Herold's family.

Fact: Dr. Mudd a medical doctor in Maryland received visit at four in the morning, from two men on the 15th April, and put a splint on one of them according to his own statement for which he was arrested, tried and sentenced to life imprisonment. He did not deny fixing someone's leg, as it was his job. And other witnesses said he did this, including the military account when they found evidence of a severed boot at his home.

Dr. Mudd must have known then or realised later this man could not have been Booth but he was said to be uncertain. In any case he could not have known the President had been shot, let alone assassinated, only 6 hours after the event with no paper, radio or telephone and the reward posters were addressed as Wanted. Murderer. $100,000 Reward but not yet distributed until the 20th April. There was no other possible reason to suspect these men as criminals except they were strangers in the night needing medical help. In any case all military telegraph lines had been cut, from Washington by the army that same night. At the trial they made out that Dr. Mudd must have found out it was Booth when he went into Bryantown the next day, to fetch supplies but he did not report it till the day after, that would be Easter Sunday. How little tolerance and mercy can be given by people who are determined to destroy you at all costs? Or for just pointing out a direction of travel to two strangers whom you have helped as a doctor in the middle of the night. It was surely a mistake of Dr. Mudd that he did not ask the two strangers for proof of identification since this might have saved him. He said they gave the names of Tyson and Hensted. It is also a pity that he did not notice that the name of JW…or J. Wilkes were stencilled inside the lame man's boot. The final letter(s) not readable perhaps from the result of wear. Why should Dr. Mudd examine the inside of a sweaty old boot which he had to cut, to get it off the man's foot? Surely, had he known it was Booth he would have destroyed the boot and not left it in the patient's room conveniently for the authorities to find it. Except he could not have known anyway, that a man called 'Booth' had assassinated the President before the 16th of April.

Fact: Four of the conspirators were hung after a military trial. Evidence photographs of the hooded victims hung on the gallows. This included the first woman Mary Surratt to be hung in the US.

There is overwhelming public evidence now to question and over-rule, that they were in any way, involved in a plot to assassinate Lincoln. If two of them were involved with Booth in his plan to kidnap the President, then Mary was found guilty only by association; since they all swore she was totally innocent of these plans as she was just the landlady. In any case her son John came to a civilian trial two years later and was acquitted of being one of the assassins. He had a top class legal team that proved he was miles away from Washington at the time. He did admit to warning Booth in a letter not to go ahead with the kidnapping however. Thus he had been a kidnap conspirator and indeed gave public lectures on the subject years later. His mother's crime was having a boarding house, being kind and having a son who was a Confederate. In fact only three of the four people hung, were really known. One was an innocent woman. One was an innocent German- American citizen of limited English language skills. The other two were ex-soldiers, one unidentified. The summation of these highlights and many others can then be applied to every other piece of the historical puzzle, and then by a rigid process of elimination start to put the facts together. However it is also necessary to find the missing pieces. The search is made easier if you can imagine the shape and colour of the these pieces and this gets easier as the puzzle progresses to take shape. One also begins to become involved in all the parts and places and then apply a certain amount of insight into the characters, as to their motivations and circumstances.

The Doctors assisted the dying President up the final stage of his Assault Course into Petersen House.

Chapter 2

President Abraham Lincoln and his Faith

1809-1865
If I Die For Thee Let All Men Be Free

If ever a man of his time was more honourable then he was unknown. This gentle giant, the son of a Baptist and illiterate backwoodsman from Kentucky, was every inch an oak tree and a natural Republican with all the whit and wisdom of his country roots. His weakness however was a certain shyness around women, nevertheless in this he could thus not be undone by them. His true weakness was men whom he thought more able than he and Stanton was such a man. He was able to deal with this however in the fashion of giving Stanton as much of a lead as possible with getting on with the war. He even told him that should he issue an instruction in which Stanton thought unsound, then he would have a certain liberty to over rule the instruction. Lincoln had once commented to a senator, I will give this man his lead until he has achieved much but I will draw him in when I know the bigger picture has to be accounted for. And so it was to be that Stanton took the Union to victory but also wanted to dictate the terms of peace i.e. no quarter or honour for the South. This is where the oak tree would not bend. Lincoln was set on giving back to the South its constitutional freedom provided slavery was abolished forever. This was the final stake and it was too much for Stanton and his radical Republican backers and the cabal of industrialists, bankers and elements of the press, indeed all right wing Republicans and radical state Governors.

In September 1862 the State of the Union and the policy of Lincoln, and his undying commitment to arrive at a just and honourable solution to the war, despite the interest of foreign governments most effected by the cotton trade, is made clear from this Civil War news circular that includes an abstract from Lincoln himself:

“From the Editor: Abraham Lincoln has many reasons for issuing the Emancipation Proclamation. Not the least of which is to prevent any possibility of foreign intervention in the war. Both England and France have showed an interest in helping the Confederates in exchange for access to the South's primary export--King Cotton. However, it should be remembered that the eight-year old Republican Party was born as an abolitionist political organization and Lincoln must have believed in this core tenet to have been chosen as the Republican candidate in the Presidential election of 1860. This was not lost on the Southern states as it was the election of Abraham Lincoln that triggered secession. In fact, Jefferson Davis was inaugurated (on a provisional basis) as President of the Confederate States of America before Lincoln made his first trip to Washington, DC. Since his inauguration, Abraham Lincoln has been very careful not to antagonize the Southern states by sticking to a moderate position regarding the South's "peculiar institution." However, with the war dragging on and the casualty list mounting to ever higher proportions, Lincoln has come to the realization that the war can no longer be contained as a war to preserve the Union. This war, if it is to be won, has to be a war for freedom.”

"The fiery trial through which we pass, will light us down, in honour or dishonour, to the latest generation....In giving freedom to the slave, we assign freedom to the free---honourable alike in what we give, and what we preserve. We shall nobly save, or meanly lose, the last, best hope of earth.”

The fact that the President was greatly loved by many people including his junior staff, is highlighted here by Mr. Field the Assistant Secretary of the Treasury, when he attended the bedside of the dying President. He had been first told of the news whilst staying at the Willard Hotel. Thus:

“The impression was prevalent however, at that time, that the President had been shot in the breast, about the region of the heart, and the wound might not prove fatal. After a few minutes we crossed the street, and endeavoured to gain admission into the house where Mr. Lincoln lay. This I effected with some little difficulty. The first person I met in the hall was Miss Harris, daughter of United States Senator Ira Harris of New York, who had been at the theater with the Presidential party. She informed me that the President was dying , but desired me not to communicate the fact to Mrs. Lincoln, who was in the front parlor. Several other persons who were there confirmed the statement as to Mr. Lincoln’s condition. I then entered the front parlor, where I found Mrs. Lincoln in a state of indescribable agitation. She repeated over and over again,

“ Why didn’t he kill me? Why didn’t he kill me?”

I asked if there was any service I could render her, and she requested me to go for Dr. Stone, or some other eminent physician. Both Dr. Stone and Surgeon-General Barnes had already been sent for, but neither had yet arrived. On my way out I met Major T. T. Eckhart, of the War Department, who told me he was himself going for Dr. Stone. I then went for Dr. Hall, one of the most distinguished surgeons in the District. I found him at home and he at once accompanied me. When we again reached the neighbourhood the house, access had become very difficult, guards having been stationed on every side.
After much effort I was enabled to obtain permission or Dr. Hall, but was not at the time permitted to enter myself; accordingly I returned to Willard's. The whole population of the city was by this time out, and all kinds of conflicting stories were being circulated. At three or four o'clock I again started for Mr. Peterson's house. This time I was admitted without difficulty. I proceeded at once to the room in which the President was dying. It was a small chamber ; in an extension or back building, on a level with the first or parlor floor. The President was lying on his back , diagonally across a low, double bed-stead, his head supported by two pillows on the outer side of the bed.
The persons in the room were the Secretaries McCulloch, Stanton, Welles, and Harlan, Postmaster General Dennison, the Attorney General, the Assistant Secretary of the Interior, Senator Sumner of Massachusetts, General Halleck, General Auger, General Meigs, General J. F. Farnsworth, of Illinois, General Todd, of Dacotah (Dakota), the President's Assistant Private Secretary, Major Hay, the medical gentlemen, and perhaps two or three others. Dr. Stone was sitting on the foot of the bed. An army surgeon was sitting opposite the President's head, occasionally feeling his pulse, and applying his fingers to the arteries of the neck and the heart. Mr. Lincoln seemed to be divested of all clothing, except the bed coverings. His eyes were closed , and the lids and surrounding parts so injected with blood as to present the appearance of having been bruised. He was evidently totally unconscious, and was breathing regularly but heavily, and with an occasional sigh escaping with the breath. There was scarcely a dry eye in the room, and the scene was the most solemn and impressive one I ever witnessed. After a while Captain Robert Lincoln , of General Grant's staff, and eldest son of the President, entered the chamber, and stood at the headboard, leaning over his father.
For a time his grief completely overpowered him, but he soon recovered himself, and behaved in the most manly manner until the closing of the scene. As the morning wore on, the condition of the President remained unchanged till about seven o'clock. In the meantime , it came on to rain heavily, and the scene from the window was in dreary sympathy with that which was going on within. Just before this Mrs. Lincoln had been supported into the chamber, had thrown herself moaning upon her husband's body. She was permitted to remain but a few minutes, when she was carried out, in an almost insensible condition. At about seven o'clock , the President's breathing changed in a manner to indicate that death was rapidly approaching. It became low and fitful, with frequent interruptions. Several times I thought that all was over., until the feeble respiration was resumed. At last, at just twenty two minutes past seven o'clock, without

a struggle, without a convulsive movement , without a tremor, he ceased breathing - and was no more.
Thus died this great, pure, kind-hearted man, who never willingly injured a human being- the greatest martyr to liberty the world has ever seen. Shortly after his death, finding that his eyes were not entirely closed, I placed my hands upon them. One of the attendant surgeons first put nickels upon them, and then substituted silver half dollars. It was twenty minutes or half an hour before the body commenced to grow cold. The lower jaw began to fall slightly, and the lower teeth were exposed. One of the medical gentlemen bound up the jaw with a pocket handkerchief. Mr. Stanton threw down the window-shades, and I left the chamber of death. Immediately after the decease, the Rev. Dr. Gurley had offered up a fervent and affecting prayer in the room, interrupted only by the sobs of those present. When I left the room, he was again praying in the front parlor. Poor Mrs. Lincoln's moans were distressing to listen to. After the prayer was over, I entered the parlor, and found Mrs. Lincoln supported in the arms of her son, Robert. She was soon taken to her carriage. As she reached the front door, she glanced at the theater opposite , and exclaimed several times,

" Oh that dreadful house! That dreadful house!"

Immediately thereafter, guards were stationed at the door of the room in which the President's body lay. In a few minutes I left myself. It is hoped that some historical painter will be found capable of portraying that momentous death-scene."
Indeed, dear Mr. Field it is you who have done it so caringly and beautifully, for us all to remember him with the greatest of love. Yes, and there are some extremely wicked 'Mystorians' about today trying to implicate his dear, kind and loyal lady, Mary Lincoln, in order to further misguide the public. The impression the President had been shot in the heart was prevalent because that was the expected target. However the President had been slightly leaning forward over the balcony when he was shot from the spy-hole. This caused a change in target height by about 6 to 8 inches, to the neck. The President was not a popular man with everyone, the war had been bitter and had dragged on for 4 years, even the ordinary soldiers had not much love left for him. Stanton had been harsh and cruel and would not exchange prisoners thinking he could allow his own to suffer terrible conditions, so that the South's elite could never match the North's numbers. Lincoln's Achilles heel however was now exposed, he thought he was wiser than Stanton, but fatefully he trusted this dark clandestine man of the McMasters clan, at the stage he should have realised was the most dangerous. Stanton's job was over and Lincoln was not to be turned back on his honour for the peace.
Stanton was a vain and supremely arrogant man yet with servile weaknesses. He would never be President but he could control presidents and had no real respect for them, rather like the butler to the lord syndrome. Hence the need for a master plan an illusion something akin to the dark secrets of the 'Masters of Illusion', the 'illuminati'. Their

kinds of skills are legendry going back even before the ancient Egyptians but carried on through the secret cults of magicians, freemason's , in America-the Scottish Rites, the Medici, the Jesuits, the Black Hand, the Knights Templar, the Rosicrucian's, the Costa Nostra and the Machiavellians amongst many others. The pyramids were build by slave labour with skills never equalled today. The stone masons of Europe carried on the secrets and the temple of Jerusalem held the Masonic line. These secrets are held in arrogance as a kind of witness to the projection of divinity from there edifices into the stars that made their rulers divine. But then what is divinity but an effigy of absolute power. Men like Stanton carry this badge and are silently contemptuous of all mortal men including presidents, unless they are members of this kind of society and have a rank of some 33 rd degree, or at least one rank above there own. It is this rank and rank only they recognise and are servile to it, because it is their path to divinity.

The President was human and listened to ordinary people and granted freeing of soldiers, the helping of widows, the everyday pleas of the atrocities of war. He certainly would never allowed the hanging of an innocent woman in a trumped up military trial. Now the war was all but finished, every hand Lincoln played went straight into the hands of the illuminati, it was inevitable. Simple hands like these: Lincoln had often regarded his security of little importance thus the illuminatti could capitalise in spades on this, as is obvious even to school children today. Lincoln liked the theatre and liked to be in public and wanted to be amongst them, because his love of his countrymen was true and not of the stone faced contempt of the servile Stanton, or the supreme arrogance of Seward. Lincoln asked for the personal security of Major Eckert but Stanton denied this small request. Had Lincoln thought it vitally important he could have given Stanton a rocket. As it was he allowed Stanton to trick him in several ways on this issue. The fact is Lieutenant George Ashum of the Ohio Light Guard had been detailed to the White house that very night as part of his rostrum; but Lincoln had been picked up earlier by Major Rathbone and had already left for the theatre. He left a message that he would see Ashum first thing in the morning when he returned.

At the theatre, Lincoln had both his messenger Charles Forbes and the questionable Parker, close at hand in the passage and the outer door but failed to notice there sudden departure, admittedly he was engrossed in the play. It should have been pointed out to the President that Parker was keeping an eye on him through the spy hole for extra security, like a nosey parker. The spy hole was only 3 feet high, so ideally more suited for a brave pygmy hunter gatherer, from the majestic forests of the Belgian Congo.

Lincoln should have realised something was amiss, when Grant had been stood down at the last minute and the effeminate Major Rathbone was to replace him as an honoured guest, or suitable escort. What was Rathbone to Lincoln he had no rank of importance (apart from being rich)? Was he to be his bodyguard? It seems likely he was because he gave a glorious if hackneyed account of his belated defence of his President.

Lincoln did not notice the spy hole level with his back, only a few feet away in the door behind him. It is easy to disguise a spy hole with a soft plug however. In any case a tiny

3/16" hole would not be noticed easily especially in a darkened theatre. Had he done so he must surely have smelt a rat because, although he had been given little security then why was there a spy hole into a closed box, that was otherwise inaccessible from below the balcony without exposure? The reason being that even Clara Harris was unaware of this spy hole until she came back with a judge on Easter Sunday.

The President was a good man and true but it was his death that catapulted him to greatness. Stanton made sure of that but Mary collapsed immediately into a state of depression and could not even attend the pomp and splendour of her husband's funeral. She accused Parker of being responsible for Abe's death. Of course she did, she saw no assassin creep up behind and shoot her husband, then fight with Rathbone and leap like an acrobatic demon from the balcony onto the stage yelling 'Sic Semper Tyrannis', the state motto of Virginia. Perhaps when she read about the prefabricated story in the press she must have thought she was going mad. Apparently the gossip has it she was not well liked in Washington, regardless of the fact that although not a young beauty, she was fashionable and cut an attractive slightly daring figure for an old 'un. Perhaps she detested hypocrisy and had a sharp tongue. Whatever, it seems she was already isolated to a certain degree. Imagine the horror and shear terror of realising that the traitors were all around her and she was powerless to do or say anything; she was up against the well oiled machinery of the illuminati. They having set the diabolical scenes of deception in an attempt to satisfy the public's insatiable desire to avenge their President's death, in a young fledgling country needing its flag wrapt around it in surrogate comfort for a crying infant child. Yes, overcome with an infinite and untapped well of undying emotions otherwise repressed from the 4 years of bitter war of brother against brother.

When we look at Lincoln today the public see a kind of giant biblical figure and a true patriot and seemingly Christian figurehead. Yet he was not overly religious but knew the bible very well, balanced and amply endowed with common sense and good natured humour. This was the man that could question extremes in all genres. He was once asked why don't you become a mason? He answered with perfect candour, I would not be a good mason because I am wayward of too much discipline and would never have the time to make even a lowly grade. Rather like Edgar Allen Poe who said chequers was a better game than chess, because the latter demanded to much time of a man's brain, to be any good. Yet, Poe was very clever, he could decipher many a cipher code and in 1840 claimed that there was no such thing as an unsolvable cipher. He challenged anyone to send him a cipher, in English, of simple substitution and one or two other limitations. He cracked scores of the ciphers sent in to him. He was also a great mind reader , at least in his books. In one story his two characters are French and they are walking along the street having an intelligent discussion, as French people do. Then suddenly in the middle of a discussion they both fall silent for a little while. After a minute or so, having both logically proceeded in their minds to exactly the same concluding remarks, with rhetoric, they immediately picked up the advanced stage of their silent conversation.

Lincoln had won the war and abolition was within his sights but he had to come to an honourable solution with Jefferson Davis. It did not help that the radical Republicans were not going to achieve there objectives, if Lincoln held his ground over the Wade-Davis bill, and Andrew Johnson the Democrat was waiting in the wings. Stanton must have figured with Lincoln gone he could control Johnson more easily but it had to be soon before the peace conditions were finally settled. The fact is the war was still going on at sea and some ships were still having skirmishes. One commander only learned the war was over months later when informed by the English. In fact the last Confederate ship sailed round the horn from the Aleutian islands near Alaska to Liverpool, finally lowering its flag in November 1865, and surrendering to the Union six months after Lincoln's death. However, the sometimes heavy drinking Johnson showed remarkable strength of character, and resisted the overtures of Stanton and finally out- manoeuvred him in a battle royal, which included pardoning Dr. Mudd, Ned Spangler, Samuel Arnold and the unfortunate Michael O' Laughlin who had already died of yellow fever, in the stinking God forsaken and disease ridden prison of the Dry Tortugas island off the coast of Florida, in the Gulf of Mexico. Stanton had even indicated stupidly to Johnson, it is said, that the conspirators would probably all die of disease before long. They in fact served over four years of there life sentences and Dr. Mudd became a true American hero by standing in for the prison doctor who had died from disease.

It showed that Johnson the Democrat did certainly care about these men and was not to be undone by Stanton and the deadly cabal of right wing Republicans. They tried to impeach him and only just failed the final 2/3 majority by one vote, because Johnson was pardoning prisoners and had broken the tenure of office act by sacking Stanton, and by allowing Grant to stand down from his new cabinet office. In fact, Stanton barricaded himself into his office, waiting for hell or high water to remove him. But finally in 1867 Johnson got rid of both Stanton and Baker by giving them their come up pence. Not however, before Johnson had received his first letter of impeachment from the House. Thus it seems that Johnson was the man that really tried to save the Union to finish Lincoln's honourable goal for him. However it was not quite the case because later the Republicans did get there way under the Republican Grant, after Johnson's term in office, but the Wade - Davis bill by then had become very much watered down. The war had taken its heavy toll in death, disease and starvation but it was also effecting the economy of Europe, and particularly England, because the cotton mills had become less productive due to the cotton embargo raised by the Union (it was also expensive at a 1 dollar per pound); so that Lincoln was under even more pressure from the industrialists and bankers of the illuminati. Indeed the Confederacy had the support of England and France to support the interest of the Rothschild banks. This was because Lincoln had printed greenbacks with no interest rate, to support the war and to forego any debts, known as fiat currency or bills of credit. The problem was it antagonised the big central and national banks such as Rothschild and they lost millions by the end of the War, instead of making so many more millions. This surely was the prime cause of

Lincoln's assassination, since the groundwork for War had long been prepared by Caleb Cushing (Attorney General under Buchanan), by the Kansas- Nebraska Act in 1851, in the North with John Brown the Mason turned Abolitionist and Albert Pike, a school principal turned World Grand Master Mason and military General, in the South; through secret financial and Masonic societies including the Golden Circle of Cincinnati, Ohio; both in the US and in Europe with the object of profits and power to them and their masters. At first their was gun running and finally the War started with the South attacking Fort Sumter on April 12th 1861. However Lincoln gained the support of Russia and they cried off their military support, but France and Spanish troops did invade Mexico and Jefferson Davis was prepared to trade off Texas and Louisiana for their support. Napoleon III made the Habsburg Austrian, Prince Ferdinand Maximilian Emperor of Mexico, of gifted scientific and romantic imagination, but it was short lived - he was executed by the Republicans, aged 34. Then in 1866 there was also an attempt to assassinate Alexander II, Tsar of Russia. It is no wonder the President was under a great strain and tinged with a great sadness, so that his keen senses must have been greatly numbed and could only be eased by appearing in public as often as possible, not giving a hoot about his own personal safety. Some of his greatest speeches- the Gettysburg address and so forth, were made to the crowd, the oak tree standing proud showing its great strength to the ordinary American people that he loved, as a father to a child. Here is the famous speech he made from the back of his train at Gettysburg, one of his briefest yet memorable, in history.

The Gettysburg Address:

'Four score and seven years ago our fathers brought forth, upon this continent, a new nation, conceived in Liberty, and dedicated to the proposition that all men are created equal. Now we are engaged in a great civil war, testing whether that nation, or any nation, so conceived, and so dedicated, can long endure. We are met here on a great battlefield of that war. We have come to dedicate a portion of it as a final resting place those who here gave their lives that that nation might live. It is altogether fitting and proper that we should do this. But in a larger sense we can not dedicate -- we can not consecrate -- we can not hallow this ground. The brave men, living and dead, who struggled, here, have consecrated it far above our poor power to add or detract. The world will little note, nor long remember, what we say here, but can never forget what they did here. It is for us, the living, rather to be dedicated here to the unfinished work which they have, thus far, so nobly carried on. It is rather for us to be here dedicated to the great task remaining before us -- that from these honored dead we take increased devotion to that cause for which they here gave the last full measure of devotion -- that we here highly resolve that these dead shall not have died in vain; that this nation shall have a new birth of freedom; and that this government of the people, by the people, for the people, shall not perish from the earth.'

That this great President should have fallen foul to those despicable servants is a measure of how vulnerable the office of the President was then, and is now in America.

It is even more important today that this great office should have greater protection. It is not a question of security, although the selection of certain few true men of proven calibre would be a start (not big muscles and guns). All the physical security of the combined services makes not one iota of difference. In fact as you will see in this book the threat comes directly through them from the illuminati. It is a question of morality and common sense(s) and true loyalty. The President himself bears a very great responsibility in behaving in a certain way and having the intelligence to circumvent and prevent; and by being able to make the right personal assessment as to who should be his closest and trusted friends and bodyguards. If he is wrong in his choice then it is his own mistake, unfortunately. Better this than blind trust. But then the man chosen as President should at least be able to select one of the best. And as you will also see the illuminati have low intelligence so they are not difficult to out-manoeuvre once detected and above all they are complete cowards. It's the closest and the most familiar that are often the most dangerous, as you will see.

A Speech Outside the Whitehouse

Lincoln's Promise To Honour The Peace With the South and Achieve Abolition In His Faith and Covenant of A Great Nation Re-United.

Chapter 3

John Wilkes Booth and his Letters

1838- ?
To Thine Own Self Be True

John was born on May 10th 1838 in Bel Air, Maryland Farm twenty six miles from Baltimore near Hickory and Oldchurch, the ninth of ten children. He went to boarding school, a solid stone mansion, of exceptional warmth and affection ran by the Elders, the Quakers at Cockeysville. One Elder philosophically said that silence was a golden rule, but that they who first break it has felt the passing of an angel's wing. And then to St. Timothy's Hall, Catonsville under the tutelage of Messrs. Van Bockelen and Guderdonk with his younger brother, to a finishing school. Here they were baptised and prepared for Confirmation in the Episcopal Church. They had entered as artillery cadets and wore the steel-grey uniform of their class. Some of the best names of Maryland were on the roll of students at this Hall. Here we have the beginnings of the supposed story of his tattoo, seemingly from Asia herself. As a boy he had clumsily marked on the back of one hand his initials in Indian ink, so the false story goes, (thus of a temporary nature yet the image was still purloined by Baker from the soldier's tattoo). Once, the boys had rebelled and withdrew to the woods, defying authority, and their fathers had to be called in and so John penned a few of Shakespeare's lines:

"Something is rotten in the state of Denmark……

Foul meat, eaten with silver forks……..

All that glitters is not gold …….."

They were punished by forfeiting some holidays.

John also loved music. His disposition was cheerful and up-beat, but he was a singular combination of gravity and joy. The songs he loved- and he was passionately fond of music, were all sad and plaintive ones. He could understand the sadness of the Jew's harp, of the black man twanging out a tuneless noise in the dark kitchen…..in doleful minor, with real improvised negro sentiment or fun, were eagerly sought by him. He was full of merriment too, but hated bad jokes, particularly theatrical ones; he used to say to a prosy narrator of worn-out stage anecdote:

"Don't bring damnation on yourself by swearing to the truth of your anecdotes, let them off as jokes."

And again ,

"I know these good old tales are only lies, but when you vouch for the truth of them so seriously, a fellow feels such a fool pretending he believes them, and trying to look surprised and to laugh always in the right place."

'This plain speaking spoilt the flavour of many a pungent joke that had never fallen flat before.'

"I cannot see why sensible people will trouble themselves to concoct such ridiculous stories of their great actors. We know that two thirds of the funny anecdotes about our own father are disgraceful falsehoods. Now for instance, that comical account of yours about the company finding him sitting on a rock in the Gunpowder river, and having to fish him out in time to get ready to act Sir Edward Mortimer. We know well enough that our father never went for a day's fishing anywhere, and that he never plied a fishing rod in his life. I often wonder where the fun is, and where merit the lies- and who invented that preposterous lie of Mrs. Siddons stabbing the potato."

'The droll thoughtful way he uttered this concluding remark caused a burst of laughter, in which the snubbed anecdotarian joined, not unwillingly.'

It sounds just like King Alfred burning the cakes. People can only hang on to the wisps of history and the characters become either jokes, saints, hero's or villains, depending on the political requirements of the era. Asia continues:

'John was a lover of botany and geology and had a collection of many specimens. He was very tender of flowers, and of insects and butterflies, lightning bugs he considered as 'bearer's of sacred torches', and would go out of his way to avoid injuring them. He once, after nights of endeavour, caught me a katy-did, just to show me what the little nuisance was like. I wanted it eagerly for my collection.'

'THE FARM'; BELAIR, MARYLAND

"No you don't, you bloodthirsty female," he said, putting the creature in his breast;

"Katy shall be free and shall sing to-night out in the sycamores."

'With that he walked over to the trees, and late the little night brawler safely among the leaves, to tune her pipes for night once more. Wilkes and I had many tastes in common; we both loved music and reading aloud, both preferred verse to prose; we went through many ponderous books together, reading histories of other countries and of our own...Bulwer, Maryatt, Byron, Longfellow, Milton, Willis, Poe, Hemans, Greek and Roman History....Plutarch's 'Lives and Morals' and Nathaniel Hawthorne. He played the flute and we sang together, accompanied by the piano or the guitar. He would recite poems and the works of Shakespeare. We took early morning rides before sun-up, when the dew lay like rain on the grass, and evening rides by moonlight, singing aloud as we rode. It was on one of these quiet nights as we let our horses walk, while we enjoyed the pungent odours of the pines and the smoky scent of the Lombardy poplars after the fierce shower, that on emerging from the long archway of trees, Wilkes broke out into a lusty song, and the horses started at a quickened pace in time with his singing. Then loosening their reigns he sang first a slow sad tune, and without a touch of ours the horses fell into measure; then we started a lively air, and they quickened their gate to our time.'

And in later years John used to attend secret meetings at the Know-Nothing Society in which Anti Slavery was there goal. The Know-Nothings were in fact a part of the new

Republican Movement. The Free Soil Party was but one expression of northern states 'popular dissatisfaction with the two major political parties' efforts, to leave slavery to the individual states; but the fear of separation into rival pro-slavery and anti-slavery American republics prevented a national resolution of the issue. By 1856 the Free Soil Party, the Know-Nothings, the Abolitionists and other anti-slavery factions had come together to form the new Republican Party. The Republicans called for the national abolition of slavery and nominated John C. Fremont to be their leader in the 1856 national election. They lost, but in 1860 the Republicans were better organized for a national campaign. They nominated Abraham Lincoln, and won the election. The country did split into two republics, and the bloody Civil War ensued. In effect Wilkes Booth was essentially a Republican and in favour of Abolition.
So where did the Baker and the illuminati and company get their information that John was a racist? It seems he was the exact opposite and in fact Lincoln got his ticket on Abolition. So Wilkes Booth and Lincoln had a common goal. Thus from Asia: 'Wilkes's bedroom was facing the east: he said,

"No setting sun view for me, it is to melancholy; let me see him rise."

Which he frequently did, coming home from the hunt and the Know-Nothing meetings, which were held at some secret place several miles distant; or in busy times when he was compelled to send the men to work at sun-up. He wanted no carpet on his floor-'he liked the smell of the oak'. A huge pair of antlers and swords pistols, daggers and a rusty old blunderbuss. A large case containing his school books, small cheaply bound volumes of Bulwer, Maryatt, Byron and a large Shakespeare, with Roman and Grecian histories, Longfellow, Whittier (Author: the anti-slavery poet from New Hampshire), Milton, N.P. Willis, Poe, and Felicia Heman's poems. These red-covered books had been purchased by himself, or presented by young friends. His bed was the hardest mattress and a straw pillow, for at this time of his life he adored Agesilaus the Spartan King, and distained luxuries. In winter I through over his bed a quilt that I had made, of Job-tears pattern.

"Oh, take away that sorrowful canopy," he said, pretending to shiver.

"I shall see old Job at the foot of my bed, naked and bent, with long white locks, and beard hanging to his knees, and shedding tears as big as these patches. I have seen a picture like that somewhere, and I don't want to be haunted and made melancholy by the thought of Job. I think God tried him to the very verge of despair."

Once he burst out with joyous exclamation,

"Heaven and Earth! How glorious it is to live! How divine! To breathe this breath of life with a clear mind and healthy lungs! Don't let us be sad," he would say.

"Life is so short-and the world is so beautiful. Just to breathe is delicious." '

It reminds me of the great British singer and comedian Ken Dodd with his 'Happiness, Happiness, the Greatest Gift that I Possess.' Although much has been written elsewhere, most of it is either false, mythological or strictly biased and derogatory, against this artistic and interesting young man. However, much can be learnt about his inner thoughts from his private letters to his sister Asia and his mother and by reading the edited book….'The Unlocked Book' (published in 1938 by Faber & Faber of London). All his artefacts and photographs and belongings in her possession were taken from her by the NDP , in effect purloined, as if owned by the state. There was also a letter from Samuel Arnold advising him to give up all thoughts of his kidnap plan because the authorities were fully aware of it, which they also took. In fact all information contained in criticisms, letters, playbills and theatrical records, has been lost in the general destruction of papers and effects belonging to him. Indeed all in the families possessions, even his picture as a baby. His books of literature and music were seized or savagely destroyed. Have we not seen this kind of propaganda many times over, that it is only the fascists that do this kind of overkill of literature, out of fear. Here is her description of what happened on his last visit to her:

' "I might need to communicate with you about my money affairs, and there is no need to let everyone know what I am worth."

I resisted, and then he said, taking a large packet from his breast,

"Lock this in your safe for me. I may come back for it, but if anything should happen -to me-open the packet alone and send the letters as directed, and the money and papers give to their owners."

It was not unusual to speak thus of possible accidents, for these reckless times the travel was rough and incessant, and a travelling actor's life is one of exposure to danger. I promised to lock up the packet. He kissed me many times goodbye, and I sat where he had left me looking at the long envelope in my lap, with the word 'Asia' written on it. In a few moments he returned and said,

"Let me see you lock up the packet."

Together we unfastened the heavy door, the heavy door , then unbarred the inner room of stone and iron, and I stooped and placed the packet in the iron safe. I hid the last key away and sat on the sofa, and he came and knelt beside me. I smoothed his black hair carelessly. He said,

"When will your child be born, my girl?"

"In five months, I think or less."

"I hope you will keep well and get stronger, dear."

Then as we rose together, he kissed me very tenderly and said,

"God bless you, sister mine-take care of yourself and try to be happy."

"Oh, my boy," with all the anxiety of my heart, " I shall never be happy till I see your face again."

There is no more to add. The rest is horror, fitted for a diary, than these pages. In time the blow fell on us, a loving, united and devoted family; and in time an enraged and furious Government did us much bitter wrong , and some justice. The packet I opened alone, and destroyed an envelope with a man's name written upon it. It is a name since numbered with the dead. The ashes of this paper I blew about the room for safety, and the letter, with another envelope addressed 'S.K. Chester', I handed to my husband, and others who stood near. The packet contained, besides this, bonds or coupons for his mother, a transfer of an oil well to Junius Booth, another for his sister Rosalie. His Boston land was afterwards given by his mother to her son Joseph, and I retained the envelope marked 'Asia.' This was afterwards taken from me.

Above all his kind love to me, I thanked him most that he left me nothing. Had he done so, it would have put a whip in my Foe's hand, to torture my remaining life. Mr. J.S. Clarke thoughtlessly gave that enclosed letter alluding to a kidnapping scheme to Mr. Stockton, his personal friend and the reporter of a daily newspaper, and, as every shred of news was voraciously accepted, the letter was published, and arrests followed in quick succession.

It was like the days of the Bastille in France. Arrests were made suddenly and in the dead of night. No reason or warning given, only let anyone breath a doubt of the most innocent person and arrest followed swift, and the incarceration meant to wait the law's leisure, innocent or guilty. Detectives women and men, decoys, and all that vile rabble of human bloodhounds infested the city. Junius Booth, who was in Cincinnati, acting, came to our house. He was arrested, but the officer politely put the handcuffs in his own pocket, and allowed the prisoner to walk nuanced at two o'clock in the morning. A few nights later J. S. Clarke was arrested, and both were placed in the Old Capitol Prison. Joseph who had just arrived after three and a half years' trip to Australia, was arrested before landing, and placed in jail in New York. Edwin was surrounded by influential friends , but with an outer guard of spies to note his movements.

This unfortunate publication , so useless now when the scheme had failed-and it led to no fresh discoveries-bought a host of miseries, for it not only served for food to newsmongers and enemies, but it directed a free band of male and female detectives to our house, and the newspapers called on 'servants to be spies upon their employers in the cause of the Government.'

John's Letter To Asia Purloined To Fabricate The Unknown Soldier's Diary

And so on. This last visit from her dear brother must have coincided with his disappearance in April , because her child was born at the end of August. Edwin wrote to her:

"Think no more of him as your brother; he is dead to us now, as soon as he must be to all the world, but imagine the boy you loved to be in that better part of his spirit, in another world."

Then the final news of her brother's death, would you believe it from another theatre, The Walnut Street Theatre and a certain T. J. Hemphill:

'The old man stood steadying himself by the centre table; he did not raise his eyes, his face was very pale and worked nervously. The attitude and pallor told the news he had been deputed to convey.

"Is it over?"

"Yes , madam."

"Taken?"

"Yes"

"Dead?"

"Yes, madam."

My heart beat like strong machinery, powerful and loud it seemed. I laid down with my face to the wall, thanking God silently, and heard the old man's sobs choking him, heard him go out, and close the street door after him. Someone sent up, by my servant a slip from the newspaper with the news that …on hearing the news Mrs. J.S. Clarke had gone mad, and was at present confined at the Asylum at West Philadelphia.'

And the horrors went on but she did not weaken but grew strong in her resolve and managed to keep her composure and her sanity. Her husband pushed ahead with his divorce plea, 'which would be his only salvation now'. Well JWB never did think much of him in the first place and John was a good judge of character. After this came tirade after tirade of abuse from every quarter whipped into a fury by the ever vigilant press, propagating their greed for slanderous stories whilst being patriotic of course. But then, they were never trained to grasp the concept, or the essence of objective truth.
One precious lady, a total stranger, managed to stop the rot:

'….all these and more were doubly, trebly outweighed by the one true womanly letter copied below. The original is treasured as precious gold.

May 3rd, 1865, Phila.

Mrs. Clarke,
Dear Madam,
Although a perfect stranger to you, I take the liberty of offering my sympathy and aid you in your great sorrow and sickness. If my mother or myself can be of the slightest use to you in any way in this world we should be only too happy. I should have offered before but illness prevented. May God help and bless you, is the Constant prayer of

Effie Germon

1129 Race Street.

There is no solidity in Love, no truth in Friendship, no steadiness in Marital Faith, and no reason in an angry nation, but above and beyond all this exceeding bitterness, this little token of rare and unsought friendliness is sufficient to set the faithlessness of the world aside, and almost revive belief in human goodness.'

There is an addendum letter of seven or eight pages which says was to be published after her death, and it includes in the last half paragraph only, of what appears to be her own writing, and is signed Asia Booth Clark. This writing at first sight appears genuine, excepting for the simple reason that it has no beginning, just the tail end. This letter mentions Sleeper Clarke and vouching for his innocence in complicity with JWB. It mentions the story of the bullet with a name engraved upon it. This story was a complete fable. It mentions Michael O'Laughlin but she herself had burned the letter with his name on it from John, never to mention it again. Also it sometimes relates to her as if in the third person. In referring to a little volume she had written called 'Memoir of Booth the Elder':

'.... in a few months of mental and bodily anguish. It was ready for the press before the 20th August 1865, on which day the sad writer gave birth to two babes.'

And babes is not Asia's style at all. And 'she' mentions 'sic semper tyrannis', the fall of the Republic, a dynasty of kings. Also …'so firmly did he believe in what he had done, he declared with his parting strength,

' Tell my mother- I died for my country!'

Even Boston Corbett the man who shot 'Booth' said he never uttered a word in all the two hours he lay dying. Also it says Doctor Mudd who assisted Wilkes Booth, was a cousin to Anne Mudd, the Abbess at the Carmelite Convent, where Asia received her education. Why would Asia bother to mention this prophetically after her death? And

'she' called her brother Wilkes Booth, not Wilkes as she normally did. It says she returned Boston Corbett's letter to him because she thought it honourable to do so and she forgave him, and thought he was a hero and there should be a memorial for him. Corbett was an honest soldier and knew he had shot a Confederate soldier, not Booth. He therefore had no reason to write to her and certainly would not write her a lying letter. He was a devout Methodist and above all he was no hypocrite. Finally it implied that she thought Wilkes Booth was mad, that his mind had lost its balance between the fall of Richmond, and the terrific end. In fact the illuminati had even tried to imply that she also was mad, in the press at the time, as they did Louis Payne, but he proved in court that he was perfectly sane. This might suggest that they were the one's that were 'mad'.
This surely is a final testimony inserted by the illuminati to get Sleeper Clarke off the hook and to reinforce yet again, all the mock evidence that her brother had slain the President. All of this was later secretly inserted into the 'Unlocked Book' published in England long after her death. Their dirty tricks never stop. This extensive malapropism and insertions in a book was a deceptive improvement on Baker's clumsy efforts, but its just as evil in 1938. The illuminati will have difficulty in subtly changing the words of this book, since it is not easily within the bounds of their intelligence to do so. The only recourse they have is propaganda, mass burning or a whole division of rogue Professors Of Mystery re-writing it. And Asia was so kind to them.

There was a certain red pocket diary supposedly belonging to Booth published by James M Crawford of St. Louis for the year of 1864 was kept in the hands of Stanton until a Senate committee demanded to see it at the time Baker was up before them. They demanded he tell them who had ripped out the '18' consecutive missing pages of this civilian pocket diary. However this red diary really belonged to a Confederate soldier, which was delivered to Baker by Conger, and then both turned it over to Stanton. Note of interest: Military diaries were kept by commissioned officers and enlisted men much later, during the 1st World war, crammed with all kinds of data. They were known as Military Field Note Books and were mainly for instruction, with only a limited space for short notes. These stapled notes could be freely ripped out (containing perforations) that were known as Combat Messages.
Baker's response to the Senate became more than insistent, he was visibly and verbally angry, when they suggested he had removed them. Instead he swore that he and Colonel Conger together had handed over the diary to Stanton intact. Yet when Stanton was summoned he denied ripping out these pages also. This might have been true if you consider that the diary they handed over, actually belonged to a soldier. Baker however had certainly already removed the pages himself and forged it to fool Stanton into believing it belonged to Booth. That is why Baker made sure he had a very senior witness to support him when he handed the forged diary over to Stanton. Booth's own letter(s) may have been handed in by another officer when his trunk at the National

Hotel had been searched by the NDP e.g. the one from Samuel Arnold telling him to desist from the kidnap plan, but the other letters were taken from Asia, and had certainly been given over to Baker. The proof of the reasoning for these certainties is given below when we examine Booth's letters and the purloined diary.
'Booth's diary' with the missing '18' pages is now at the Ford Theatre and can be best read on the Web as exhibited by the FBI. Apart from being an out of date 1864 diary and a leap year, the handwriting in the dated section begins on June 17th 1864, but this is over-written and the writing actually begins Friday-April 14th 1865. This date is hand written, (even this already raises the question of authenticity). It seems there are actually 28 pages missing up till mid-June, since there are 6 days per page. In fact the writing in this section of the diary is distinctly different from the Booth's actual letter writing in the plain sections, in a number of ways:

1. The handwriting is quite different in the diary. The letters are not joined up so well ; it is scruffy and the writing is un-even and varies in slope but often to the vertical.

2. There are no apparent dates on the letters of Booth and no sign that they are notes from a diary.

3. The sentences are much shorter in the diary. Booth wrote with a much more flowing style. This style is very distinctive in that all the letters lean at a gentle slope to the right, written with natural ease and artistic beauty.

4. The writing lines are not straight in the diary. Booth's lines are perfectly straight and much longer.

5. There is much more crossing out in the diary but Booth's errors in the letters are very few.

6. Booth underlines many words to stress his points. The notes in the diary sections have few underlines.

7. The writing flows over the dates in the diary, thus appearing continuous and without bothering to chronologies or reference to the real days, as would be expected in keeping a real diary.

8. The words are simpler, in the diary; of shorter span, strictly limited in literature and with a hopeless brevity of expression.

9. There are several copied lines, as if copied from Booth's letters word for word.

Baker's fabrication of the soldier's diary:

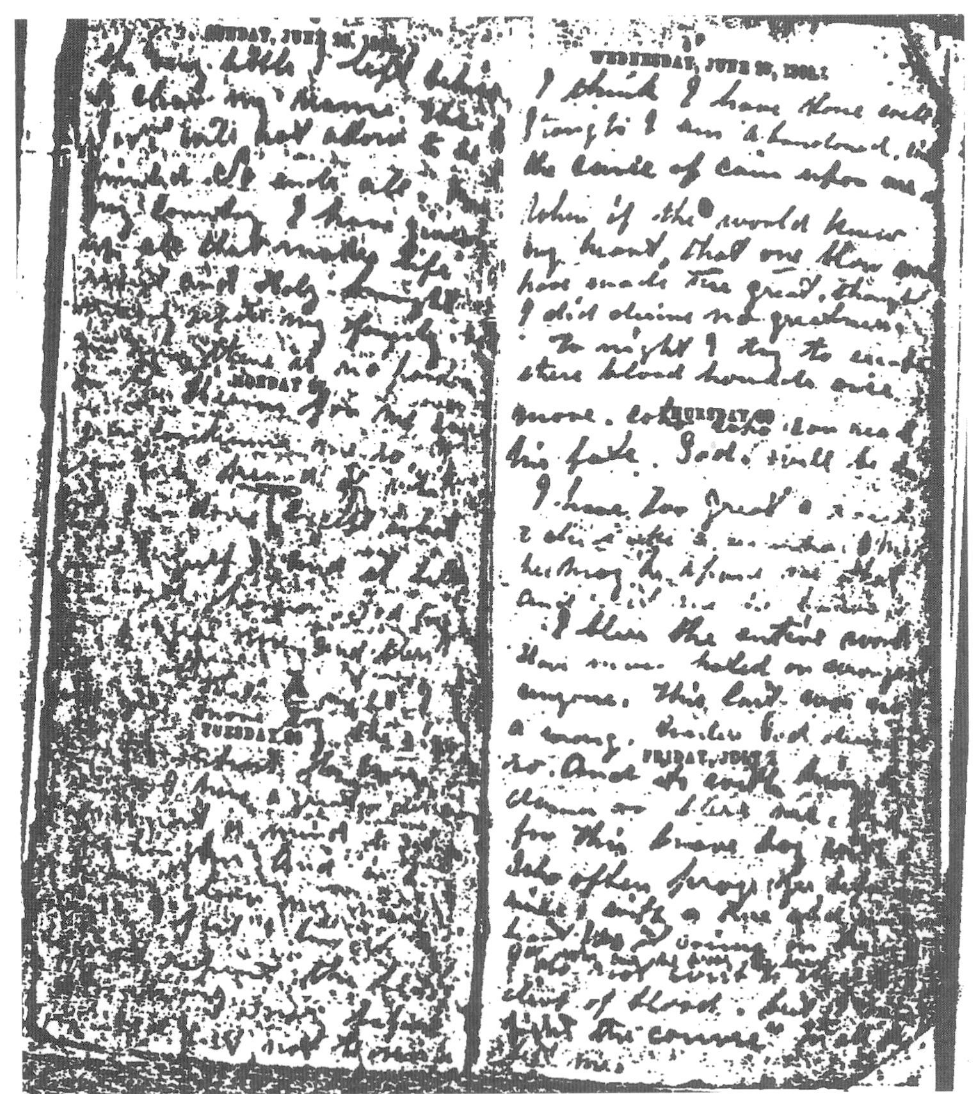

Baker's Handiwork in All Its Wavy, Waning and Wayward Wanderings

In regards to content, the diary sections are written by another hand because:

10. In the diary he is talking to his mother in the third person and about bringing misery on his family, whereas in the genuine letters, in one soliloquy, he is addressing to her directly several times 'my dear mother' confessing his undying love to her and his happy home, and signed John. There is also another letter where he signs John Wilkes Booth in a long flowing style and this is more philosophical, however this is also genuine and he signs the page as if it was a letter, not a diary.

11. He suggests in the diary 'the very little I left behind to clear my name, the Government will not allow to be printed.' Why would he say this if he had done the deed? (Note: The little he left behind refers to his belongings kept in a trunk, at the National Hotel, that were taken by the NDP).

12. It says in the diary, he has a desire to return to Washington to clear 'his' name. How could he want to do this, since the next sentence says ' I do not repent the blow I struck.'? And in another two lines he says: 'God cannot pardon me.......for striking down a greater tyrant than they ever knew.' This surely is a confession to the deed that would stand zero chance of clearing his name.

13. It says he shouted 'Sic semper before I fired. In jumping broke my leg.' Yet the official version is that he shouted this line on the stage to the audience, after shooting Lincoln. And why didn't he complete the line ......tyrranis? And neither did the 'New York Times' complete this line.

14. The diary confession is hand written dated, beginning on the Friday 14th the assassination day, followed by 'The Ides' then begins 'Until today.....I struck boldly, and not as the papers say.'
How or why would he have digested the papers, all the time on the run in the swamps and wilderness of Southern Maryland? And what is the reference to 'The Ides' (of March and Ceaser's assassination). The line in the next paragraph explains this, just dated April... (perhaps days later), that is 'I am here in despair . And why? For doing what Brutus was honoured for.' What nonsense is this? Yes, more thespian rubbish in a continuous daily theme, from a hit man on the run in the swamps.

15. In fact the only thing these different accounts have in common are the several copied lines and they both use black ink; and the copies are photographically black, anyway.

John's letter to his mother:

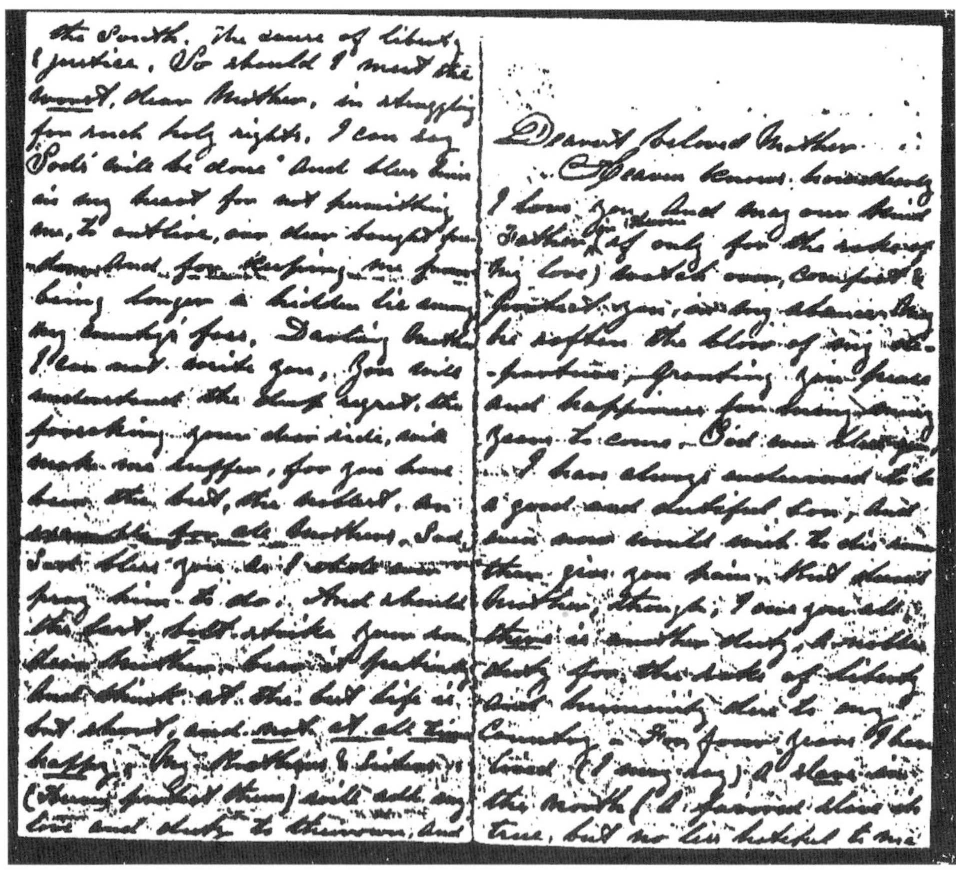

the South. the cause of liberty & justice. So should I meet the worst, dear Mother, in struggling for such holy rights. I can say "Gods will be done" And bless Him in my heart for not permitting me, to outlive, our dear bought freedom. And for keeping me from being longer a hidden lie among my country's foes. Darling Mother I can not write you. You will understand the deep regret, the forsaking your dear side, will make me suffer, for you have been the best, the noblest, an example for all mothers. God, God bless you as I shall ever pray him to do. And should the last, bitter strike you, dear Mother bear it patiently And think at the best life is but short, and not at all times happy. My Brothers & Sisters (Heaven protect them) will add my love and duty to theirs, and

Dearest beloved Mother
Heaven knows how dearly I love you. And may our kind Father in Heaven (if only for the sake of my love) watch over, comfort & protect you, in my absence. May He soften the blow of my departure, granting you peace and happiness for many, many years to come. God ever bless you.
I have always endeavored to be a good and dutiful son, And even now would wish to die sooner than give you pain. But dearest Mother, though I owe you all, there is another duty, a noble duty for the sake of liberty and humanity due to my Country. For four years I have lived (I may say) A slave in the north (A favored slave its true, but no less hateful to me

The Beautiful Artistic writing of Wilkes is evident in this letter to his mother Line after Line in Perfect Line and Perfect Style with no trace of Error.

16. In regards to the letters it is clear that in his letter to his mother, two pages have been placed side by side from right to left, so this is not a logical sequence in a diary. Besides there is no central shadows of a diary here, just a clean line.

In Chapter 13 you will see what the true contents of the 28 missing pages were.

And in reference to point 13) Baker, 3 years later, in his book says:

" About ten o'clock in the evening of April 14, 1865, while the play, "Our American Cousin," was progressing, a stranger who proved to be John Wilkes Booth, an actor of some note, worked his way into the proscenium box, occupied by the presidential party, and levelling a pistol close behind the head of Mr. Lincoln, he fired, and the ball was lodged deep in the brain of the President. The assassin then drew a dirk, sprang from the box, flourishing the weapon aloft, and shouted , as he reached the stage, the motto upon the escutcheon of the State of Virginia, "Sic Semper Tyrannis"! He dashed across the stage, and before the audience could realise the position of affairs, the murderer had mounted a fleet horse in waiting in an alley in the rear of the theater and galloping off, he escaped for a time."

Baker's secret image of Booth was of ancient Roman good looks, having dark features and a Roman nose, and he imagined that women adored him even though he was just a 'knocked kneed' actor. To continue now with the genuine writing in the letters:

The genuine writing describes him addressing his mother where he pours out his heart about his feelings. It does appear he his thinking of kidnapping Mr. Lincoln (but it is not dated here) intending to get an exchange of prisoners. He felt the South was being blamed for slavery as a means for the North to justify the war. He thought their policies were becoming more and more unjust and cruel and puts the blame on Lincoln. He feels the Union government was the real cause of initiating the war and the prime mover in the upsetting of peace, for financial gain, and they were maliciously guilty of national fratricide. He says he would gladly give up all and die for the South but above all, for justice. He says he loves his mother and family even though they do not concur with his politics. He honestly felt that African people were long taken from their home-lands where they belonged, thus implicating that it was wrong that they should have been brought over as slaves to be used by white people to gain profit. But that the South was not the main blame and the North were capitalising on this, even in the freeing of slaves, they would be used as cheap labour in the North; be it inevitable and for all people and freedom's sake. In effect the South would suffer badly from this division of labour. He said his income was $20,000 a year, yet he felt like a political slave in the North without freedom of speech, and his career he would gladly sacrifice, and his happy home. He does not mention a wife or any girlfriend here. The writing and thoughts of Booth in this section without doubt, are authentic and indicate no sign or indeed no single thought of assassination. In the false dated section (in the diary) however, which is the most often publicised, the confessions are self evident and totally fabricated. In one letter to a friend, or possibly to his sister, Asia, he signs it with a beautiful flowing style saying what he might do, he claims is 'on his own responsibility'. This implicates Baker most clearly in the purloining of his letters, because Baker refers directly to this line in his book. Thus:

" When Booth began, 'on his own responsibility,' to hunt for accomplices, he found his theory at fault. The bold men he had dreamed of refused to join him in the rash attempt at kidnapping the President, and were too conscientious to meditate in murder. All those who presented themselves, were military men, unwilling to be subordinate to a civilian, and a mere play actor, and the mortified bravado found himself, therefore, compelled to sink to a petty rank in the plot to make use of base and despicable assistants. His vanity found it easier to compound with the second alternative than the first".

It also indicates how ridiculous that such an alternative deed, intending to assassinate Lincoln, Grant and half the cabinet in Washington by Booth, would turn out to be. Thus, accompanied by a non-professional band described by Baker, as being 'of base and despicable assistants' that Booth had chosen, because of his vanity. This would take the mind of an idiot to imagine, let alone contemplate. However the 'idiot' in fact was

Baker, and he got away with it because of the 'invisible assassin' and the powers of the illuminati. If one takes a kinder view of Booth you will find he was first a gentleman in the truest sense of the word, his class, in his dress, outlook, profession, good looks, courage, charming manner, sense of duty, generosity, and self made style and success in his profession. How the illuminati could turn him into an evil killer shows how clever they were with the full backing of the press playing upon the weakness of the public mood after the assassination. He was particularly attractive to women although not tall he had classic dark good looks, the famous black moustache and a flock of jet black hair, not a single blemish on his pure white skin and walked with a confident and flamboyant air. A man gifted with talent and a good future guaranteed. By then he was earning top rates as a classic actor and not by any means second rate, although the critics even tried to rob him of that afterwards. His gait was slightly bent and he cut a slightly tragic figure faintly resembling Charlie Chaplain. He could ride extremely well and was probably familiar with firearms as he had been an agent delivering dispatches and medicines to and from Richmond and for General Robert E. Lee, where he may have seen action. However he does say in his letters that he never took part as a soldier in any battlefield. The stories are thick and thin of him carrying pictures of women including Lucy Hale when 'his body' was searched. These stories of course are not true (except the photographs in the purloined diary would have belonged to the brave soldier) and only serve to enrich the legends of an heroic villain who was also a red blooded American (not to let the side down). It is rumoured he did have another girlfriend besides Lucy to visit, and she lived in Pennsylvania, her name was Kate Scott an army nurse, who later claimed he was still alive. One might suspect it was just another lady's claim that she once loved a handsome hero. However there are also many stories of other girlfriends that have multiplied over the years. He did of course have liaisons with other girls at times, as evidenced when starring at the Woods theatre in Nashville, Tennessee, when he and his friend Andrew Johnson (later the President) hit it off with two sisters there between shows. An actor of course is a traveller and like musicians they spend many lonely nights in many lonely towns on the road. And in those days being 'on the road' was a far more rugged affair than today. If they are famous they try to project their love to all their fans, a somewhat daunting task, to which their hearts must ever be true and not just settling for the singular. Indeed one of his younger peers the great actress Clara Morris described him thus:

"In glancing back over two crowded and busy seasons, one figure stands out in clearness and beauty. In this case so far as my personal knowledge goes, there is nothing derogatory to dignity and manhood in being called 'beautiful' for he was that bud of splendid promise blasted to the core before its full triumphant blooming, known to the world as a madman and assassin, but to the profession as 'that unhappy boy, John Wilkes Booth.' He was so young, so bright, so kind. I could not have known him well? Of course, too, there are two or three different people in every man's skin. Yet when we remember that stars are not in the habit of showing their brightest, best side at

rehearsals, we cannot help feeling both respect and liking for the one who does.
There are not many men who can receive a gash over the eye at a scene at night without at least a momentary outburst of temper, but when the combat between Richard and Richmond was being rehearsed, John Wilkes Booth had again and again, urged McCullom—that six foot tall and handsome man who used to entrust me with the care of his watch during such encounters, 'Come on hard, come on hot, old fellow! Harder, faster!' That he would take the chances of a blow if only they could make a hot fight of it. Mr. McCullom, who was a cold man at night, became nervous in his efforts to act like a fiery one. He forgot that he had struck the full number of hard blows and when Booth was expecting a thrust, McCullom wielding his sword with both hands brought it down with an awful force fair across Booth's forehead. A cry of horror arose, for in one moment his face was marked in blood, one eyebrow was cut through. Then came simultaneously one deep groan from Richard (Booth) and an exclamation of 'Oh good God, good God!' from Richmond (McCollum) who stood trembling like a leaf and staring at his work. Booth, flinging the blood from his eyes with his left hand, said as gently as a man could speak: 'That is all right, old man. Never mind me, only come on hard, and save the fight,' which he resumed at once. And although he was perceptibly weakened, it required a sharp order from Mr. Ellsler to ring the first curtain bell to force him to bring the fight to a close a single blow shorter than usual. There was a running to and fro with ice and vinegar, raw steak and raw oysters, and when the doctor placed a few stitches where they were most required, Booth laughingly declared that there were provisions enough to start a restaurant. McCullom came to try to apologize, to explain, but Booth would have none of it. He held out his hand saying.
"Why, old fellow, you look as if you lost the blood. Don't worry—now, if my eye had gone, that would have been bad".
So, with light words he turned to set the unfortunate man at ease, and though he must have suffered much mortification and pain from the eye, he never made a sign showing it. John Wilkes Booth, like his next elder brother, was rather lacking in height, but his head and throat and the manner of their rising from his shoulders were truly beautiful. His coloring was unusual, the ivory pallor of his skin, the inky blackness of dusky curly hair, the heavy lids of his glowing eyes, were all oriental, and they gave a touch of mystery to his face when it fell into gravity, but there was generally a flash of white teeth behind his black silky moustache. Now it is scarcely exaggerating to say that the fair sex was in love with John Wilkes Booth, or John Booth as he was called, the name Wilkes apparently being unknown to his family and close friends. I played with John Wilkes to my great joy, playing Player Queen in the Marble Heart. I was one of the group of three statues in the first act, then a girl in my teens.
With all my admiration for the person and genius of John Wilkes Booth, his crime I cannot condone. The killing of that homely, tender-hearted father, Abraham Lincoln, a rare combination of courage, justice, and humanity, whose death at the hands of an actor will be a grief of horror and shame to the profession forever. And I cannot believe that

John Wilkes Booth was the leader of a band of bloody conspirators. Who shall draw the line and say, 'Here genius ends and madness begins'? There was that touch of strangeness, in Edwin it was a profound melancholy; in John it was an exaggeration of spirit, almost a madness. There was a natural vanity of the actor too who craves a dramatic selection in real life. There was also his passionate love and sympathy for the South, which was easier to play upon than a pipe. Undoubtedly he conspired to kidnap the President; that would appeal to him. But after that I truly believe he was a tool; certainly he was no leader. Those who led him knew his courage, his belief in fate, his loyalty to his friends, and because they knew these things he drew the lot as it was meant he should from the first. Then, half mad, he accepted the part fate cast him for and committed the murderous crime. 'God moves in a mysterious way And His wonders to perform. And God shutteth not up his mercies forever in displeasure.' We can only shiver and turn our thoughts away from the bright light that went out in such utter darkness; poor guilty, unhappy, John Wilkes Booth."

And Booth did project this image and not just to his peers and fans but to all the staff in the theatre as evidence from witnesses at the Ford theatre. In short he could charm and impress people at any level or station. Even lesser men looked up to him because he must have given them inspiration and lifted them from their care torn moods for a brief moment in time. This talent is not without its downside and must have engendered envy from his peers and others, and even jealousy from slighted women. His most famous girlfriend was the senator's daughter Lucy Hale with whom he had become attached to and was seen with in listening to a speech made by Lincoln at the White House. He was also seen chatting to her out front at the intermission of 'Our American Cousin' by a female witness but this is unconfirmed. It might explain why he arrived late from his horse ride to and from Crystal City in the hope of seeing her their because he was not bothered about the play. And perhaps also to see Lincoln the object of his passion to kidnap but had finally, through good sense and advice from Samuel Arnold and John Surratt, counter sanctioned. Now compare Clara's view of Booth with that of the envious Baker, who had never met him:

"Half applauded, half rebuffed by the rebel agents in Canada., Booth's impressions of his visit were just those which would whet him soonest for the tragedy. His vanity had been fed by the assurance that success depended upon himself alone, and that as he had the responsibility he would absorb the fame; and the method of correspondence was of that dark and mysterious shape which powerfully operated on his dramatic temperament. And so he grew into the idea of murder. It became his business thought. It was his recreation and his study. He had not worked so hard for histrionic success as for his terrible graduation into an assassin. He had fought often on the boards, and had seen men die in well imitated horror, with flowing blood on the keen sword's edge and the strong stride of mimic victory with which he flourished his weapon at the closing of the curtain. He embraced conspiracy like an old diplomatist, and found in the women and the spot subjects for emulation."

What kind of complex man, that lay within this suave debonair man of his actor's generation, can we deduce. The war effected everyone and in Maryland, where Booth was born of the great English tragic actor Junius Brutus Booth, had become a hotbed of insurrection because geographically it marked the Mason-Dixon line, the dividing line between North and South. The Mason - Dixon line was surveyed and delineated in 1763 to 1767 by two Englishmen, one a Surveyor the other an Astronomer. Charles Dixon and Jeremiah Mason essentially vertically split the Delaware peninsula with northern Maryland, then horizontally in a dead straight line demarking Pennsylvania from then, all Virginia, along the latitude of 39 degrees and 43 minutes North, every mile marked with stones, and every 10 miles, engraved Crown stones from England, along to where it joins the Ohio River. This was in part, to resolve a dispute between Lord Calvert 6th Baron of Baltimore and the William Penn family under a settlement by the English Crown. But this was also a cultural divide between the North and the South and Washington was well south of it. Pennsylvania had abolished slavery in 1781, just after Independence (1776), but Delaware and Virginia had not. Maryland was thus stuck in the middle of this cultural divide, much to its distress.

Note, Slavery was effectively abolished by the following States and Capitols in:

Vermont:	1777.	Montpellier.	Missouri:	1865.	Jefferson City
Pennsylvania	1780	Harrisburg.	Florida:	1865.	Tallahassee.
Maine:	1783.	Augusta.	North Carolina:	1865.	Raleigh.
Massachusetts:	1783.	Boston.	South Carolina:	1865.	Columbia.
Rhode Island:	1784.	Providence.	Arkansas:	1865.	Little Rock.
New Jersey:	1787.	Trenton.	Texas:	1865.	Austin
Illinois:	1787.	Springfield.	Alabama:	1865.	Montgomery
Ohio:	1787.	Columbus.	Virginia:	1865.	Richmond
Wisconsin:	1787.	Madison.	Oklahoma:	1865.	Oklahoma C
Michigan:	1787.	Lansing.	Kansas:	1865.	Topeka.
Indiana:	1787.	Indianapolis	Louisiana:	1865.	Baton Rouge.
New York:	1799.	Albany.	Hawaii	1865	Honolulu
Oregon	1844	Salem. .	Maryland	1865	Annapolis
Washington	1848	Seattle.	Mississippi:	1865.	Jackson.
Idaho:	1848	Boise	Delaware	1865	Dover.
Iowa:	1848	De Moines.	Kentucky:	1865	Frankfurt.
California:	1848.	Sacramento.	Tennessee:	1865.	Nashville
Connecticut:	1848.	Hartford.	Georgia:	1865.	Atlanta.
Nebraska	1848.	Lincoln	Virginia	1865	Richmond
Montana	1848	Helena	W. Virginia	1865	Charleston
North Dakota	1848	Bismarck	Alaska	-	Anchorage
South Dakota	1848	Pierre			
New Mexico	1848	Santa Fe.			
Nevada:	1848.	Reno.			
Colorado	1848	Denver.			
Arizona	1848	Phoenix			
New Hampshire:	1857	Concord.			
Delaware:	1860.	Dover.			
Minnesota	1862	St. Paul			
Utah	1862	Salt Lake City			

And in the following countries by:

Sweden & Finland:	1335.
Japan	1588.

Portugal:	1761	
England and Wales:	1772.	In 1807 The Royal Navy was tasked with suppressing it, even when carried on by non-British subjects
Scotland:	1776.	
Haiti:	1791.	
Upper Canada:	1793	by Act Against Slavery
France (first time):	1794 -	1802, including all colonies (although abolition was never carried out in some colonies under British occupation)
Lower Canada:	1803	William Osgoode, then Chief Justice of Lower Canada, but some remained enslaved until the abolition of slavery in the entire British Empire 1834.
Spain	1811	Including some Colonies except Cuba, Trinidad & Tobago.
Chile:	1811	Partially.
Argentina:	1813	
Gran Colombia	1821	Ecuador, Colombia, Panama, and Venezuela, through a gradual emancipation plan Colombia in 1853, Venezuela in 1854.
Central America Federation	1824	Guatemala, El Salvador, Honduras, Nicaragua and Costa Rica.
Mexico:	1829.	
South Africa	1834-1838.	Including Basutoland, Swaziland and magnificent Zululand.
British Empire:	1834.	Including Gambia, Gibraltar, Kenya, Uganda & Tanganyika, Malaya, Malta,, Singapore, Mauritius, Montserrat, Natal, New Guinea, New Hebrides, Australia, NewZealand, Nigeria, Rhodesia Nyasaland, Orange Free State, Papua, New Guinea, Pitcairn Isles, St. Helena, St. Lucia, St. Christopher, Nevis & Anguila, St. Vincent, Seychelles, Sarawak, Shanghai, Somaliland, Transvaal, Virgin Isles, Antigua, Barbados, Bermuda, Bahrain, Basutoland, Bechuanaland, Solomon Isles, Caymen Isles, Cyprus, Dominica, Falkland Isles, Fiji, Gold Coast, Gilbert & Ellice Isles, Grenada, Hong Kong, India, Pakistan, Jamaica and all other colonies.
East Indies	1838.	
Mauritius:	1835	under the British government.
Portugal Colonies:	1836	
Denmark:	1848	including all colonies.
France (second time):	1848	including French Equatorial Africa, Camaroons, Anjouan, Annam, Tonquin, Benin, Cochin-China, Comoro Islands, Cambodia Dahomey, Diego Suarez, Djibouti, Fezzan, French Congo, French Guiana, Somali, French Sudan, Gabon, Ghadames, Comoro, Guadelope, Indo-China, Inini, Ivory Coast, Laos, Martinique Mauratania, Mayotte, Middle Congo, Moheli, New Caledonia, New Hebrides, Niger, Nossi-Be, Obock, Oceanic Settlements, Oubangui-Chari, Reunion, St Marie de Madagascar, St. Pierre and Miquelon, Senegal, Senegambia,, Niger, Tahiti, Tchad, Togo, Upper Volta, Viet-nam, Wallis and Fortuna Islands and all other colonies.
Peru:	1851	
Moldavia:	1855.	
Walachia(S. Rumania):	1856.	

Russia:	1861 The Serfs
The Netherlands:	1863 including colonies, but kept using Recruits from Africa until 1940
United States:	1865 after the U.S. Civil War
Puerto Rico	1873
Cuba:	1880 both were colonies of Spain at the time.
Ottoman Empire:	1876. As late as 1908 women slaves were still sold in the Ottoman Empire.
Brazil:	1888. The last country to do so in the Americas. The Imperial Princess Isabel De Braganca abolished all forms of slavery.
Korea:	1894 hereditary slavery ended in 1886
Madagascar:	1896
Zanzibar:	1897 slave trade abolished in 1873
China:	1910
Nepal:	1921
Sudan:	1924 actually still practiced today.
Iran:	1928
Burma:	1929
Morocco:	1930s.
Ethiopia:	1936. by order of the Italian occupying forces.
Qatar:	1952
Tibet:	1959 by order of the People's Republic of China
Saudi Arabia:	1962
Yemen:	1962
United Arab Emirates:	1963
Oman:	1970
Mauritania:	1980 formally abolished by French authorities in 1905, but finally criminalized in 2007.
Niger:	2003. Slave markets

Many of these dates are approximate due to varying degrees of abolition proceeding in a gradual process and some may not be totally accurate, if so in some cases, the author begs corrections.

Where must a man cast his loyalty and how must he help the cause to be a man? Booth's family were strictly pro-union. Indeed Edwin had saved Robert Lincoln from being hit by a train, not that John would not have done the same for any man. However John was a man of the world and had probably seen or heard first hand of much suffering in both northern and southern prisons. Potter the Detective said he had followed 'Booth' to a farm house at Harpers Ferry, West Virginia which is highly unlikely; but he did have his brother's house in New York city to visit, and often visited the 'Old Dominion' and Canada. His mother had lived at the family home in Harford County, twenty six miles from Baltimore, but she had long moved to Edwin's house in New York. At that time his sister Asia was married to John Sleeper Clarke in Philadelphia, and was always accompanied by a Detective and all letters and photographs relating to Booth were taken from her. They were to steal everything that belonged to him. He played mostly in the South whereas Edwin acted mainly in the North and East. Edwin was scheduled to perform in Boston that Easter but it was cancelled. It is interesting how bad news travels fast. Here we have a letter generated at 7 a.m. by H.C. Jarrett, a Boston theatre manager:

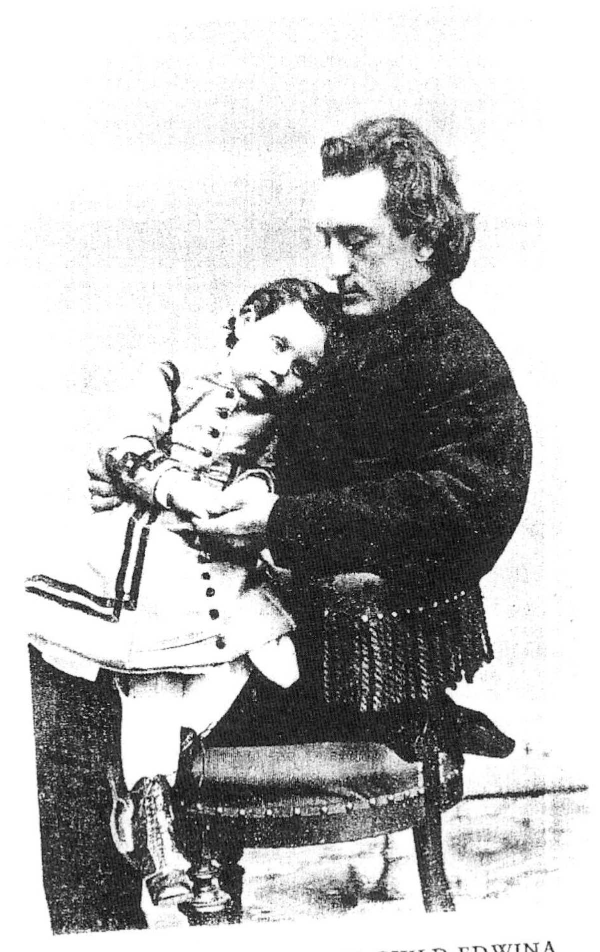

EDWIN BOOTH AND HIS CHILD EDWINA

Edwin had once saved Robert Lincoln from being hit by a train

Parker House, Boston, 7 o'clock a. m.
Saturday, April 15th, 1865

Edwin Booth Esq.
My Dear Sir:
A fearful calamity is upon us. The President of the United States has fallen by the hand of an assassin, and I am shocked to say suspicion points to one nearly related to you as the perpetrator of this horrid deed. God grant it may not prove ! With this knowledge, and out of respect to the anguish which will fill the public mind as soon as the appalling fact shall be fully revealed, I have concluded to close the Boston theatre until further notice. Please signify to me your co-operation in this matter.

In great sorrow and in haste,
I remain yours, very truly.
Henry C. Jarrett.

OK he his advising Edwin, but how did he get the news that it was someone nearly related to Edwin. Even the press had no conclusive evidence, except it was a young man. See Press report of New York Times, 15th April. And what does 'nearly related' mean? The best information is that John had visited this theatre himself on the 5th according to Surratt. And everyone in the business knew they were brothers. Is he being kind, or did he also have inside information? And at 7am Stanton was still waiting for Lincoln to die, whilst his secretary was taking notes from Rathbone of the assassin's identity, inside a guarded house (as indicated by Mr. Field above and Baker below).

Thus, 'Edwin' replied to Jarrett:

Franklin Square, Boston, April 15th, 1865.

My dear Sir:
With deepest sorrow and great agitation, I thank you for relieving me from my engagement with yourself and the public. The news of the morning has made me wretched indeed, not only because I have received the unhappy tidings of a brother's crime, but because a good man, has fallen, in an hour of national joy, by the hand of an assassin. The memory of the thousands who have fallen in the field, in our country's defence , during this struggle, cannot be forgotten by me, even in this, the distressing day of my life. And I most sincerely pray that the victories we have won may stay the brand of war and the tide of loyal blood. While mourning in common with all other loyal hearts, the death of the President, I am oppressed by a private woe not to be expressed in words. But whatever calamity may befall me and mine, my country, one and indivisible, has my warmest devotion. EDWIN BOOTH

It seems however that 'Edwin' has become convinced that it was his brother, yet Jarrett had only said it was someone 'nearly related' to him. And the letters are far too formal, considering they were business friends. In fact Edwin's letter mentions little relating to the business and only seemingly admits to his 'brother's' crime, with no possible evidence. The rest is hype. In fact it literally gloats about 'the victories we have won' with 'the tide of loyal blood', hardly the words of a man who has been confronted with the news that a near relation, might be an assassin. It is yet another forgery. These letters are contained in the edited book called the 'Unlocked Book' . But they are outside of the Chapters of Asia Booth's accounts, so have to be taken with more than a pinch of salt. Indeed you will need all the vast resources of a Siberian salt mine, throughout this whole sorry 'Booth saga'. This book opens with a forward by Eleanor Farejeon, a distant relative of JWB and was published by Faber & Faber Ltd. of London in 1938. The strange thing about this Forward is that it straight away begins with his supposed tattoo. Thus:

"J.W.B are the initials of John Wilkes Booth, the American actor who assassinated Abraham Lincoln. They are the initials branded on his hand in boyhood, by which he identified himself to a Southerner whose help he sought during his attempt to escape-the initials stamped on the leather cover of the book in which his sister Asia wrote the memoir, now printed for the first time."

So first we have the assassin. Then we have a branded tattoo. Was it done with a branding iron perhaps? The dictionary defines 'branded', as a permanent mark deliberately made by a hot iron, or a stigma or a trade mark. Considering this is a refined lady of the 1930's it seems out of character, to say the least. Yet elsewhere in her Forward there is not a bad word to say about Booth. In fact it was published in 1938, just one year after Otto Eisensmichl's book 'Why Was Lincoln Murdered'. Could it be the publisher's influence to some degree to get the book published. I.e. The publisher wanted an admittance of guilt in the first paragraph together with the 'proof' of a branded tattoo. How strange, after all of 72 years later and in a foreign country.

Then there is a quantum leap from Booth's boyhood to identifying himself to a Southerner some 20 years later, by showing him his tattoo. So are we too assume from this bizarre statement that when he met this Southerner, during his escape, it was in order to prove he was Booth by showing him his tattoo, as a means of identification? Then the Southerner helped him! (JWB is not proof as even historians today are still trying to prove these initials stood for another JWB). Well the only Southerner that helped 'him' was a Confederate. Except it wasn't Booth with the tattoo. It was another Confederate, a soldier. In any case 'she' (actually Faber & Faber) has gotten the supposed story wrong because his friend 'Herold' was supposed to be with him all along according to Baker. And so this story in fact supports the truth of a Confederate soldier meeting another Southerner that helped him as a fugitive, therefore disproving that he was an assassin.

When you read Asia's account of them growing up together at their rustic rambling,

country home isolated and remote from Baltimore you will see how they lived close to nature. The pages are beautifully written in all its innocent charm but with astute and incisive observations into human character. Their famous father had died and they lived frugally but with open generosity to any visitors, treating them with southern hospitality often leaving themselves short. John once came in from the farm work and would not even eat if others were hungry. He and Asia were very close and would take long walks and read poetry and the classics together. In the woods he would scald his sister for even daring to kill a fire-fly or a frog. He said these were the natural lights and sounds of nature long before even the birds awakened the majestic stillness of the forests. Her writing is nothing short of poetic beauty and does make considerable insights into her family and the division of labour and social comments. But it mainly revolves around John and is growing into a strong, sensitive, warm, passionate and caring young man, who had a long way to go in fulfilling his future role as one of the greatest actors of his generation.. A man with honour, strength, humour and compassion for all. Naturally, later in life, his spirit for some just or noble cause was in line with the South became to powerful and led him astray. The South was like an abstract love and in its strength therein lay his weakness, for this just and noble cause. It lifted him above mere mortal men as indeed many actors become overly mesmerised by their heroic roles. But with John it became a fixation for the under-dog and Virginia was his vanquished and ravaged Queen.
It is by now patently clear that Booth was an honourable gentleman and his destiny was to be forged against another man of devious cunning whom he did not know and would never meet, but hounded John and his family till the ends of the earth. This other man's background was of the most extreme opposite nature, versed and moulded in the treacherous denizens of the Barbary Coast to become head of the notorious NDP.
It was in the South that John's heart could speak more freely, un-surrounded by rampant paranoia. The favoured just, are cogniscent of what is rampantly unjust be they sometimes blind to their own convention and accepted norms of morality. He was comfortable as an actor and was in demand in many cities North and South. However he was not a soldier and did not volunteer but had undoubtedly been involved in running messages, and medical drugs such as quinine (anti-malaria) and morphine, between Canada and Richmond parallel with John Surratt a blockade runner, so to be involved in the cause. That does not make him a traitor especially as he had lived and often worked in the South and Maryland, astride the political dividing line. Asia said he would come into her married home during the war and speak, too passionately, and she had a great fear in her heart for him. His hands were extremely course and worn, and he confessed it was due to the river runs where he had often rowed long and hard, on these expeditions. Often he would visit in the early hours, exhausted, to fall asleep on the settee, where she would find him in the morning. One day she asked of Michael O'Laughlin and he would not talk about him. It seemed he was another involved in the cause. And so gradually, in this way he eventually took on a bolder plan to kidnap

Lincoln in order to force an exchange of prisoners. After all he probably felt that Lincoln was to blame for all the unnecessary suffering when in fact it was Stanton's policy, albeit not over ruled by Lincoln.

Here was a man trying to do his duty as a patriot just like any other Southerner. Of course to the North he would be just another 'Johnny Reb' however they might class them, otherwise as rebels not traitors; just like all Americans were all rebels in the eyes of the British, when they tossed the tea in Boston harbour and struck a blow for freedom. Booth was a passionate man above all else and threw himself into this mad scheme like a devil possessed and did make, with John Surratt, at least one failed attempt to kidnap Lincoln. Beyond this is pure speculation but the probability of Booth becoming involved with Lafayette Baker is definitely another saga generated as a red herring and to fill the '18' missing pages (actually 28) of a purloined diary. If one reads Baker's own unpublished book (at the time), 'The United States Secret Service', you will find he mentions nothing about ever meeting Booth. However Baker is more than a pathological liar he is an author that creates chapter and verse of gothic fiction mainly from his ghost writer's imagination, with a few questionable facts thrown in for good measure. The book would rival Henry Rider Haggard's fictional African romances if the truth of this man's deeds were not pure evil. What is truly amazing about it is that he has a good grasp of written English with full punctuation, good grammar and quite good spelling. It is a quicksand of envious malice, sinister and malignant slander mixed with unbelievable false pathos, dark deeds, macabre and inventive adventures all carved out with vitriolic artistic licence. However within the lines of his lies one can glean certain elements of what might have actually happened, such that bits of the truth are discovered by deduction. He even admits in one paragraph that :

"Within fifteen minutes after the murder the wires were severed entirely round the city, excepting only a secret wire for Government uses, which leads to Old Point. I am told that by this wire the Government reached the fortifications around Washington, first telegraphing all the way to Old Point, and then back to the out-lying forts. This information comes to me from so many credible channels that I must concede it."

Baker had kept the diary but any direct liaisons between he and Booth are not accounted for in his own book at all. The 28 pages themselves are not in the public realm and never will be since the pages must have been destroyed by Baker. They referred to this man's journey including a fall from his horse that injured his leg, and the shooting of his lamed horse, and keeping warm that night between the dead horse's legs. He then met another soldier and they attempted to cross Rappahannock River and eventually stayed at Garrett's Barn. In what remains of this out of date pocket diary there is an indirect reference to the first attempt at crossing this river, in the fabricated text. Thus:

"Tonight I will once more try the river with the intent to cross."

And according to a Confederate officer called Ruggles, Boyd (the name Ruggles said this man's friend had called himself) had asked to join Ruggle's Confederate officer trio, since the ferryman was waiting for more passengers to cross in order to make it a cost worthy trip. Further this also suggests that it was through Baker's hand that fabricated the diary, since it was he who detailed Doherty's cavalry and Conger, directly to the Rappahannock River, to capture this man. The Algonquian Indian literal meaning of this is "river of quick, rising water" or "where the tide ebbs and flows." And of this, the Rappahannock tribe, is of such poetic power and beauty.
These were the probable facts Baker never intended even Stanton to find out, let alone showing any change in 'Booth's plan', to include assassination. Indeed why was it put about that John had penned a letter in Gautier's restaurant amongst his busy retinue on the 14th April, that he supposedly gave to John Mathews a fellow actor, to be handed in to the National Intelligencer the very next day detailing his assassination plot. Why bother with this if it was all in his diary a copy of which he could have posted it to Washington on another day, when he wasn't quite so busy with carrying out the assassination? In fact Baker said in his book, that he had in is hand a sealed letter of Booth's confession, along with further evidence for a hiding place in Washington, should he capture the President. This was a place of ill repute, run by a practising madam called Mrs. Greene, with various devices of bondage including manacles and a dungeon. Thus:

" Booth shrank at first from murder, until another and less dangerous resolution failed. This was no less than the capture of the President's body, and its detention or transportation to the South. I do not rely for this assertion upon his sealed letter, where he avows it; there has been found upon a street within the city limit's a house belonging to one Mrs. Greene, mined and furnished with underground apartments, furnished with manacles, and all the accessories of private imprisonment. Here the President , and as many as could be gagged and conveyed away with him, were to be concealed, in the event of failure to run them into the confederacy. Owing to his failure to group around him as many men as he desired, Booth abandoned the project of kidnapping ; but the house was discovered, as represented, ready to be blown up at a moment's notice."

This supposed letter from Booth also tallies with the false account in the diary, again implicating Baker's hand. Thus:

"The night before the deed I wrote a long article and left it for one of the editors of the National Intelligencer, in which I fully set forth our reasons for our proceeding."

If Booth was larger than life it was the illuminati that made him so and transformed him into a devil. He must have been a silent invisible devil to go through two supposedly guarded and locked doors, creep up on the President in a theatre full of officers and men, kill then fight and stab at close quarters, an impotent Major, and then swoop down to the stage, then spirit away on his horse, straight through the sentries, to ride 60 miles through swamp and trackless forest in a day, with a broken leg. Here is the full contents of the fabricated diary writing seemingly addressed to his sister. A blatant and easily

proven forgery in any court of law in any land.
Note : the spelling stands as it is and uncorrected:

"To Asia.
April 14th. Friday. The Ides.
Until today nothing was ever thought of sacrificing to our country's wrongs. For six months we had worked to capture, but our cause being almost lost, something decisive and great must be done. But its failure was owing to others, who did not strike for their country with a heart. I struck boldly, and not as the papers say. I walked with a firm step through a thousand of his friends, was stopped, but pushed on. A colonel was at his side. I shouted Sic semper before I fired. In jumping broke my leg. I passed all his pickets, rode sixty miles that night with the bone of my leg tearing the flesh at every jump. I can never repent it, though we hated to kill. Our country owed all her troubles to him, and God simply made me the instrument of his punishment. The country is not what it was. This forced Union is not what I have loved. I care not what becomes of me. I have no desire to outlive my country. The night before the deed I wrote a long article and left it for one of the editors of the National Intelligencer, in which I fully set forth our reasons for our proceedings.

He or the gov'r-
After being hunted like a dog through swamps, woods, and last night being chased by gunboats till I was forced to return wet, cold, and starving, with every man's hand against me, I am here in despair. And why? For doing what Brutus was honored for. What made Tell a hero? And yet I, for striking down a greater tyrant than they ever knew, am looked upon as a common cutthroat. My action was purer than either of theirs. One hoped to be great himself. The other had not only his country's but his own, wrongs to avenge. I hoped for no gain. I knew no private wrong. I struck for my country and that alone. A country that groaned beneath this tyranny, and prayed for this end, and yet now behold the cold hands they extend to me. God cannot pardon me if I have done wrong. Yet I cannot see my wrong, except in serving a degenerate people. The little, the very little, I left behind to clear my name, the Government will not allow to be printed. So ends all. For my country I have given up all that makes life sweet and holy, brought misery upon my family, and am sure there is no pardon in the Heaven for me, since man condemns me so. I have only heard of what has been done (except what I did myself), and it fills me with horror. God, try and forgive me, and bless my mother. Tonight I will once more try the river with the intent to cross. Though I have a greater desire and almost a mind to return to Washington, and in a measure clear my name - which I feel I can do. I do not repent the blow I struck. I may before my God, but not to man. I think I have done well. Though I am abandoned, with the curse of Cain upon me, when, if the world knew my heart, that one blow would have made me great, though I did desire no greatness. Tonight I try to escape these bloodhounds once more. Who, who can read his fate? God's will be done. I have too great a soul to die like a criminal. Oh, may He, may He spare me that, and let me die bravely. I bless the entire world. Have never hated or wronged anyone. This last was not a wrong, unless God deems it so, and it's with Him to damn or bless me. As for this brave boy with me, who often prays (yes, before and since) with a true and sincere heart - was it crime in him? If so, why can he pray the same? I do not wish to shed a drop of blood, but 'I must fight the course.' 'Tis all that's left to me."

This was the hand that was picked to run the US Secret Service?; then God save all our souls. In fact it was 'Baker's Secret Service' the National Detective Police or NDP. The origin of Secret Service was supposedly Lincoln's idea, formed initially just to protect the President and it was formed well after his assassination. Well, Lincoln was right he would have been better off with a loyal friend guarding the door that night. Just that one true friend outside the door, would have made the assassination impossible. Baker was fascinated with Julius Ceaser (here likening his assassination to Lincoln's) and mentions him in his book several times in relation to Booth, in an envious manner. Thus:

"What would please an actor, and the son of an actor, better than to mingle as a principal in a real conspiracy, the aims of which were pseudo-patriotic, and the ends so astounding that at its coming the whole globe would reel. Booth reasoned that the ancient world would not feel more sensitivity the death of Julius Ceaser, than the new sudden taking off of Abraham Lincoln".

And as for Brutus:

" John Wilkes Booth was the projector of the plot against the President , which accumulated in the taking of that good man's life. He had rolled under his tongue the sweet paragraphs of Shakespeare referring to Brutus, as his father had so well, that the old man named one son Junius Brutus, and the other John Wilkes, after the wild English agitator, until it became his ambition, like the wicked Lorenzino de Medici, to stake his life upon one stroke for fame, the murder of a ruler obnoxious to the South."

So who then who is the real Brutus? Is it Booth or is it Baker? Baker also liked to use common terms or words, sprinkled everywhere in his literature. For example the word cut-throat is used to fabricate the diary and in his book. Thus:

" Here began the first resolve, which in its more animal state, we may name courage. Booth found that a tragedy in real life could no more be enacted without greasy-faced and knock-kneed supernumeraries than upon the mimic stage. Your 'First Citizen' who swings a stave for Marc Antony , and drinks hard porta behind the flies, is very like the brave of real life, who murders between his cocktails at the nearest bar. Wilkes Booth had passed the ordeal of a garlicky green-room, and did not shrink from the broader and ranker green room of life. He assembled around him , one by one, the cut-throats at whom his soul would have revolted, except that he had become, by resolve a cut-throat in himself."

In fact it was Baker himself who had spent more time in bars as a bouncer on the Barbary Coast and had lynched many a cut-throat, so this would be a favourite word of his, and he also used it for Booth in the soldier's diary '.....am looked upon as a common cut-throat.'

It almost seems as if Baker had substituted the actor for his own real villainous life. Is this the mind of a psychopath or a schizophrenic? Also: 'The Colonel at his side...' he refers to was in fact Major Rathbone but Baker was oft in the habit of 'promoting' officers in his book. Indeed Lieutenant Conger was one other of them, duly promoted to Lieutenant-Colonel Conger. The hand of Baker is also clearly exposed in the diary by using the line 'I shouted sic semper before I fired...'. This quote was supposed to have been called out after he had fired the shot, when he had landed on the stage in front of the audience. And why didn't he complete the line '....sic semper......' .....tyrannis?

And what of ‘Tell’, yes another hero….. Tell of Switzerland.

William Tell and Son. Heroic 15th Century Swiss Hero who split the apple on his son’s head but his second arrow split Lamberger Gessler’s head and Switzerland was born. This legend is of Viking or Germanic origins however.

True American Hero

1866 - 1955

Mathew Henson First Man to Reach the North Pole

Chapter 4

Dr. Samuel Alexander Mudd and his Valour

DR. SAMUEL A. MUDD
Born December 20, 1833
Died January 10, 1883

Doctor of Healing, Faith and Valour

If ever there was such an American hero then or anytime, in terms of courage and fortitude under extreme mental torture and physical conditions, this man must be in the top ten along with Payne in the bravery section. The absent mindedness of pseudo-historians such as Hall and Steers who both live in Virginia and West Virginia beggar's all Christian or moral belief. How nice to live there, compos-mentis and sublimely safe and happy in their malignant hypocrisy. Some historians are able to coldly ignore the evidence of 300 prison staff, of Dr. Mudd's dedicated and selfless sacrifice, in saving so many people's lives in the malaria scourged and Yellow Fever infected prison. Not only this, they even refute claims that he was a good doctor. How can anyone defy this evidence and signed affidavit of 300 enlisted men and NCO's and one brave Lieutenant Zabriskie. Perhaps they choose to ignore the NCO's and men so that it would cut it down to just one officer. President Johnson at the risk of impeachment was brave enough to grant Dr. Mudd and the other's, there rightful pardons. What kind of substance are these so called historians made of? One suspect's many earn too much money propagating pastel truths, than to worry about authenticity. After all they have tons of qualifications and universities to back them up and behind that is officialdom and their myth of 'history' and misguidance on a global scale. The writer has spent eight weeks and almost completed this book from first seriously reading about this

unmentionably wicked deed, plus his regular work. So what has been going on all these years, whole divisions of 'historians' getting round on countless combinations of spin offs-no doubt?
As will be proven in this book for anyone who understands logical reasoning or even common sense and for those who are not of the un-dead, Booth did not assassinate Lincoln. Indeed the forged diary is enough to prove Booth's innocence in the courts but this book will show how the whole plot was engineered; in case any one cares to counter logic with woffle and need a full explanation for every single part of the gambit.

So, the evidence against Dr. Mudd boils down to only one point :

Yes, he had met Booth, but he had met him on one occasion only, according to his defence team, in relation to the sale of a horse, in November 1863, 18 months beforehand. The prosecution argued that they had met on two more occasions including Dec. 23rd 1864 but this was from Louis Weichman and John Lloyd, two of the conspiracy trial witnesses, who are both proven to be treacherous. And as further explained even if his visitors had assassinated Lincoln, Dr. Mudd could not have known about it, unless they had told him so. But, even Baker admitted in his book that 'Booth' gave Dr. Mudd a false name. And Dr. Mudd himself said they gave the names Tyson and Hensted (sometimes quoted as Henson). The evidence for this comes straight from Baker himself. Thus:

"On Saturday, before sunrise, Booth and Harold, without stopping elsewhere, reached the house of Dr. Mudd, three miles from Bryantown. They contracted with him, for 25 dollars in greenbacks, to set the broken leg. Harold, who knew Dr. Mudd, introduced Booth under another name, and stated that he had fallen from his horse during the night. The doctor remarked of Booth that he draped the lower part of his face while the leg was being set; he was silent and in pain".

In addition it is clear they were bent on deception by saying that 'Booth' had fallen from his horse. This is interesting because it's the same story attributed by Baker in his book that he got from the diary account of the unknown Confederate soldier's horse fall, at a later date i.e. that 'fact' has followed fiction. Also, Baker is playing off the devil's alternative. That is, he needs to try to disguise Booth, as played by Tyson, but he knew that Dr. Mudd did not in fact know Herold, as played by Hensted. And this information Baker knew to be true from ex PC John Lloyd and the government clerk, Louis Weichmann. (See these below). And remember Dr. Mudd had met the real Booth only once, the year before, in regards to the sale of a horse. Besides it wasn't Herold at all, it really was Hensted. Further they spent only twelve hours with him and this was only six hours after the President had been shot. The prosecution tried to make out that because Dr. Mudd went into Bryantown at midday he must have picked up the news of the assassination. This is line of reasoning can be torn apart quite easily:
1) Even today I can go into town and buy stuff and it is very rare that anyone will give me news of anything. It depends if you like gossip.

2) In those days it is true that news would travel much faster by word of mouth, especially in a small town; but how can anyone be sure whether this kind of news is true or just a rumour, and the President had only just died 5 or 6 hours ago.

3) Let us then assume the news came into Bryantown by telegraph, newspaper or coach. Bryantown is about 30 miles from Washington, that is about a good 7 hour carriage ride, or possibly a 5 hour horse ride. In fact it took Tyson and Hensted nearly 6 hours to get there at night with a change of fresh horses at Surrattsville. It was Easter Saturday perhaps not so busy. How fast would this news travel in the town? If you just went in to do some shopping you might still not discover this news, because you don't buy a paper or not enough people are yet aware of the news, or the people you might speak to do not yet know either and you may be in a hurry, or un-communicative.

Of course you could argue the opposite way to prove the counter point of view. However the odds might still only be 50/50 for arguments sake. This then is certainly not proof. In fact some of these districts were remote in those days, as Major O'Bierne described thus:

"Others, like the taking of Dr. Mudd, simultaneously occurred. But the district suspected being remote from the railway routes, and broken by no telegraph station, the Colonel, to place himself nearer the theater of events, ordered an operator, with the necessary instrument to tap the wire running into Chappell's Point, and send him prompt messages".

Dr. Mudd's house in Beantown 3 miles from Bryantown. When 'Booth' crossed the Navy bridge he gave his name and his destination of Beantown, said Baker. In fact it was Tyson the decoy detective giving his destination as Beantown, and hell bent for Treachery with his side-kick Hensted. This is the reason the Telegraph wires were de-commissioned at 10.30 pm that night.

The New-York Times.

VOL. XIV....NO. 4230. NEW-YORK, SATURDAY, APRIL 15, 1865. PRICE FOUR CENTS.

Department and two male nurses, disabling them all, he then rushed upon the Secretary, who was lying in bed in the same room, and inflicted three stabs in the neck, but severing, it is thought and hoped, no arteries, though he bled profusely.

The assassin then rushed down stairs mounted his horse at the door, and rode off before an alarm could be sounded, and in the same manner as the assassin of the President.

It is believed that the injuries of the Secretary are not fatal, nor those of either of the others, although both the Secretary and the Assistant Secretary are very seriously injured.

Secretaries STANTON and WELLES, and other prominent officers of the government, called at Secretary SEWARD's house to inquire into his condition, and there heard of the assassination of the President.

They then proceeded to the house where he was lying, exhibiting of course intense anxiety and solicitude. An immense crowd was gathered in front of the President's house, and a strong guard was also stationed there, many persons evidently supposing he would be brought to his home.

The entire city to-night presents a scene of wild excitement, accompanied by violent expressions of indignation, and the profoundest sorrow—many shed tears. The military authorities have dispatched mounted patrols in every direction, in order, if possible, to arrest the assassins. The whole metropolitan police are likewise vigilant for the same purpose.

The attacks both at the theatre and at Secretary SEWARD's house, took place at about the same hour—10 o'clock—thus showing a preconcerted plan to assassinate those gentlemen. Some evidence of the guilt of the party who attacked the President are in the possession of the police.

Vice-President JOHNSON is in the city, and his headquarters are guarded by troops.

ANOTHER ACCOUNT.

Special Dispatch to the New-York Times.

WASHINGTON, Friday, April 14, 11:16 P. M.

A stroke from Heaven laying the whole of the city in instant ruins could not have startled us as did the word that broke from Ford's Theatre a half hour ago that the President had been shot. It flew everywhere in five minutes, and set five thousand people in swift and excited motion on the instant.

It is impossible to get at the full facts of the case, but it appears that a young man entered the President's box from the theatre, during the last act of the play of "Our American Cousin," with pistol in hand. He shot the President in the head and instantly jumped from the box upon the stage, and immediately disappeared through the side scenes and rear of the theatre, brandishing a dirk knife and dropping a kid glove on the stage.

The audience heard the shot, but supposing it fired in the regular course of the play, did not heed it till Mrs. LINCOLN's screams drew their attention. The whole affair occupied scarcely half a minute, and then the assassin was gone. As yet he has not been found.

The President's wound is reported mortal. He was at once taken into the house opposite the theatre.

As if this horror was not enough, almost the same moment the story ran through the city that Mr. SEWARD had been murdered in his bed.

Inquiry showed this to be so far true also. It appears a man wearing a light coat, dark pants, slouch hat, called and asked to see Mr. SEWARD, and was shown to his room. He delivered to Major SEWARD, who sat near his father, what purported to be a physician's prescription, turned, and with one stroke cut Mr. SEWARD's throat as he lay on his bed, inflicting a horrible wound, but not severing the jugular vein, and not producing a mortal wound.

In the struggle that followed, Major SEWARD was also badly, but not seriously, wounded in several places. The assassin rushed down stairs, mounted the fleet horse on which he came, drove his spurs into him, and dashed away before any one could stop him.

Reports have prevailed that an attempt was also made on the life of Mr. STANTON.

MIDNIGHT.

The President is reported dead. Cavalry and infantry are scouring the city in every direction for the murderous assassins, and the city is overwhelmed with excitement. Who the assassins were no one knows, though every body supposes them to have been rebels.

SATURDAY MORNING—1 O'CLOCK.

The person who shot the President is represented as about 30 years of age, five feet nine inches in height, sparely built, of light complexion, dressed in dark clothing, and having a genteel appearance. He entered the box, which is known as the State box, being the upper box on the right hand side from the dress-circle in the regular manner, and shot the President from behind, the ball entering the skull about in the middle, behind, and going in the direction of the left eye; it did not pass through, but apparently broke the frontal bone and forced out the brain to some extent. The President is not yet dead, but is wholly insensible, and the Surgeon-General says he cannot live till day-break. The assassin was followed across the stage by a gentleman, who sprang out from an orchestra chair. He rushed through the side door into an alley, thence to the avenue and mounted a dark bay horse, which he apparently received from the hand of an accomplice, dashed up F, toward the back part of the city. The escape was so sudden that he effectually eluded pursuit. The assassin cried "*sic semper*" in a sharp, clear voice, as he jumped to the stage, and dropped his hat and a glove.

Two or three officers were in the box with the President and Mrs. LINCOLN, who made efforts to stop the assassin, but were unsuccessful, and received some bruises. The whole affair, from his entrance into the box to his escape from the theatre, occupied scarcely a minute, and the strangeness of the action found everybody wholy unprepared. The assault upon Mr. SEWARD appears to have been made almost at the same moment as that upon the President. Mr. SEWARD's wound is not dangerous in itself, but may prove so in connection with his recent injuries. The two assassins have both endeavored to leave the city to the northwest, apparently not expecting to strike the river. Even so low down as Chain Bridge, cavalry have been sent in every direction to intercept them.

SATURDAY, 1:30 o'clock A. M.

The President still lies insensible. Messrs. STANTON, WELLES, MCCULLOCH, SPEED and USHER are with him, as also the Vice-President, the Surgeon-General, and other Surgeons.

There is a great throng about the house, even at this hour.

2 o'clock A. M.

The President still lives, but lies insensible, as he has since the first moment, and no hopes are entertained that he can survive.

The most extravagant stories prevail, among which one is to effect, that Gen. GRANT was shot while on his way to Philadelphia, of course this is not true.

Another is, that every member of Mr. SEWARD's family was wounded in the struggle with the assassin there. This also is untrue. Mr. FRED. SEWARD, the Assistant Secretary, and Major CLARENCE SEWARD, of the army, were wounded, neither of them dangerously.

THE CONDITION OF THE PRESIDENT.

WASHINGTON, April 15—2:12 A. M.

The President is still alive; but he is growing weaker. The ball is lodged in his brain, three inches from where it entered the skull. He remains insensible, and his condition is utterly hopeless.

The Vice-President has been to see him; but all company, except the members of the Cabinet and of the family, is rigidly excluded.

Large crowds still continue in the street, as near to the house as the line of guards allows.

THE SIEGE OF MOBILE.

Fierce Bombardment of the Spanish Fort—Mobile Papers Announce the Capture of Selma.

NEW-ORLEANS, Saturday, April 8, via CAIRO, Friday, April 14.

A special dispatch to the New-Orleans *Times*, from the Spanish Fort, dated April 5, says:

"A furious fire was opened on the rebel forts last night from our entire line. During the bombardment a small magazine in the Spanish Fort exploded. The damage is unknown. Quiet prevailed on the 6th. *Deserters* report from 15,000 to 20,000 troops in and about Mobile, including all the State Reserves, and about 2,000 in the Spanish Fort. The loss outside the Spanish Fort up to the 4th instant amounted to about 800 killed and wounded. The rebel loss exceeds ours."

Adjt.-Gen. THOMAS arrived at New-Orleans on the morning of the 7th.

Mobile papers of the 4th inst. announce the capture of Selma, Alabama, with 32 pieces of artillery, and a large amount of Government property.

Fort Sumter Celebration in Bangor.

BANGOR, Me., Friday, April 14.

The restoration of the Old Flag to Fort Sumter was celebrated here to-day by a national salute at noon, by a display of all the flags on public and private buildings, and by the raising of the Stars and Stripes one thousand feet above the city by means of a monster kite bearing the name of U. S. GRANT.

The Madrid *Epoca* says if the Pope should leave Rome, Spain would confer upon him the Balearic Isles.

The *Politica* says the Pope would rather inhabit the Montpensier Palace at Seville.

Straight from the Horse's Mouth at 11.16 pm. No mention of Booth nor his fight with Rathbone. And the whole affair lasted scarcely 30 seconds.

Even if Dr. Mudd had received the news how could he relate it so quickly to his visitors, even if he really knew it was Booth, despite Booth's disguise and having given him a false name. (And even Stanton's poster issued six days later did not mention a lame Booth, only John Surratt and a man called Daniel C. Harrold, not David E. Herold). There could be no other reason for a false name other than deception. This meant the decoy, Tyson (as Booth) did not intend to let on that he had 'assassinated' the President. In any case the assassin whoever he was, did not know for certain that he had killed the President that Saturday morning, that far away, because Lincoln did not die until 7.22 am; and that was nearly 4 hours after Tyson and Hensted, the two decoys playing off Booth and Herold, had turned up at Dr. Mudd's house. Indeed the present school of medical thought is that the President would have lived had he received careful treatment. Well, Booth as we all know was indeed a fast mover, like grease lightning or a German Blitzkrieg.

Also if Dr. Mudd was in on the plot why did Baker say that 'Booth' gave him a false name? The fact is that this was standard operational procedure for the NDP in order to pretend they were Confederates- known as a ruse or a deception, normally used to locate possible rebel houses or indeed any friendly houses. If you were hospitable you were done for. If you showed a weapon they would clear off and leave you be. For proof of this see below. You might stupidly or wickedly reply that the man was lame, so he must be the assassin. However, the press did not yet even state that the assassin was lame. And the wanted posters were not even issued till the 20th according to Baker who initiated the second lot with photographs, and still no mention of a lame Booth on them. Take a look at the New York Times who were given the privilege of receiving the story from its official source at 11.16 pm that night (then it takes hours to write and print and many more hours after dawn to deliver to Bryantown). Even with this news all it said was the President had been shot by a young man, unknown and certainly no mention of a lame person. The idea he had become a lame assassin was being unwittingly initiated right there and then at Dr. Mudd's home by Tyson to gain sympathy at 4 in the morning, as engineered by Baker (perhaps un-intentionally regarding the bust leg) who knew where Dr. Mudd lived, from Lloyd or Louis Weichmann. But most probably from Lloyd since he would have been able to give them exact navigational instructions from their last port of call in Surrattsville. And of course the truth is even simpler, Dr. Mudd did not recognise Booth because it really was Tyson and Hensted playing off Booth and Herold, as Baker had 'played off' his agents many times before, both in fact and in his distinctive style of prose. In fact 'Booth' didn't really become lame till it was reported that a possible lame rebel soldier was crossing the Rappahannock River on the 24th of April.

Dr. Mudd really made two mistakes:
a) he should have tried to find out their true identities and,
b) should have discovered Tyson was not really lame.

The writer once as a young lad jumped about 13 feet or so into some hay in a barn. I felt something give in my ankle but otherwise felt ok and walked several miles home and it did not bother me till the next day, when it swelled up real bad and I was in agony for days. But I had seen no bruising or swelling right away. In other words you can sprain your ankle and not know it. On the other hand you can also pretend you have just sprained your ankle or injured your leg internally. Doctors usually give you an X-ray to see if its broken. In the old days they would have to manoeuvre it, to locate the source of the pain by the patients response. If the patient is a good actor he can easily feign the pain. In fact Tyson had invented the lame ruse himself to ensure that Dr. Mudd would give them medical aid and hospitality at four in the morning. It was just another variation on a common theme, as you will see below. As you will also see later the arresting officer Lieutenant Lovett who went into Dr. Mudd's home and found the boot, was the same officer who accompanied Major O'Bierne's team of six, of the NDP near Leonardstown. They used the same ruse to arrest Mr. Claggert and others by asking favours and in some cases paying greenbacks for services rendered, (just as they paid Dr. Mudd 25 dollars). This in order to effect a small pretence in plain clothes, that they might be Confederates on the run. One man however showed the two of them the barrel of his gun, so they got scared and all of them stopped using this ruse. It's all in Baker's book where he boasts about using this ruse as a standard operational procedure.

Courtesy of Ron Williams

This man from Pennsylvania ranks among the finest of Americans ever

The New-York Times.

NEW-YORK, SATURDAY, APRIL 15, 1865. PRICE FOUR CENTS

AWFUL EVENT.

President Lincoln Shot by an Assassin.

The Deed Done at Ford's Theatre Last Night.

THE ACT OF A DESPERATE REBEL

The President Still Alive at Last Accounts.

No Hopes Entertained of His Recovery.

Attempted Assassination of Secretary Seward.

DETAILS OF THE DREADFUL TRAGEDY.

[OFFICIAL.]

WAR DEPARTMENT,
WASHINGTON, April 15—1:30 A. M.

Maj.-Gen. Dix:

This evening at about 9:30 P. M., at Ford's Theatre, the President, while sitting in his private box with Mrs. Lincoln, Mrs. Harris, and Major Rathburn, was shot by an assassin, who suddenly entered the box and approached behind the President.

The assassin then leaped upon the stage, brandishing a large dagger or knife, and made his escape in the rear of the theatre.

The pistol ball entered the back of the President's head and penetrated nearly through the head. The wound is mortal. The President has been insensible ever since it was inflicted, and is now dying.

About the same hour an assassin, whether the same or not, entered Mr. Seward's apartments, and under the pretence of having a prescription, was shown to the Secretary's sick chamber. The assassin immediately rushed to the bed, and inflicted two or three stabs on the throat and two on the face. It is hoped the wounds may not be mortal. My apprehension is that they will prove fatal.

The nurse alarmed Mr. Frederick Seward, who was in an adjoining room, and hastened to the door of his father's room, when he met the assassin, who inflicted upon him one or more dangerous wounds. The recovery of Frederick Seward is doubtful.

It is not probable that the President will live throughout the night.

Gen. Grant and wife were advertised to be at the theatre this evening, but he started to Burlington at 6 o'clock this evening.

At a Cabinet meeting at which Gen. Grant was present, the subject of the state of the country and the prospect of a speedy peace was discussed. The President was very cheerful and hopeful, and spoke very kindly of Gen. Lee and others of the Confederacy, and of the establishment of government in Virginia.

All the members of the Cabinet except Mr. Seward, are now in attendance upon the President.

I have seen Mr. Seward, but he and Frederick were both unconscious.

EDWIN M. STANTON,
Secretary of War.

DETAIL OF THE OCCURRENCE.

WASHINGTON, Friday, April 14—12:30 A. M.

The President was shot in a theatre tonight, and is, perhaps, mortally wounded.

Secretary Seward was also assassinated.

SECOND DISPATCH.

WASHINGTON, Friday, April 14.

President Lincoln and wife, with other friends, this evening visited Ford's Theatre for the purpose of witnessing the performance of the "American Cousin."

It was announced in the papers that Gen. Grant would also be present, but he took the late train of cars for New-Jersey.

The theatre was densely crowded, and everybody seemed delighted with the scene before them. During the third act, and while there was a temporary pause for one of the actors to enter, a sharp report of a pistol was heard, which merely attracted attention, but suggesting nothing serious, until a man rushed to the front of the President's box, waving a long dagger in his right hand, and exclaiming "*Sic semper tyrannis*," and immediately leaped from the box, which was in the second tier, to the stage beneath, and ran across to the opposite side, making his escape amid the bewilderment of the audience from the rear of the theatre, and, mounting a horse, fled.

The screams of Mrs. Lincoln first disclosed the fact to the audience that the President had been shot, when all present rose to their feet, rushing toward the stage, many exclaiming "Hang him! hang him!"

The excitement was of the wildest possible description, and of course there was an abrupt termination of the theatrical performance.

There was a rush toward the President's box, when cries were heard: "Stand back and give him air." "Has any one stimulants." On a hasty examination, it was found that the President had been shot through the head, above and back of the temporal bone, and that some of the brain was oozing out. He was removed to a private house opposite to the theatre, and the Surgeon-General of the army, and other surgeons sent for to attend to his condition.

On an examination of the private box blood was discovered on the back of the cushioned rocking chair on which the President had been sitting also on the partition and on the floor. A common single-barreled pocket pistol was found on the carpet.

A military guard was placed in front of the private residence to which the President had been conveyed. An immense crowd was in front of it, all deeply anxious to learn the condition of the President. It had been previously announced that the wound was mortal; but all hoped otherwise. The shock to the community was terrible.

The President was in a state of syncope, totally insensible, and breathing slowly. The blood oozed from the wound at the back of his head. The surgeons exhausted every effort of medical skill, but all hope was gone. The parting of his family with the dying President is too sad for description.

At midnight, the Cabinet, with Messrs. Sumner, Colfax and Farnsworth, Judge Curtis, Gov. Oglesby, Gen. Meigs, Col. Hay, and a few personal friends, with Surgeon-General Barnes and his immediate assistants, were around his bedside.

The President and Mrs. Lincoln did not start for the theatre until fifteen minutes after eight o'clock. Speaker Colfax was at the White House at the time, and the President stated to him that he was going, although Mrs. Lincoln had not been well, because the papers had announced that Gen. Grant and they were to be present, and, as Gen. Grant had gone North, he did not wish the audience to be disappointed.

He went with apparent reluctance and urged Mr. Colfax to go with him; but that gentleman had made other engagements, and with Mr. Ashman, of Massachusetts, bid him good bye.

When the excitement at the theatre was at its wildest height, reports were circulated that Secretary Seward had also been assassinated.

On reaching this gentleman's residence a crowd and a military guard were found at the door, and on entering it was ascertained that the reports were based on truth.

Everybody there was so excited that scarcely an intelligible word could be gathered, but the facts are substantially as follows:

About 10 o'clock a man rang the bell, and the call having been answered by a colored servant, he said he had come from Dr. Verdi, Secretary Seward's family physician, with a prescription, at the same time holding in his hand a small piece of folded paper, and saying in answer to a refusal that he must see the Secretary, as he was entrusted with particular directions concerning the medicine.

He still insisted on going up, although repeatedly informed that no one could enter the chamber. The man pushed the servant aside, and walked heavily toward the Secretary's room, and was then met by Mr. Frederick Seward, of whom he demanded to see the Secretary, making the same representation which he did to the servant. What further passed in the way of colloquy is not known, but the man struck him on the head with a "billy," severely injuring the skull and felling him almost senseless. The assassin then rushed into the chamber and attacked Major Seward, Paymaster of the United States army and Mr. Hansell, a messenger of the State

The wound is already Mortal at 1 AM yet the President lived till 7.22 AM. Stanton has seen Seward After 'His Attack'. The news at 1.30 AM says Seward's throat is cut but the Bowie Knife narrowly misses the Jugular. Seward also expected to die.

Now follows the pardon for Dr. Mudd by Andrew Johnson which nearly cost him his presidency. Had he fully vindicated him he would probably have lost it altogether. But it shows that he really cared, and in his mind he knew Dr. Mudd and the others were innocent, especially as he had gotten rid of Baker and Stanton in the same swoop:

"And whereas, upon occasion of the prevalence of the Yellow Fever at that military station, and the death by that pestilence of the medical officer of the Post, the said Samuel A. Mudd devoted himself to the care and cure of the sick, and interposed his courage and his skill to protect the garrison, otherwise without adequate medical aid, from peril and alarm, and thus, as the officers and men unite in testifying, saved many valuable lives and earned the admiration and the gratitude of all who observed or experienced his generous and faithful service to humanity. And whereas, the surviving families and friends of the Surgeon and other officers who were the victims of the pestilence earnestly present their dying testimony to the conspicuous merit of Dr. Mudd's conduct, and their own sense of obligation to him and Lieut. Zabriskie and two hundred and ninety nine non-commissioned officers and privates stationed at the Dry Tortugas have united in presenting to my attention the praiseworthy action of the prisoner and in petitioning for his pardon; And whereas the Medical Society of Hartford County, Maryland, of which he was an associate, have petitioned for his pardon, and thirty nine members of the Senate and House of Representatives of the Congress of the United States have also requested his pardon; Now, therefore be it known that I, Andrew Johnson, President of the United States of America, in consideration of the premises, divers other good and sufficient reasons me thereunto moving, do hereby grant to the said Dr. Samuel A. Mudd a full and unconditional pardon. In testimony thereof, I have hereunto signed my name and caused the Seal of the United States to be affixed.
Done at the City of Washington, this Eighth day of February, A. D. (Seal) 1869, and the Independence of the United States the ninety third.
ANDREW JOHNSON By the President".

He cleverly used the word officers in the plural, indeed the Surgeon had died, and their families petitioned. In fact there was only one commissioned officer, a certain brave Lieutenant Zabriskie, that signed the petition. The remainder were all non-commissioned officers and men. Andrew Johnson had struck a blow for the people. These officers and men having the hearts of free men not that of cloned servants.

Edward (Edman) Spangler:

It was Ed's statement that gave me the vital clue as to what really happened that night, and it highlights the importance of selection, in listening to evidence. The statement makes small observations, like the alley door would not shut properly and the key to the stable was always kept on a nail, on this door and no one went out. These little pointers are obviously not biased but simple and practical observations. And the key line is: A man ran across the stage <u>immediately</u> after the shot rang out.

True Hero

1825-1875
Edman Spangler
Saved Dr. Mudd

Here is his statement found in his tool box by Dr. Mudd after he had died:

I was born in York County, Pennsylvania, and am about forty-three years of age, I am a house carpenter by trade, and became acquainted with J. Wilkes Booth when a boy. I worked for his father in building a cottage in Harford County, Maryland, in 1854. Since A. D. 1853, I have done carpenter work for the different theaters in the cities of Baltimore and Washington, to wit: The Holiday Street Theater and the Front Street Theater of Baltimore, and Ford's Theater in the City of Washington. I have acted also as scene shifter in all the above named theaters, and had a favorable opportunity to become acquainted with the different actors. I have acted as scene shifter in Ford's Theater, ever since it was first opened up, to the night of the assassination of President Lincoln. During the winter of A. D. 1862 and 1863, J. Wilkes Booth played a star engagement at Ford's Theater for two weeks. At that time I saw him and conversed with him quite frequently. After completing his engagement he left Washington and I did not see him again until the winters of A. D. 1864 and 1865. I then saw him at various times in and about Ford's Theater.
Booth had free access to the theater at all times, and made himself very familiar with all persons connected with it. He had a stable in the rear of the theater where he kept his horses. A boy, Joseph Burroughs, commonly called "Peanut John," took care of them whenever Booth was absent from the city. I looked after his horses, which I did at his request, and saw that they were properly cared for. Booth promised to pay me for my trouble, but he never did. I frequently had the horses exercised, during Booth's absence from the city, by "Peanut John," walking them up and down the alley. "Peanut John" kept the key to the stable in the theater, hanging upon a nail behind the small door, which opened into the alley at the rear of the theater. Booth usually rode out on horseback every afternoon and evening, but seldom remained out later than eight or nine o'clock. He always went and returned alone. I never knew of his riding out on horseback and staying out all night, or of any person coming to the stable with him, or calling there for him. He had two horses at the stable, only a short time. He brought them there some time in the month of December. A man called George and

myself repaired and fixed the stable for him. I usually saddled the horse for him when "Peanut John" was absent. About the first of March Booth brought another horse and a buggy and harness to the stable, but in what manner I do not know; after that he used to ride out with his horse and buggy, and I frequently harnessed them up for him. I never saw any person ride out with him or return with him from these rides.

On the Monday evening previous to the assassination, Booth requested me to sell the horse, harness, and buggy, as he said he should leave the city soon. I took them the next morning to the horse market, and had them put up at auction, with the instruction not to sell unless they would net two hundred and sixty dollars; this was in accordance with Booth's orders to me. As no person bid sufficient to make them net that amount, they were not sold, and I took them back to the stable. I informed Booth of the result that same evening in front of the theater. He replied that he must then try and have them sold at private sale, and asked me if I would help him. I replied, "Yes." This was about six o'clock in the evening, and the conversation took place in the presence of John F. Sleichman and others. The next day I sold them for two hundred and sixty dollars. The purchaser accompanied me to the theater. Booth was not in, and the money was paid to James J. Gifford, who receipted for it. I did not see Booth to speak to him, after the sale, until the evening of the assassination. Upon the afternoon of April 14 I was told by "Peanut John" that the President and General Grant were coming to the theater that night, and that I must take out the partition in the President's box. It was my business to do all such work. I was assisted in doing it by Rittespaugh and "Peanut John."

In the evening, between five and six o'clock, Booth came into the theater and asked me for a halter. I was very busy at work at the time on the stage preparatory to the evening performance, and Rittespaugh went upstairs and brought one down. I went out to the stable with Booth and put the halter upon the horse. I commenced to take off the saddle when Booth said, "Never mind, I do not want it off, but let it and the bridle remain." He afterward took the saddle off himself, locked the stable, and went back to the theater.

Booth, Maddox, "Peanut John," and myself immediately went out of the theater to the adjoining restaurant next door, and took a drink at Booth's expense. I then went immediately back to the theatre, and Rittespaugh and myself went to supper. I did not see Booth again until between nine and ten o'clock. About that time Deboney called to me, and said Booth wanted me to hold his horse as soon as I could be spared. I went to the back door and Booth was standing in the alley holding a horse by the bridle rein, and requested me to hold it. I took the rein, but told him I could not remain, as Gifford was gone, and that all of the responsibility rested on me. Booth then passed into the theater. I called to Deboney to send 'Peanut John' to hold the horse. He came, and took the horse, and I went back to my proper place.

In about a half hour afterward I heard a shot fired, and immediately saw a man run across the stage. I saw him as he passed by the center door of the scenery, behind which I then stood; this door is usually termed the center chamber door. I did not recognize the man as he crossed the stage as being Booth. I then heard some one say that the President was shot. Immediately all was confusion. I shoved the scenes back as quickly as possible in order to clear the stage, as many were rushing upon it. I was very much frightened, as I heard persons halloo, "Burn the theater!" I did not see Booth pass out; my situation was such that I could not see any person pass out of the back door. The back door has a spring attached to it, and would not shut of its own accord. I usually slept in the theater, but I did not upon the night of the assassination; I was fearful the theater would be burned, and I slept in a carpenter's shop adjoining.

I never heard Booth express himself in favor of the rebellion, or opposed to the Government, or converse upon political subjects; and I have no recollection of his mentioning the name of

President Lincoln in any connection whatever. I know nothing of the mortise hole said to be in the wall behind the door of the President's box, or of any wooden bar to fasten or hold the door being there, or of the lock being out of order. I did not notice any hole in the door. Gifford usually attended to the carpentering in the front part of the theater, while I did the work about the stage. Mr. Gifford was the boss carpenter, and I was under him.

Notes:

A man ran across the stage, immediately the shot was fired and it was not Booth, whom he knew very well.

He was located behind the centre stage chamber door, so had a clear view of the back alley door and saw no one exit this way, after the muffled shot rang out.

Booth could hardly kidnap the President without a horse and buggy, as they had planned it this way before. So the illuminati would have us believe he intended to assassinate the President and Grant instead.

They were all still expecting Grant to attend as late as the afternoon.

Ed was obviously doing his job to the best of his ability and was able to make clear and concise observations in carrying out his duties. He sensed trouble and tried to avert chaos and damage by clearing the stage of scenery. He was clearly worried about the situation getting out of hand but did not panic. However he was already being set up by the illuminati and his helper Jake Ritterspaugh was the one who lied to get him convicted of aiding and abetting 'Booth'. Rittespaugh wanted to change his statement later, according to Harry Ford, because he was wretched about it afterwards. It was too late, the illuminati had their man, and he got six years hard labour for doing his job and being honest, just like Dr. Mudd.

He mentioned Mr. Sleichman the prompts man as a witness, whom he obviously trusted to be relied upon. He also trusted Mr. Gifford his boss. Booth was obviously expecting Ed to stable his horse for him, for the night. It was the intermission but Ed was still too busy and got Burroughs to do it instead. Indeed, good old Ed was a bit of a drudge for Booth, but a kind, brave and honest man with high intelligence and un-impeachable honour.

Louis J Weichmann

1842-1862
Friend of John Surratt

Chapter 5

John Harrison Surratt and his Lectures

1844-1916
He Ventured Much But
Lost His Mother's Heart

John was born a Catholic in at Congress Heights in Washington in 1844 and trained as a divinity student at St. Charles College. His father John was the postmaster at Surrattsville (now Clinton) Maryland. He owned farm-land and property and was a pillar of the community and John Jr. took over when he died in 1862. His mother's maiden name was Mary Jenkins and was a refined and kind lady of strong breeding, good discipline, and impeccable dress and a good, honest Christian woman and originally a Presbyterian. John was a blockade runner, carrying messages for the Confederacy, and had took pride in how easy it was to get past Union troops and sentries. He and Booth had a lot in common in their taste for adventure that was to undo them both; but both were masters of survival and indeed masters of disguise. Both had influence over others but Surratt was foolishly more trusting otherwise he should have clocked Louis Weichmann sooner; perhaps because they had been divinity students together his judgement was clouded.

At the time of the assassination he was in Canandaigua, NY on his way to Canada and then, while his mother was on trial, he tried to get back to Baltimore where he lived and had a servant there. Earlier he had made his last attempt to contact with Booth at his home in New York on the 5th April 1865 but Booth had left for a theatre engagement in Boston, according to Booth's house servant. This in fact may have been Edwin's house where his mother lived. The following is the first part of his lecture account of his role in the kidnap plans and his flight from the Government and his two years abroad capture and trial. He gave lecture tours in at least three cities but in Washington it was banned:

"Ladies and gentlemen: - Upon entering that door a few moments ago the impression on my mind was so strong as to vividly recall scenes of three years ago. I am not unacquainted with court room audiences. I have stood before them before; true, not in the character of a lecturer, but as a prisoner at the bar, arraigned for the high crime of murder. In contrasting the two positions I must confess I felt more ease as the prisoner at the bar than I do as a lecturer. Then I felt confident of success; now I do not. Then I had gentlemen of known ability to do all my talking for me; now, unfortunately, I have to do it for myself, and I feel lily capable of performing the task; still I hope you will all judge me kindly. I am not here to surprise you by any oratorical effort - not at all - but only to tell a simple tale. I feel that some explanation, perhaps, indeed an apology is due you for my appearance here this evening. In presenting this lecture before the public I do it in no spirit of self-justification. In a trial of sixty-one days I made my defence to the world, and I have no need or desire to rehearse it; nor do I appear for self-glorification. On the contrary, I dislike notoriety, and leave my solitude and obscurity unwillingly. Neither is it an itching for notoriety or fame. My object is merely to present a simple narrative of events as they occurred. I stand here through the force of that which has obliged many other men to do things quite as distasteful - pecuniary necessity, for the supply of which no more available channel presented itself. This is a reason easily appreciated. So you will take it kindly, I trust, and the ground we will have to go over together will guarantee sufficient interest to repay your kind attention. In this my first lecture I will speak of my introduction to J. Wilkes Booth, his plan - its failure - our final separation - my trip from Richmond, and thence to Canada - then my orders to Elmira - what was done there - the first intimation I had of Mr. Lincoln's death, my return to Canada and concealment there, and final departure for Europe.

At the breaking out of the war I was a student at St. Charles College, in Maryland, but did not remain long there after that important event. I left in July, 1861, and returning home commenced to take an active part in the stirring events of that period. I was not more than eighteen years of age, and was mostly engaged in sending information regarding the movements of the United States army stationed in Washington and elsewhere, and carrying dispatches to the Confederate boats on the Potomac. We had a regular established line from Washington to the Potomac, and I being the only unmarried man on the route, I had most of the hard riding to do. I devised various ways to carry the dispatches - sometimes in the heel of my boots, sometimes between the planks of the buggy. I confess that never in my life did I come across a more stupid set of detectives than those generally employed by the U.S. government. They seemed to have no idea whatever on how to search men. In 1864 my family left Maryland and moved to Washington, where I took a still more active part in the stirring events of that period. It was a fascinating life to me. It seemed as if I could not do too much or run too great a risk.

In the fall of 1864 I was introduced to John Wilkes Booth, who, I was given to understand, wished to know something about the main avenues leading from Washington to the Potomac. We met several times, but as he seemed to be very reticent with regard to his purposes, and very anxious to get all the information out of me he could, I refused to tell him anything at all. At last I said to him, "It is useless for you, Mr. Booth, to seek any information from me at all; I know who you are and what are your intentions." He hesitated some time, but finally said he would make known his views to me provided I would promise secrecy. I replied, "I will do nothing of the kind. You know well I am a Southern man. If you cannot trust me we will separate." He then said, "I will confide my plans to you; but before doing so I will make known to you the motives that actuate me. In the Northern prisons are many thousands of our men whom the United States Government refuses to exchange. You know as well as I the efforts that have been made to bring about that much desired exchange. Aside from the great suffering they are

compelled to undergo, we are sadly in want of them as soldiers. We cannot spare one man, whereas the United States Government is willing to let their own soldiers remain in our prisons because she has no need of the men. I have a proposition to submit to you, which I think if we can carry out will bring about the desired exchange." There was a long and ominous silence which I at last was compelled to break by asking, "Well, Sir, what is your proposition?" He sat quiet for an instant, and then, before answering me, arose and looked under the bed, into the wardrobe, in the doorway and the passage, and then said, "We will have to be careful; walls have ears." He then drew his chair close to me and in a whisper said, "It is to kidnap President Lincoln, and carry him off to Richmond!" "Kidnap President Lincoln!" I said. I confess that I stood aghast at the proposition, and looked upon it as a foolhardy undertaking. To think of successfully seizing Mr. Lincoln in the capital of the United States surrounded by thousands of his soldiers, and carrying him off to Richmond, looked to me like a foolish idea. I told him as much. He went on to tell with what facility he could be seized in various places in and about Washington. As for example in his various rides to and from the Soldiers' Home, his summer residence. He entered into the minute details of the proposed capture, and even the various parts to be performed by the actors in the performance. I was amazed - thunderstruck - and in fact, I might also say, frightened at the unparalleled audacity of this scheme. After two days' reflection I told him I was willing to try it. I believed it practicable at that time, though I now regard it as a foolhardy undertaking. I hope you will not blame me for going thus far. I honestly thought an exchange of prisoners could be brought about could we have once obtained possession of Mr. Lincoln's person. And now reverse the case. Where is there a young man in the North with one spark of patriotism in his heart with would not have with enthusiastic ardor joined in any undertaking for the capture of Jefferson Davis and brought him to Washington? There is not one who would not have done so. And so I was led on by a sincere desire to assist the South in gaining her independence. I had no hesitation in taking part in anything honorable that might tend toward the accomplishment of that object. Such a thing as the assassination of Mr. Lincoln I never heard spoken of by any of the party. Never! Upon one occasion, I remember, we had called a meeting in Washington for the purpose of discussing matters in general, as we had understood that the government had received information that there was a plot of some kind on hand. They had even commenced to build a stockade and gates on the navy yard bridge; gates opening towards the south as though they expected danger from within, and not from without. At this meeting I explained the construction of the gates, etc., and stated I was confident the government had wind of our movement, and the best thing we could do would be to throw up the whole project. Everyone seemed to coincide in my opinion, except Booth, who sat silent and abstracted. Arising at last and bringing his fist upon the table he said, "Well, gentlemen, if the worst comes to the worst, I shall know what to do."
Some hard words and even threats then passed between him and some of the party. Four of us then arose, one saying, "If I understand you to intimate anything more than the capture of Mr. Lincoln I for one will bid you goodbye." Everyone expressed the same opinion. We all arose and commenced putting our hats on. Booth perceiving probably that he had gone too far, asked pardon saying that he "had drank too much champagne." After some difficulty everything was amicably arranged and we separated at 5 o'clock in the morning. Days, weeks and months passed by without an opportunity presenting itself for us to attempt the capture. We seldom saw one another owing to the many rumors afloat that a conspiracy of some kind was being concocted in Washington. We had all the arrangements perfected from Washington for the purpose. Boats were in readiness to carry us across the river. On day we received information that the President would visit the Seventh Street Hospital for the purpose of being present at an entertainment to be given for the benefit of the wounded soldiers. The report only reached us about three quarters of an hour before the time appointed, but so perfect was our communication that we were instantly in our saddles on the way to the hospital. This was between one and two o'clock in the afternoon. It was our intention to seize the carriage , which was drawn by a splendid pair of horses, and to have one of our men mount the box and drive direct for southern Maryland via Benning's bridge.

We felt confident that all the cavalry in the city could never overhaul us. We were all mounted on swift horses, besides having a thorough knowledge of the country, it was determined to abandon the carriage after passing the city limits. Upon the suddenness of the blow and the celerity of our movements we depended for success. By the time the alarm could have been given and horses saddled, we would have been on our way through southern Maryland towards the Potomac river. To our great disappointment, however, the President was not there but one of the government officials - Mr. [Salmon P.] Chase, if I mistake not. We did not disturb him, as we wanted a bigger chase than he could have afforded us. It was certainly a bitter disappointment, but yet I think a most fortunate one for us. It was our last attempt. We soon after this became convinced that we could not remain much longer undiscovered, and that we must abandon our enterprise. Accordingly, a separation finally took place, and I never saw any of the party except one, and that was when I was on my way from Richmond to Canada on business of quite a different nature - about which, presently. Such is the story of our abduction plot.

Rash, perhaps foolish, but honorable I maintain in its means and ends; actuated by such motives as would under similar circumstances be a sufficient inducement to thousands of southern young men to have embarked in a similar enterprise. Shortly after our abandonment of the abduction scheme, some dispatches came to me which I was compelled to see through to Richmond. They were foreign ones, and had no reference whatever to this affair. I accordingly left home for Richmond, and arrived there safely on the Friday evening before the evacuation of that city. On my arrival I went to [the] Spotswood Hotel, where I was told that Mr. Benjamin, the then Secretary of War of the Confederate States, wanted to see me. I accordingly sought his presence. He asked me if I would carry some dispatches to Canada for him. I replied "yes." That evening he gave me the dispatches and $200 in gold with which to pay my way to Canada. That was the only money I ever received from the Confederate government or any of its agents. It may be well to remark here that this scheme of abduction was concocted without the knowledge or the assistance of the Confederate government in any shape or form. Booth and I often consulted together as to whether it would not be well to acquaint the authorities in Richmond with our plan, as we were sadly in want of money, our expenses being very heavy. In fact the question arose among us as to whether, after getting Mr. Lincoln, if we succeeded in our plan, the Confederate authorities would not surrender us to the United States again, because of doing this thing without their knowledge or consent. But we never acquainted them with the plan, and they never had anything in the wide world to do with it. In fact, we were jealous of our undertaking and wanted no outside help. I have not made this statement to defend the officers of the Confederate government. They are perfectly able to defend themselves. What I have done myself I am not ashamed to let the world know. I left Richmond on Saturday morning before the evacuation of that place, and reached Washington the following Monday at 4 o'clock P.M., April 3d, 1865. As soon as I reached the Maryland shore I understood that the detectives knew of my trip South and were on the lookout for me. I had been South several times before for the secret service but had never been caught. At that time I was carrying the dispatches Mr. Benjamin gave me: in a book entitled "The Life of John Brown." During my trip, and while reading that book, I learned, to my utter amazement, that John Brown was a martyr sitting at the right hand of God. I succeeded in reaching Washington safely, and in passing up Seventh street met one of our party, who inquired what had become of Booth. I told him where I had been; that I was then on my way to Canada, and that I had not seen or heard anything of Booth since our separation. In view of the fact that Richmond had fallen, and that all hopes of the abduction of the President had been given up, I advised him to go home and go to work. That was the last time I saw any of the party. I went to a hotel and stopped over that night, as a detective had been to my house inquiring of the servant my whereabouts. In the early train next morning, Tuesday, April 4, 1865, I left for New York, and that was the last time I was ever in Washington until brought there by the U.S. Government a captive in irons, all reports to the contrary notwithstanding.

The United States, as you will remember, tried to prove my presence in Washington on the 15th of

April, the day on which Mr. Lincoln met his death. Upon arriving in New York, I called at Booth's house, and was told by the servant that he had left that morning suddenly, on the ground of going to Boston to fulfill an engagement at the theater. In the evening of the same day I took the cars for Montreal, arriving there the next day. I put up at the St. Lawrence Hotel, registering myself as "John Harrison" such being my first two names. Shortly afterwards I saw General Edward G. Lee, to whom the dispatches were directed, and delivered them to him. Those dispatches we tried to introduce as evidence on my trial, but his Honor Judge Fisher ruled them out, despite of the fact that the government had tried to prove that they had relation to the conspiracy to kill Mr. Lincoln. They were only accounts of some money transactions - nothing more or less. A week or so after my arrival there, General Lee came to my room, and told me he had a plan on foot to release the Confederate prisoners then in Elmira, N.Y. He said he had sent many parties there, but they always got frightened, and only half executed their orders. He asked me if I would go there and take a sketch of the prison, find out the number of prisoners, also minor details in regard to the number of soldiers on guard, cannon, small arms, etc. I readily accepted these new labors, owing to the fact that I could not return to Washington for fear of the detectives. The news of the evacuation of Richmond did not seem to disturb the General much in his plan, as he doubtless thought then that the Confederacy wanted men more than ever, no one dreaming that it was virtually at an end. I was much amused at one expression made use of by an ex-reb with regard to the suddenness of its demise: "D---n the thing, it didn't even flicker, went right out." In accordance with Gen. Lee's order, I went to Elmira, arriving there on Wednesday, two days before Mr. Lincoln's death, and registered at the Brainard House, as usual as "John Harrison." The following day I went to work, and made a complete sketch of the prison and surroundings. About 10 o'clock on Friday night I retired, little thinking that on that night a blow would be struck which would forever blast my hopes, and make me a wanderer in a foreign land. I slept the night through, and came down the next morning little dreaming of the storm then brewing around my head. When I took my seat at the table around 9 o'clock A.M., a gentleman to my left remarked: "Have you heard the news?" "No, I've not," I replied. "What is it?" "Why President Lincoln and Secretary Seward have been assassinated." I really put so little faith in what the man said that I made a remark that it was too early in the morning to get off such jokes as that. "It's so," he said, at the same time drawing out a paper and showing it to me. Sure enough, there I saw an account of what he told me, but as no names were mentioned, it never occurred to me for an instant that it could have been Booth or any of the party, for the simple reason that I never had heard anything regarding assassination spoken of during my intercourse with them. I had good reason to believe that there was another conspiracy afloat in Washington, in fact we all knew it. One evening, as I was partially lying down in the reading-room of the Metropolitan Hotel, two or three gentlemen came in and looked around as if to sure that no one was around. They then commenced to talk about what had been done, the best means for the expedition, etc. It being about dusk, and no gas light, and partially concealed behind a writing desk, I was an unwilling listener of what occurred. I told Booth of this afterward, and he said he had heard something to the same effect. It only made us all the more eager to carry out our plans at an early day for fear some one should get ahead of us. We didn't know what they were after exactly, but we were all well satisfied that their object was very much the same as ours. Arising from the table I thought over who the party could be, for at that time no names had been telegraphed. I was pretty sure it was none of the old party. I approached the telegraph office in the main hall of the hotel for the purpose of ascertaining if J. Wilkes Booth was in New York. I picked up a blank and wrote "John Wilkes Booth," giving the number of the house. I hesitated a moment, and then tore the paper up, and then wrote one "J.W.B.," with directions, which I was led to do from the fact that during our whole connection we rarely wrote or telegraphed under our proper names, but always in such a manner that no one could understand but ourselves. One way of Booth's was to send letters to me under cover to my quondam friend, Louis J. Weichman.

Doubtless you all know who Louis J. Weichman is. They were sent to him because he knew of the plot to abduct President Lincoln. I proclaim it here and before the world that Louis J.Weichman was a party to the plan to abduct President Lincoln. He had been told all about it, and was constantly importuning me to let him become an active member. I refused, for the simple reason that I told him that he could neither ride a horse nor shoot a pistol, which was a fact. These were two necessary accomplishments for us. My refusal nettled him some; so he went off, as it afterwards appeared by his testimony, and told some government clerk [Captain Gleason] that he had a vague idea that there was a plan of some kind on hand to abduct President Lincoln. This he says himself: that he could have spotted every man on the party. Why didn't he do it? Booth was sometimes rather suspicious of him, and asked me if I thought he could be trusted. Said I, "Certainly he can. Weichman is a Southern man," and I always believed it until I had good reason to believe otherwise, because he had furnished information for the Confederate government, besides allowing me access to the government records after office hours. I have very little to say of Louis J. Weichman. But I do pronounce him a base-born perjurer; a murderer of the meanest hue! Give me a man who can strike his victim dead, but save me from a man who, through perjury, will cause the death of an innocent person. Double murderer!!!! Hell possesses no worse fiend than a character of that kind. Away with such a character. I leave him in the pit of infamy, which he has dug for himself, a prey to the lights of his guilty conscience.

I telegraphed Booth thus: "J.W.B., in New York: If you are in New York telegraph me. John Harrison, Elmira, N.Y." The operator, after looking it over, said, "Is it J.W.B.?" to which I replied, "Yes." He evidently wanted the whole name, and had scarcely finished telegraphing when a door right near the office, and opening on the street, was pushed open, and I heard someone say, "Yes, there are three or four brothers of them, John (actually, Joseph: Author), Junius Brutus, Edwin, and J. Wilkes Booth." The whole truth flashed on me in an instant, and I said to myself, "My God! What have I done?" The dispatch was still lying before me, and I reached over and took it up for the purpose of destroying it, but the operator stretched forth his hand and said, "We must file all telegrams." My first impulse was to tear it up, but I pitched it back and walked off. The town was in the greatest uproar, flags t half mast, bells tolling, &c., &c. Still I did not think that I was in danger, and determined to go immediately to Baltimore to find out the particulars of the tragedy. But here I wish to say a few words concerning the register of the Brainard House. When my counsel, by my own direction, went to seek that register, it could not be found. Our inability to produce it on the trial naturally cast a suspicion over our alibi. For weeks, months, did we seek to find its whereabouts, but to no purpose. Every man who was connected with the hotel was hunted up and questioned. Every register of the hotel before and after the one which ought to contain my name was to be found, but the most important one of all was gone. Now the question is what became of that register? The U.S. Government, by one of its witnesses, Doctor McMillan, knew in November, 1865, that I was in Elmira at the time of the assassination. They knew it, and they naturally traced me there to find out what I was doing. That some of the government emissaries abstracted that register, I firmly believe, or perhaps it is stored away in some of the other government vaults, under charge of some judge high in position, but this is only a surmise of mine. But the circumstance involves a mystery of villainy which the All Seeing God will yet bring to light. The dispatch I sent to Booth also from Elmira it was impossible to find. We had the operator at Washington during my trial, but he said the original was gone though he had a copy of it. In telegraph offices they are compelled to keep all dispatches filed. Of course we could not offer this copy in evidence, because the original alone would be accepted, and that had been made away with. So sure was the government that they had destroyed all evidence of my sojourn in Elmira, that in getting me in Washington in time for Mr. Lincoln's death they brought me by way of New York City, but so completely were they foiled in this that in their rebutting testimony they saw the absolute necessity of having me go by way of Elmira, and they changed their tactics accordingly. That was enough to damn my case in any man's mind. This is a strange fact, but nevertheless true that the government having in its possession this hotel register as well as my dispatch to Booth and knowing moreover by one of its witnesses that I was in

Elmira, yet tried to prove that I was in Washington on the night of Mr. Lincoln's death, giving orders and commanding in general as they were pleased to say. The gentlemen in Elmira, by whom I proved my alibi, were men of the highest standing and integrity whose testimony the United States government could not and dare not attempt to impeach. I left Elmira with the intention of going to Baltimore. I really did not comprehend at that time the danger I was in. As there was no train going South that evening I concluded to go to Canandaigua and from there to Baltimore by way of Elmira and New York. Upon arriving at Canandaigua on Saturday evening I learned to my utter disappointment that no train left until the Monday following, so I took a room at the Webster House, registering my self as "John Harrison." The next day I went to church, I remember it being Easter Sunday. I can here safely say that the United States government had not the remotest idea that I stopped anywhere after I left Elmira. They thought, when I left there, I went straight through to Canada. It was a very fortunate thing for me that I could not leave Canandaigua. Now mark, ladies and gentlemen, if you please, my name was signed midway of the hotel register, with six other parties before and after. There was no doubt as to the genuineness of my signature, because the very experts brought by the United States to swear to my signatures in other instances, swore also that that was my handwriting. After all this register was ruled out by Judge Fisher, because he was well aware if he admitted it my case was at an end. I could not be in two places at once, though they tried to make me so. Listen to his reason for so ruling: "The prisoner might have stepped down from Canada to Canandiagua during his concealment and signed his name there for the purpose of protecting himself in the future." It was a likely idea that the proprietor of a hotel would leave a blank line in the register for my especial benefit. Need I say that the ruling was a most infamous one, and ought to damn the Judge who so ruled as a villain in the minds of every honest and upright man. Had Judge Fisher been one of the lawyers for the prosecution, he could not have worked harder against me than he did. But, thanks to him, he did me more good than harm. His unprincipled and vindictive character was too apparent to everyone in the court room. I could not help smiling at the time to think of the great shrewdness and foresight he accorded me by that decision. At times, really, during my trial, I could scarcely recognize any vestige of my former self. Sometimes I would ask myself, "Am I the same individual? Am I really the same John H. Surratt?" When that register was produced in court, the Hon. Judge Pierrepont, the leading counsel for the United States, became exceedingly nervous, especially, when Mr. Bradley refused to show it to him, and he tore up several pieces of paper in his trembling fingers. He evidently saw what a pitiful case he had, and how he had to make the dupe of his precious, worthy friend, Edwin M. Stanton. At the time of my trial the proprietor of the Webster House, in Canandaigua, could not find the cash book of the hotel, in which there should have been an entry in favor of "John Harrison" for so much cash. When he returned to Canandaigua, my trial being then ended, he wrote Mr. Bradley that he had found the cash book, and sent it to him. It was then too late. My trial was over. If we had had that cash book at the time of my trial it would have been proved beyond a doubt that I was in Canandaigua and not in Washington city.

On Monday when I was leaving Canandaigua I bought some New York papers. In looking over them, my eye lit on the following paragraph which I have never forgot, and don't think I ever will. It runs thus: "The assassin of Secretary Seward is said to be John H. Surratt, a notorious secessionist of Southern Maryland. His name, with that of J. Wilkes Booth, will forever lead the infamous role of assassins." I could scarcely believe my senses. I gazed upon my name, the letters of which seemed to sometimes to grow as large as mountains and then to dwindle away to nothing. So much for my former connection with him I thought. After fully realizing the state of the case, I concluded to change my course and go direct to Canada. I left Canandaigua on Monday 12 M., going to Albany arriving there on Tuesday morning in time for breakfast. When I stepped on the platform at the depot at St. Albans I noticed that one of the detectives scanned every one, head and foot, as well as the rest. Before leaving Montreal for Elmira, I provided myself with an Oxford cut jacket and a round-top hat, peculiar to Canada at that time. I knew my trip to Elmira would be a dangerous one, and I wished to pass myself off as a Canadian, and I succeeded in so doing, as was proved by my witnesses in Elmira. I believe that costume guarded me safely through St. Albans. I went in with others, and moved around, with the detectives standing there most of the time looking at us. Of course I was obliged to talk as loud as anybody about the late tragedy. After having a hearty meal I lighted a cigar and walked up town. One of the detectives approached me, stared me directly in the face, and I looked him quietly back. In a few moments I was speeding on my way to Montreal, where I arrived at two o'clock in the afternoon, going again to the St. Lawrence Hotel. Soon after I called on a friend, to whom I explained my former connection with Booth, and told him I was afraid the United States government would suspect me of complicity in the plot of assassination. He advised me to make myself scarce. I immediately went to the hotel, got my things, and repaired to the room of a friend. When my friend's tea-time came I would not go to the table with him, but remained in the room. The ladies wanted to know why he didn't bring his friend to tea with him. He replied that I didn't want any. One of the ladies remarked, "I expect you have got Booth in there." "Perhaps so," he answered laughingly. That was rather close guessing. At night-fall I went to the house of one who afterwards proved to be a most devoted friend. There I remained until the evening of the next day, when I was driven out in a carriage with two gentlemen, strangers to me. One day I walked out and saw Weichman on the lookout for me.

He had little idea I was so near. One night about 11 o'clock, my friend, in whose house I was, came to me and said, in a smiling way: "The detectives have offered me $20,000 if I will tell them where you are." "Very well," said I, "give me one half, and let them know." they suspected this gentleman of protecting me, and they had really made him the offer. One day about 12 o'clock, I was told that they were going to search the house, and that I must leave immediately, which I did. They searched it before morning. This gentleman was a poor man, with a large family, and yet money could not buy him. I remained with this gentleman until I left Montreal, within a week or so afterwards. The detectives were now hunting me very closely, and would doubtless succeeded in capturing me, had it not been for a blunder on the part of my friend Weichman. He had, it appears, started the detectives on the wrong track, by telling them that I had left the house of Mr.Porterfield in company with some others, and was going north of Montreal. Soon that section was swarming with detectives. I was not with that party, but about the same time, I too, left Montreal in a hack, going some 8 or 9 miles down the St. Lawrence river, crossing that stream in a small canoe. I was attired as a huntsman. At 3 o'clock Wednesday morning, we arrived at our destination, a small town lying south of Montreal. We entered the village very quietly, hoping no one would see us. It has been asserted over and over again, and for the purpose of damning me in the estimation of every honest man that I deserted her who gave me birth in the direst hour of her need. Truly would I have merited the execration of every man had such been the case. But such was not the case. When I left Montreal there was no cause for uneasiness on my part, and upon my arrival in the country I wrote to my friends in Montreal to keep me posted in regard to the approaching trial, and to send me the newspapers regularly. I received letters from them frequently, in all of which they assured me there was no cause of anxiety; that it was only a matter of time, and it would all be well. After a while papers did not come so regularly, and those that did, spoke very encouragingly. A little while afterwards, when they came, sentences were mutilated with ink and pen.

I protested against such action, and for some time I received no papers at all. I became very uneasy, and wrote for publication an article signed by myself, which I sent to Montreal to be forwarded for publication in the New York World. It is needless to say it never went. Things continued in this way for some time, until I could stand the suspense no longer. I determined to send a messenger to Washington for that purpose, and secured the services of an intelligent and educated gentleman. I started him off immediately, I paying all expenses. I gave him a letter to a friend of mine in Washington, with instructions to say to him to put himself in communication with the counsel for the defense, and to make a correct report to me as to how the case stood; if there was any danger; and also, to communicate with me if my presence was necessary, and inform me without delay; with an urgent request that he would see and inquire for himself how matters stood. He left me, and God alone knows the suspense and anxiety of my mind during the days of his absence. I imagined and thought all kinds of things; yet I was powerless to act. At last he returned, and so bright and cheerful was his countenance that I confess one-half of my fears were dispelled. He represented everything as progressing well, and brought me the message from the gentleman in Washington to whom I had sent him:

> "Be under no apprehension as to any serious consequences. Remain perfectly quiet, as any action on your part would only tend to make matters worse. If you can be of any service to us, we will let you know; but keep quiet."

These were the instructions I received from my friend in Washington, in whom I felt the utmost reliance, and who I thought would never deceive me. He also sent me copies of the National Intelligencer, containing evidence for the defense. I certainly felt greatly relieved, though not entirely satisfied. This news reached me sometime in the latter part of June, just before the party of gentlemen of whom I have spoken arrived. They, too, assured me there was no cause for fear. What else could I do but accept these unwavering assurances? Even had I thought otherwise, I could not have taken any action resulting in good.

Just on the eve of my departure to join a party of gentlemen on a hunting excursion, while I was waiting at the hotel for the train, the proprietor handed me a paper, and said, "Read that about the conspirators." Little did the man know who I was, or how closely that paragraph bore upon me or mine. That paper informed me that on a day which was then present, and at an hour which had then come and gone, the most hellish of deeds was to be enacted. It had been determined upon and carried out, even before I had intimation that there was any danger. It would be folly for me to attempt to describe my feelings. After gazing at the paper for some time I dropped it on the floor, turning on my heel, and going directly to the house where I had been stopping before. When I entered the room, I found my friend sitting there. As soon as he saw me, he turned deadly pale, but never uttered a word. I said, "You doubtless thought you were acting a friend - the part of a friend - towards me, but you have deceived me. I may forgive you, but I can never forget it."

"We all thought it for the best, Charley," he commenced to say, but I did not stay to hear more. I went to my room, remained there until dark, and then signified my intention to leave the place immediately. I felt reckless as to what should become of me.

After visiting Quebec and other places, with the reward of $25,000 hanging over my head, I did not think it safe to remain there, and so I concluded to seek an asylum in foreign lands. I had nothing now to bind me to this country, save an only sister, and I knew she would never want for kind friends or a good home. For myself, it mattered little where I went, so that I could roam once more a free man. I then went on a venture, and now, ladies and gentlemen, I go forth again on a venture. Gladly would I have remained hidden among the multitude, but the stern necessities arising from the blasting of my earthly prospects have forced me to leave my solitude and to stand again before the public gaze as the historian of my own life. One mitigation to its distastefulness in this and my first attempt, however, is the kindness with which I have been received, and the patience with which I have been listened to, for which I return you, ladies and gentlemen, my sincere and heartfelt thanks."

The highlights of this lecture are:

He remarks that Washington seemed to be preparing a stockade at the navy bridge, as if to contain a threat from within. (Author: Or perhaps for a dummy controlled escape.)

He first met Booth in the fall of 1864. He was confident the Union had wind of their

movements.
He mentions that his erstwhile friend Louis E. Weichmann had informed a Captain Gleason of their plans for a kidnap. But he did not identify any names at that stage, so he thought, but little did he realise.
He says that Weichmann, a prison clerk showed him government records.
He said that Weichmann traced him to Montreal and informed government detectives to look for him in the north of the city. His trial lasted 61 days. He said that Weichmann was in on the conspiracy to kidnapping. They tried to kidnap the president at the Seventh Street Hospital. But Salmon Chase and not the president was there. No mention of Booth or any other names. He decided to give up the whole idea after this and warned Booth.
He left for New York on the 4th April and visited Booth's house, the following morning. The servant said Booth had left that very morning for a theatre engagement in Boston. In fact Edwin Booth was performing in Boston that very Easter, so this was probably Edwin's house. And John seldom performed in the North. In fact the only time they had recently performed together was at the New York Winter Gardens when all three brothers, Junius, John and Edwin, played in Shakespeare's Julius Ceaser.
He said he never heard any talk about assassination at any time. The reason for the kidnap was to force an exchange of prisoners by taking Lincoln to Richmond. He said the kidnap plot was their own idea and they did not want to involve the Confederate government, until they had got to Richmond. (Booth had also indicated this in his letter to a friend, or to his sister- 'my own responsibility').
He was named by the press already as the assassin of Seward. So later the press had to change their 'facts' and decided it was Payne instead. Whilst in Washington he had overheard another group were plotting something similar.

Captain William E. Doster

16th Pennsylvania Cavalry Regt.

Chapter 6

Lewis Payne, His Bravery And His Defence

1845-65
He Was Their Bravest Soldier

There is no doubt that Payne was a very sure and brave young man of only 20 years when he was brutally hung in the public eye. At the trial he stood-up for Mary Surratt and swore on his honour as a soldier that she was not involved in the kidnap plot and to let them hang him in her place. He had somehow managed to rip his hood of and shouted that Mary Surratt was totally innocent. Baker said he was a professional murderer, one of three outlawed brothers from Kentucky. The photographs show a very strong, handsome young man with piercing eyes, and no fear and it is said he went to his death with a brave remark. He obviously knew that if he could not escape, he was willing to accept his fate in the honour of his country men, and so did not feel any remorse whatsoever. For what is remorse but a feeling of guilt for a crime he did not commit? The following glowing account is the result of genuine research courtesy of Mcfarland Press to which this author is exceptionally grateful:

"Lewis (Payne) Thornton Powell's early Civil War years included his enlistment June 4, 1861 for twelve months in Company I, 2nd Florida, at Jasper, Hamilton County, Florida at the age of 19. He was wounded in the wrist and captured during the Gettysburg Campaign on July 2, 1863. On August 10, 1863 he was a POW at Letterman General Hospital, Gettysburg then moved to the U.S.A. General Hospital, Baltimore where he escaped and joined Mosby's 43rd Virginia Battalion in September 1863. He participated in the attack on the Union troops stationed at Salem and in the engagement at Myerstown, West Virginia on November 18th 1864, where Munson cited Powell in quite favourable light; after that he participated in the capture of Union Captain Richard Blazer, as part of the Berryville Raid. Payne captured three Federal prisoners near Warrenton, on December 25, 1864. He occasionally took the name where he boarded, of General William H. Payne's relatives, who were complimentary of Louis and then Dr. Alban T. Payne of Upperville, Virginia. He was executed on July 7th, 1865 at the Old Capitol Prison, Washington, DC. "

Also mentioned in this account was William Jett and another soldier by the name of

Bainbridge of Company G, 43rd Battalion. Thus all three fought with Moseby's, Virginia Partisian Rangers. These last two soldiers along with Lieutenant Ruggles were the Confederate officers that intercepted, helped and reported the lame soldier and his comrade, in the crossing of the Rappahannock river from Port Conway to Port Royal, Virginia. Baker's view of Payne however was completely different:

" Someone or all of these agents furnished Booth with a murderer-the fellow Wood, or Payne, who stabbed Mr. Seward, and was caught at Mrs. Surratt's house in Washington. He was one of three Kentucky brothers, all outlaws, and had himself, it is believed, accompanied one of his brothers, who is known to have been at St. Albans on the day of the bank delivery. This Payne, besides being positively identified as the assassin of the Sewards, had no friends or haunts in Washington. He was simply a dispatched murderer, and after the night of the crime struck northward for the frontier, instead of southward in the company of Booth. The proof of this will follow in the course of the article".

This account of Baker's is to support his plan that Booth went south, which of course is true in terms of the dummy run (of Tyson and Hensted), in which he says the proof will follow, and in this author's case, the counter proof to this will also follow. It also takes pains to exhibit boldly, as you will see later in another passage, how Payne rode north and then became plastered with mud, in order to effect his disguise for returning to the heart of the lion's den, Washington. Whereas in fact there was a much simpler explanation. He was arrested all muddy with a pick in his hand because he had been digging a culvert for his landlady, the dear and tragic Mrs.Surratt.
What is truly worrying about this passage however, is that Baker intimates perhaps mistakenly, since Baker was never the one to worry much about detail, that Payne had assassinated the Sewards, in plural. Was this a big part of the original plot? You will see below in a coded letter that an agent called 'Red Shoes' suddenly got a bad case of cold feet. And a young soldier called Robinson was acting as a nurse for Seward, at his very bedside that night, whilst Seward was recovering from a carriage accident. Also the original rumours and some press reports, said that the President and Secretary of State plus half the Cabinet had been assassinated. And one of Seward's sons-Frederick was an army Major. He together with his brother and sister were all at risk that night, if any one of them had interfered, all at home with the house man William Bell and other staff. Seward had become estranged from his wife Frances who lived in Auburn, New York. Well, we know he was an extremely rich and arrogant man, but there must have been a lot of hate for him too, and he was already badly injured by the carriage accident. Why not capitalise on this? This would be perfectly logical to the illuminati in order to help achieve their stated objective - half the Cabinet.

Here we have one of the many books by the late Victorian, English publisher, Heath W. Robinson later made into the famous ballet and then a film starring Marius Goring in 1948. However the connection is not to Heath Robinson himself since Red Shoes was a Fairy Tale written by Hans Christian Anderson, in Copenhagen in 1845, that lives in folk lore. Robinson is associated with Red because of that ubiquitous and highly territorial bird and man's friend, the Robin. The putting on of the shoes by the girl representing vanity and boldness. And since the Union had a highly associative, character system of giving nicknames in their ciphers, this one is easy to de-cipher. I.e. Red Shoes was Robinson, who suffered from a 'loss of nerve' but had then later 'recovered well'.

Red Shoes
Published by
Heath W. Robinson

So it is logical that Red Shoes was the code name for Robinson the young soldier acting as nurse at the bedside of the Secretary of State. The writer remembers himself this film as a kid and always had haunting memories, as it was such a haunting and visually moving film with hidden esoteric meaning, even to a child. Such was the writing power and imagination of Hans Christian Anderson. It was a fairy tale story about a young girl who could not stop dancing, after she had put on the red shoes. Anderson got his idea for the story from a vivid piece of red cloth his father brought home one day.

Seward- Kenai Peninsula Alaska

Seward's wife Frances died in June 1865
His nurse Fanny died in Oct 1866

Now follows the most diabolical defence of an innocent young man that could ever exist in the annals of recorded history and another example of rampant Victorian hypocrisy.

The Defence Of Lewis Payne

The defence admitted unreservedly their clients guilt on all three counts without having investigated or brought forward one shred of evidence in his defence. In addition, at the scene of the crime he is supposed to have shouted to William Bell 'I'm mad, I'm mad' but the defence argued that he was perfectly sane. Of course he was, he was the sanest man in Washington that day but also the most brave and strongest. No man in that court room was fit enough to polish his shoes. Then followed the most painful and impotent, filibuster of a mitigation plea ever to wax lyrical across a court room floor. It defies all known logic but its political intentions are plain and are not lost upon the hierarchy. This defence was engineered to make out a case against the South's morality, in the fullest cognisance that this pseudo-actor Doster speech would send young Lewis, on the threshold of man-hood, straight to the gallows. Indeed it was a futile, repetitive, broadside barrage against the South, such that its only victim was the young man he was charged to defend. Even by Doster's own standards it may be un-matched, in the extensive annals of Victorian hypocrisy.
It is included here, this whole sad and sorry politically motivated plea, because it will give you an insight to the kind of 'honourable' creatures that this period threw up, to become senior officers, entrusted to preserve and defend an innocent young man, in the name of justice..

Note; The author has not corrected any spelling, or mistaken words such as rot and stink, common words in the Victorian vernacular.

ARGUMENT IN DEFENSE OF LEWIS POWELL, BY W.E. DOSTER, ESQ.

May it please the Court:

I. There are three things in the case of the prisoner, Powell, which are admitted beyond civil or dispute:

1. That he is the person who attempted to take the life of the Secretary of State.
2. That he is not within the medical definition of insanity.
3. That he believed what he did was right and justifiable.

The question of his identity and the question of his sanity are, therefore, settled, and among the things of the past. The sole question that remains is, how far shall his convictions serve to mitigate his punishment? I use the word punishment deliberately, and with the consciousness that in so doing I admit that if he is a responsible being he ought to be punished. And I say it, because I can not allow my duties as counsel to interfere with my convictions as a man so far as to make me blind to the worth of the life of a distinguished citizen, and the awful consequences of an attempt to take it away. If, indeed, such an attempt be allowed to go without rebuke, then it seems to me the office is but a perilous exposure to violence; then the highest compensation for public services is the distinction which follows assassination, and then our public servants are but pitiable and defenseless offerings to sedition. And surely, if any public servant deserved to be excepted from that fates it was he, the illustrious and sagacious statesman, who, during a long life of arduous services, has steadfastly checked all manner of factious and public discontent; who, in the darkest days of discord, has prophesied the triumph of concord, and who at all times has been more ready to apply antidotes than the knife to the nation's wounds. How far, then, shall the conviction of the prisoner that he was doing right go in extenuation of his offense? That we may accurately, and as fully as the occasion demands, understand the convictions of the prisoner, I invite your attention to sketch of his life, the customs under which he was reared, and the education which he received. Lewis Thornton Powell is the son of the Rev. Geo. C. Powell, a Baptist minister, at present supposed to live at Live Oak Station, on the railroad between Jacksonville and Tallahassee, in the State of Florida, and was born in Alabama in the year 1845. Besides himself, his father had six daughters' and two sons. He lived for some time in Worth and Stewart counties, Georgia, and in 1859 moved to Florida. At the breaking out of the war, but four years ago, the prisoner was a lad of sixteen, engaged in superintending his father's plantation and a number of slaves. We may safely presume that, occupied in the innocent pursuits of country life, he daily heard the precepts of the Gospel from his father; that, in the society of his sisters, the hardy life of a planter was softened by the charms of a refined and religious circle, and that, in the natural course of events, he would be today, as he was then, a farmer and an honest man. But, in 1861, war broke out--war, the scourge and pestilence of the race. The signal, which spread like a fire, was not long in reaching Live Oak Station. His two brothers enlisted, and Lewis, though but sixteen, enlisted in Capt. Stuart's company, in the Second Florida Infantry, commanded by Col. Ward, and was ordered to Richmond.

Let us pause a moment in this narrative, and consider what, in the eyes of this Florida boy, was the meaning of war, and what the thoughts that drove him from a pleasant home to the field of arms. At another time I might picture to you the scene, but too familiar, of his taking leave; a mother, like the mothers of Northern boys, shedding tears, less bitter, because she was dedicating a son to her country; sisters, whose sorrow, like the sorrow of the sisters of Northern boys, was alleviated with pride that they had a brother in the field; the father's blessing; the knapsack filled with tributes of affection, to be fondled by distant bivouac fires, and the heavy sigh, drowned in the rolling of the drum. But this is not a stage for effect. We know this was mistaken pride and sorrow in a mistaken cause, though the object of them was a son and brother, and we must not consider them, though the boy was but sixteen when he launched on the terrible sea of civil war.

In the State of Florida were two separate races--one white and the other black--of which the one was slave to the other, and Lewis belonged to the race which was master. It was a custom of this State for masters to whip their slaves, sell them, kill them, and receive the constant homage which the oppressed offer to the powerful. It was the custom of this State to whip and burn men who preached against the custom. It was the custom to defend this institution in meeting-houses, at political gatherings, in family prayers. It was the custom to hunt fugitives with bloodhounds--even those who tried to help them to freedom.

In this custom the prisoner was bred; education made it a second nature; politicians had taught him to find it in the Constitution, preachers had taught him to find it in the Bible, the laws taught him to regard it as property, habit had made it a very part of his being. In the eyes of the lad, the war meant to abolish this custom and up heave society from its foundations. His inheritance was to be dissipated. It is vassals equals, his laws invaded, his religion confounded, his politics a heresy, his habits criminal. Hereafter, to strike & slave was to be an assault, to sell one felony, to kill one murder. For this, then, the lad was going to fight--the defense of a social system. That was the reason. It was a traditional political precept of the State in which the prisoner lived, that the State, like its elder sisters, had reserved the right of divorcing itself at pleasure from the Union, and that great as the duty of a citizen might be to the Union, his first duty was to Florida. Schoolmasters taught that the relative rights of State and Nation had been left unsettled; politicians taught that the local power was greater than the central, and in support of it men were sent to Washington. The war, in the eyes of the boy, meant to reverse this, to subordinate the

State to the Nation, the Governor to the President, Tallahassee to Washington City. And, therefore, he was going to fight; to defend State rights. That was the second reason.

It was a deep-seated conviction of the people in this State that their blood and breeding were better than the blood and breeding of Northerners; that they had more courage, more military prowess, and were by nature superiors. This conviction the war threatened to overthrow, this boast the war was to vindicate, this superiority was, by the war, intended to be proved. And this was the third reason he was going to fight--to show that he was a better man than Northerners.

There was a frantic delusion among these people that Northern men were usurping the Government, were coveting their plantations, were longing to pillage their houses, ravage their fields, and reduce them to subjection. The war was to defend mother, sister, home, soil, and honor, and beat back an insolent invader. This was the fourth reason? to repel invasion. These were, in the mind of this lad, the incentives to war. Let us not pass unnoticed how he was schooled in the instincts and morals of war. Under the code of slavery we know that the murder of a companion with a bowie-knife or in a duel was an index of spirit; the torture of negroes evidence of a commanding nature; concubinage with negroes a delicate compliment to wives; spending wealth earned by other men in luxuriance, chivalric; gambling the, sweet reprieve for confinement to plantations. Instead of morals bad sprung up a code of honor--perhaps a false, but surely an exacting and imperious code, that kept bowie-knives in the belt and pistols in, the pocket. and had no hesitation in using them when slavery was assailed, and a code that remembered friends an never forgave enemies. These, then, were the morals and instincts of the lad--it is right to kill negroes, right to kill abolitionists; it is only wrong to break promises, to forget a friend, or forgive an enemy ; and to do right is to be ready with bowie-knife and pistol.

Now let me ask whether in the wide world there is another school in which the prisoner could so well have been trained for assassination as in this slave aristocracy?... But who is to blame that he, with five millions more, was so instructed, so demoralized, so educated to crime? Is it his father and mother? They found their precepts in the Bible; they gave their son but the customs they had themselves inherited. Is it the society of Florida? It was a society that ruled this country until within four years, and occupied the seats of Government. Is it the laws of Florida? They were but rescripts of the Constitution. Is it the Constitution? That is but the creation of our forefathers. Who, then, is responsible that slavery was allowed to train assassins? I answer, it is we; we, the American people ' we who have cherished slavery, have compromised with it, have for a hundred years extended it, have pandered to it, and have at last, thanks be to God, destroyed it. Let us, then, not shrink from our responsibility. If there be any Southerner here who has sought to foster slavery, lie is in part father of the assassin in this boy. If there be any Northerner here who has been content to live with slavery, he is also in part father of the assassin in this boy. If there be any American that has been content to be a citizen of a slaveholding republic, he is part father of the assassin in this boy. Nay, all of us--such as he is we have made him--the murderous, ferocious, and vindictive child of by-gone American Constitution and laws and what is to be the fate of our offspring Let us see. That it is criminal, let us reform it; that it, is deluded, let us instruct it. But let us not destroy it, for therein we punish others for our own crimes. Let the great American people rather speak thus: "For twenty years we have sent you to a wicked school, though we knew not the wickedness thereof, until our own child rebelled against us. Now we have torn down the school? house and driven out the master. Hereafter you shall be taught in a better school, and we will not destroy you, because you learnt but as instructed." II. But there is another school before him--the school of war. At Richmond his regiment joined the army of Gen. Lee, and was joined to A. P. Hill's corps; with it he shared the fate of the rebel army, passed through the Peninsular campaign, the battles of Chancellor Ville and Antietam. Here he heard that his two brothers were killed at Murfreesboro. Finally, on the 3d of July, 1863, in the charge upon the Federal center, at Gettysburg, he was wounded, taken prisoner, and detailed as a nurse in Pennsylvania College Hospital. Let us pause again to consider the effect of two years' campaigning as a private in the army of Gen. Lee upon the moral nature of the accused. He was one of that army who made trinkets and cups out of the bones of Union soldiers--an army where it was customary to starve prisoners by lingering agonies, which supplied its wants by plundering the dead, which slew men after surrender, that was commanded by officers who bad violated their sacred oaths to the United States, and who taught their subordinates that such violation was justifiable; an army who were taught by Jackson that God was the champion of their cause; an army that held the enemy in quest of "booty and beauty;" an army which believed no means that helped the cause of Southern independence unjustifiable, but glorious; an army who for two years explained victory by the righteousness of the cause--finally, an army that held the person and Cabinet of the President in holy execration. Surely he could not pass through these two terrible years without being in his moral nature the same as the army of which he formed a part. He is now eighteen, and the last two years have formed his character. He also abhors the President of the Yankees; he also believes that victory comes because God is just; he also believes that nothing is bad so the South be free; he also regards a Federal as a ravisher and robber; he also prays with Jackson to God for the victory. He further believes in Heaven and General Lee; dresses himself in the clothes of Union dead; stands guard over starving prisoners; also has his cup carved out of some Federal skull. Besides, he has learned the ordinary soldier's lessons, to taste blood and like it; to brave death and care nothing for life; to hope for letters and get none; to hope for the end of the war and see none; to find in victory no more than the beginning of another march; to look for promotion and get none; to pass from death and danger to idleness and corruption; to ask for furloughs and get none, and finally, to despair, and hope for death to end his sufferings. The slave-driver has now become a butcher...Now, I hear it said, true, the boy has been a rebel soldier. and we can forgive him; but we can not forgive assassins. Let us, for a moment, compare a rebel soldier with the prisoner, and see wherein they differ. The best rebel soldiers are native Southerners. So is he. The best rebel soldiers have for four years longed to capture Washington, and put its Government to the sword. So has he. The best rebel soldiers have fought on their own hook, after the fashion of the provincials during the Revolution, finding their own knives, their own horses, their own pistols. So has he. The best rebel soldiers have fired at Mr. Lincoln and Mr. Seward, have approached the city by stealth from Baltimore, and aimed to destroy the Government by a sudden blow. So has he. The best rebel soldiers have picked off high officers of the Government? Kearney, Stevens, Baker, Wadsworth, Lyon, Sedgwick. So has he. What, then, has he done that every rebel soldier has not tried to do? Only this--he has ventured more; he has shown a higher courage, a bitterer hate, and a more ready sacrifice; he has aimed at the head of a department, instead of the head of a corps; he has struck at the head of a nation, instead of at its limbs; be has struck in the day of his humiliation, when nothing was to be accomplished but revenge, and when he believed lie was killing an oppressor. .If, then, you praise men because they kill such as they believe oppressors, you must praise him; if you praise men who are ready to die for their country, you will praise him; and if you applaud those who show any courage superior to the rest of mankind you will applaud him. III. But there is a third school before him From Gettysburg he was sent to West Building Hospital, Pratt street, Baltimore, and remained until October, 1863, when, seeing no hope of an exchange, he deserted for his regiment, and, walking through Winchester, met a regiment of cavalry at Fauquier. Not being able to get through our lines, he was joined to this arm of the service ' and remained in that service until January 1, 1865. On that day, as we see by the narrative of Mrs. Grant, he saved the lives of two Union soldiers. About the same time be, like many of the Southern soldiers, began to despair of the Confederacy, came to Alexandria, sold his horse, gave his name as Payne, took the oath of allegiance as a refugee from Fauquier, went to Baltimore, took a room at the house of Mrs. Branson , the lady be had met at Gettysburg, and resolved to wait for the return of peace. Now, let us see what he learned in the third school. The rebel cavalry of Northern Virginia, as we now know, was considered, in the Southern army, the elite of their horsemen. Dismounted cavalrymen of the army of the Potomac were sent to Northern Virginia, re-mounted and then returned to their commands. In the spirit of war, however, they differed materially from the rest of the Southern forces. First, they came intimately in contact with the people of Loudon and Fauquier, who had suffered most from the war, and whose hatred of Northern troops was more bitter, so that they fought rather from personal hate, and in individual contests, than from political sentiments, and in battle. Accordingly, whatever edge of acrimony was wanting in the temper of Powell he gained at the houses of ruined slaveholders in Leesburg, Aldie, Middleburg, and Upper Ville. IV. But there is a fourth the school of necessity. Arrived at Baltimore and having taken up his residence with Mrs. Branson, he looked around for something to do. He had no trade or profession. The period in which he would have learned one was spent in the army; and we know how abhorrent it was to men of the South to engage in manual labor; and as his hands attest, he has never engaged in any. Accordingly, in perplexity about his future for the little money be got for his horse was fast going--he whiled away the time in reading medical books and brooding in his chamber. While in this condition, unable to get home, unable to Bee bow he was to live at Baltimore, the fracas occurred by which he was arrested, brought before the Provost Marshal, and ordered north of Philadelphia. Picture to yourself the condition of this unfortunate victim of Southern fanaticism, suddenly again cast into the street and exiled from Baltimore, a stranger, sundered from his only friends, in a strange land. He thinks of big own home in far-off Florida, but between him and it are a thousand miles and a rebel army on whose rolls he is a deserter. He thinks of rejoining that army, but between him and it is a Union army. He thinks of the unknown North into which he is banished, but his fingers refuse the spade; he thinks of a profession, but the very dream of one is now a mockery; be thinks of going where no one knows him, but he fears that after all the curse of secession will follow him; he thinks of eluding the authorities and staying at Baltimore, but then he is afraid of compromising his friends, and leaves them. Everywhere the sky is dark. Among Northern men he is persecuted, for be is a rebel; among Southern men at Baltimore he is despised, for he is a recreant Southerner; among Southern men at home he is a by-word, for he is a deserter. The earth seems to reject him, and God and man to be against him. Now, if there be any man in this Court who has ever wandered, penniless, houseless, friendless, in that worst of solitudes, the streets of a strange city, with hunger at his stomach, and school before him a great sense of wrong at his heart, in rags, and these very rags betraying him as a, thing to be despised and spurned; afraid of meeting at every corner the peering eyes of a Government detective; too proud to beg, and, when hunger overcame pride, rejected with a frown, that man will understand how the prisoner felt in the beginning of March, 1865. If there be any man who has ever been hunted down by misery in his youth, and before much sorrow had made the burden easy, until he wondered why he was born, and hid his face in his hands, praying to God to end his pain forever, he also can understand how, in the fullness of suffering, he has been brother to the accused. Well, indeed, had it been for him if some angel of mercy had on that day, as he wandered a hungry specter through the streets of Baltimore, with flashing eyes and disordered hair, stretched forth her band and said: "Here is bread; take, eat, and live." A loaf of bread might have saved him; a single word of kindness might have saved him; the gracious lick of a friendly dog might have saved the glow of a once generous heart from going out forever. We have all, my friends, had these turning points in our lives, and we all reckon back to a time when we stood in the midst of gloom, and suddenly it was glorious day, for we found a plank and reached the shore. His Creator, in His inscrutable wisdom, thought it good there should be no ray of light, no beckoning band, no hope for the prisoner. Perhaps it had been better if he had dragged himself to the pier and ended his career in suicide. It was ordered that his very weakness should make him the prey of a human devil. We can already fore see the consequences. He is desperate, an you; for death, only he is a soldier, and he will not die ingloriously, after having faced death an hundred times. He is pursued by the Government in which he had confided, and for which he had deserted his own; pursued, tracked, followed like an outlaw among mankind will show that Northern Government that he is, not a dog, and that Southern Government, that he is not a traitor; and give him but a chance, and he will, with one stroke, pay off the scores he owes the abolitionists, restore himself in the eyes of his comrades in arms, and throw himself into the arms of a pitiful eternity. And who is to blame that he was urged to desperation and consequent revenge? I answer, this civil war. The civil war took him from the magnolias and orange groves of Florida, and left him a waif upon the pavements of a Northern city. The civil war took the independent farmer from his fields, and left him a beggar among strangers. The civil war took, him from honest pursuits and professions, and left him to make his living without ar 'he, accomplishments than dexterity in murder. The civil war forbade him a home among Northern men, after it had taken him from his home in the South. The civil war made him an outcast and a fugitive on the face of the earth; took the bread out of his mouth, and gave him the alternative of dying obscurely by his own hand, or notoriously by the, death of a public officer. V. The education of our farmer's boy is now complete. He has been in four schools. Slavery has taught him to wink at murder, the Southern army has taught him to practice and justify murder, cavalry warfare has taught him to love murder, necessity has taught him resolution to commit murder. lie needs no further education ; his four terms are complete, and he graduates an assassin! And of this college we, the re-united people of the United States, have been the stern tutors, guides and professors. It needs now only that some one should employ him. I need not pursue this dolorous history further. You know the rest. If you did not know it, you could infer it from what has gone before. That he should meet Booth at Barnum's Hotel, enter into his plans eagerly, and execute them willingly, are matters of course. That he should care nothing for money, but only for revenge; that he should hate the Lincoln Government like a slaveholder; that be should enter the house of a cabinet officer like a guerrilla; that lie should try to murder, and justify his murder like a Southern soldier; that he should then give himself up willingly, as one who exchanges the penalties of assassination for suicide; that lie should sit here like a statue, and smile as one who fears no earthly terrors, and should tell the doctors, calmly and stoically, that he only did what he thought was right--all these things are as certain to follow as use, education and employment necessity. Now, in considering the condition of Powell at this crisis, I do rot ask you to believe he was insane. That is a declaration of mental disease of which I am no judge. I only ask you to believe that he was human?& human being in the last stage of desperation, and obeying self-preservation, nature's first law. It is acknowledged by all that the possession of reason only makes man responsible for crime. Now, there are two ways in which reason is vanquished. One is when the passions make war against reason and drive her from her throne, which is called insanity. Another is when the necessities of the body overcome the suggestions of the mind, a state in which the reason is a helpless captive. And if you find that while his reason was so in captivity, he surrendered to temptation, I am sure you will set it to the credit, not of reason, but of the body, whose wants were imperious while there was yet no reason in it, in childhood, and which will again exist without reason after death. At the beginning of the war, Powell, one night, secured a pass and went to the theater at Richmond. It was the first play that Powell ever saw, and he was spellbound with that magical influence wielded by the stage over such, to whom its tinsel is yet reality. But he was chiefly attracted by the voice and manner of one of the actors. He was a young man of about twenty-five, with large, lustrous eyes, a graceful form, features classical and regular as a statue, and a rich voice that lingered in the ears of those who heard him. Although only a private soldier, Powell considered himself the equal of any man, and after the play was over sought and gained an introduction to the actor. Never were two natures thrown together so different, yet so well calculated, the one to rule, the other to be ruled. The soldier was tall, awkward, rough, frank, generous and illiterate. The actor was of delicate mold, polished, graceful, subtle, with a brilliant fancy, and an abundant stock of reading. Each was what the other was not, and each found in the other an admirer of the other's qualities. The actor was pleased to have a follower so powerful in his muscles, and Powell was irresistibly drawn to follow a man so wondrously fascinating and intellectual. They saw enough of one another to form a close intimacy, and confirm the control of the actor over Powell, and parted, not to meet for nearly four years. In the twilight of that memorable day in March, which I have described, Powell was dragging himself slowly along the street past Barnum's Hotel--a poor creature overcome by destiny. Suddenly a familiar voice hailed him looking up the steps, he saw the face of the Richmond actor. The actor on his side expressed astonishment to find Powell in such a plight--for the light in the eyes of a desperate man needs no translation--and in that distant city. Powell answered him in few words: "Booth, I want bread--I am starving." In ordinary circumstances, I do not doubt but Booth would have said, come in and eat; but just now he was filled with a mighty scheme, for he had just been to Canada, and was lying in wait for agents. So he did not give him to eat; he did not tell him to go and die, but he seized with eagerness upon this poor man's hunger to wind about him his accursed toils, saying, "I will give you as much money as you want, but first you must swear to stink by me. It is in the oil business." An empty stomach is not captious of oaths, and Powell then swore that fatal oath, binding his soul as firmly to Booth as Faust to Mephistopheles, and went in and feasted. Next morning Booth gave him money enough to buy a change of clothing and keep him for a week. Powell now became anxious to know what plan it was that was to make; him rich, but Booth answered evasively that it was in the oil business. He knew well enough that he had to do with a desperate man, but he knew, also, that any proposition of a guilty character might as yet be rejected. He must get full control of this desperate tool, and instil into his nature all the subtle monomania of his own. Accordingly he proceeded to secure every thought and emotion of Powell. With a master pencil he painted before the eyes of this boy the injuries of the South and the guilt of her oppressors. He reminded him of devastated homes, Negroes freed, women ravished, the graves of his brothers on a thousand hillsides. He reminded him that he was a traitor to the Southern cause, and that it was necessary he should regain the favor of his country. He pointed out to him his desperate condition--a fugitive from his friends, and an exile among strangers. He touched him upon his pride, and showed him how he was born a gentleman, and ought to live as a gentleman. He touched upon his helplessness, and showed him that there was no hope for him, in peace or war, in heaven or earth, except by rendering a great service to the South. He touched upon his melancholy, and said if he must die, he should offer up his life in a manner that would bequeath his name as a blessing to posterity. Powell now awoke from the depth of' despair to the highest pinnacle of agonized excitement, It was as if he had been breathing that subtle Eastern poison, wherein the victim sees swimming before his eyes a vision of more than celestial felicity, but far off and unattainable. What wonder he swam in dreams of delicious pain I Instead of that former melancholy, he felt an eager desire to live. Instead of that long torpor, he felt all the old wounds bleeding again, and burned to avenge the South. Instead of laboring like a negro, he saw a vague vision of rolling in boundless wealth. Instead of being coursed by his kinsmen, he was fired with zeal to be cherished as one of her chief martyrs. Instead of being the toy of fortune, he dreamed of being her conqueror. But yet he saw no avenue to all this, and, spell? Bound as he was, turned to his tormentor, who held him as firmly as ever Genii did their fabled imps, for the explanation, for the, means and quick road to happiness. Booth saw his victim was ready, and hastened to impart his mysterious plans. The first plan was to go to Washington, take a ride with confederates, on horseback, to the Soldiers' Home, capture the President, and deliver him to the Rebel authorities. This failed. The second plan was to kill the heads of the State--a plan first broached to Payne on the evening of the 14th of April, at eight o'clock. Booth, on the evening of the 14th, at eight o'clock, told him the hour had struck; placed in his hands the knife, the revolver, and the bogus package of medicine; told him to do his duty, and gave him, horse, with directions to meet beyond the Anacosta bridge; and he went and did the deed. I have asked why he did it. His only answer is: "Because believed it my duty." VI. Now, let us not be deceived by the special name of assassination, and confound it with the conscientious killing of what is believed to be an oppressor. When we read of is assassination we involuntarily bring to mind examples of men hired by statesmen to make away with princes....I say he is the fanatic, and not the hired tool; the soldier who derived his orders from conscience, and who, in the applause of that tribunal, smiles at all earthly trials. How else do you explain his bearing? He smiles at all that you can do against him. To him the clanking of these chains is the sweet music of his triumph. The efforts of the prosecution and its bitter witnesses to convict him are but the confirmation of his glory. The power and majesty of the Government brought upon his head seem but clear and pleasant praise's of his deed. He lives in that land of imagination where it seems to him legions of the souls of Southern Soldiers wait to crown him as their chief commander. He sits here like a conqueror; for four weeks he has held his head erect when all others have quailed; he meets the stare of curiousity as a king might face his subjects; he keeps his state even in his cell, and the very keepers, in admiration, acknowledge him their master. Now, I know I dare not call him mad--the doctors have forbidden it. I might say that if ever man fell within that definition of Chief Justice Shaw of insanity, "A very common instance is where a person fully believes the act he is doing is done by the immediate command of God, and lie acts under the delusive but sincere belief that what he is doing is by command of a superior power, which supersedes all human laws and the laws of nature," this is the man. But the doctors have said he is not insane, and though he fills the legal definition he does not fill the medical, and, therefore, I can not hope that you will hold him insane. But I appeal from medical definitions and from legal definitions to your good sense, and I ask you to explain for me the riddle of this man's conduct in any other way than that he is a political fanatic; a monomaniac on the subject of his duty--call him sane or insane--yet one who is responsible only to that God from whom he derives his commandments. Before another tribunal, where all his previous life might be inquired into, and where time would be given for all this mystery to be unraveled, I do not hesitate to say I could convince the judges beyond a doubt that he is no more responsible for what he has done to the laws of the United States than a Chinaman whom custom and religion give the right to strangle his daughters. You have not the time, and I must end the inquiry. But as you are sworn to try this man on your consciences, so I charge you to give him the benefit of his, Gentlemen, when I look at the prisoner, and see (as it has been my duty for four weeks to see) the calm composure with which he has gone through the horrors of this trial; the cheerful and firm fortitude with which he has listened to the evidence against him, and with which he has endured the gaze of the public, as well as the ignominy of fetters; the frank and honest way in which he speaks of his crime, as a thing revolting in itself, but due to a cause which he thinks holy; and, more than all, the settled conviction, which robs the trial of all terrors, that he has but obeyed the voice of custom, education, and conscience; and the calm serenity with which he regards all pains that men can inflict upon him as contemptible, and part of his duty to endure, I can not help being proud--though blood is on his hands? That such fortitude, unparalleled in history, is the growth of American soil; and I can not help wishing that throughout all the coming vicissitudes of life, in all perplexities and doubts, on all occasions of right and wrong, in all misconstructions and trials, I may have so cheering, so brave, so earnest a conviction that I have done my duty. And what is this duty? What is this doing right? Ask the Indian, as he returns to his wigwam, laden with the dripping scalps of the dispossessors of his soil, why he has done it, and he will answer you, with a flourish of his tomahawk and his face turned toward Heaven, that lie is doing right? the Great Spirit has commanded it. Ask the Hindoo, as he disembowels some English officer by the Ganges, and riots in his blood, the reason of his crime, and, he will tell you it is his duty, he is doing right--the Brahmiris have decreed it. Consult the records of Vendee, and see why Charette and Gastou murdered the Republican soldiery in ambuscades and thickets, and you will find they entered, at the bar of the Parisian Court, the plea that they were doing right; it was their duty. Now go through the devastated South; speak with a few of the five millions, and ask them why they have thirsted for and taken Northern blood in secret places, murdered stragglers, waylaid orderlies, and killed by stealth, and they will answer you, pointing to the charred remains of some ancestral home and sonic neighboring bill dotted with graves Because it was our duty; because we felt bound in conscience to do it. Let us not undervalue the force of conscience. It is man's sole director, his highest judge, his last resort. Without it he is but an erring wanderer, tossed by every wind of passion, interest, and caprice. With it, his course is as certain and regular as the stars. In labor it cheers him; in pleasure it restrains him; to all manner of good it prompts him; from all manner of evil it defends him. In peace it teaches him to labor; in war to fight; for religion it tells him to fear God; for his country it says, protect and defend it; for himself it says, thy country, thy home, thy friends first, and thyself last. It is this spark of heavenly fire which has supported martyrs at the stake; which has sustained good men on the scaffold; which brought liberty and preserved it in this land for you and me and all of us. Let us, then, respect it, even when it speaks in a voice which we can not understand. Let us honor it as the same voice which directs us, even when it directs others to a grievous fault his brothers. We know, further, that this man desires to die, in order to gain the full crown of martyrdom; and that, therefore, if we gratify him, he will triumph over us; but if we spare him, we will triumph over him. We know, also, that the pWe are but men. The same God who created us all, may reconcile all that, and find in our difference but ignorance on the one side and ignorance on the other. And if we dare to judge the dictates of conscience, do we not arrogate to ourselves the prerogatives of the Sovereign Lawgiver of the Universe, who gave the rule, "Judge not, that ye be not judged?" Therefore, considering that we have the limit set, and that we can not go beyond without becoming in turn transgressors, let us leave that cause with Him who measures the conduct of men by no standard of success, but by obedience to the invariable dictates of conscience. For us it is enough that we are weak judges of weak men. If we were beasts, unconscious of the sacred limits of right and wrong, we might excuse him; if we were Gods and superior to destiny, we might destroy him; but as we are men who know our duties, but also our weakness, often seek good but do evil, therefore let us do the work of man to man--punish and reform him. VII. Gentlemen, I have done with narrative and reflections. We now know that this Florida boy is not a fiend, but an object rather of compassion. We now know that slavery made him immoral, that war made him a murderer, and that necessity, revenge, and delusion made him an assassin. We now know that in all regards he is like us, only, that he was taught to believe right what we were taught to believe wrong; and that if we had been taught in his school, we would be like him, and if he had been taught in ours, he would be like us. We know that, from his point of view, he justifies the murder of our Secretary of State; we know that, from our standpoint, we would gladly have seen, for four years, the death of the rebel Secretary of State. We know that we were on the side of the Government, because we were born North; we know that he was against it, because he was born South; and that had we been born South we would have been in his place, and had he been born North he would be in ours. We know, also, that all the enemy desired the death of the President, and that he surpassed them only in courage; and that if we forgive them who killed our brothers, we must, in consistency, forgive him who tried to kill Mr., Seward, because he thought Mr. Seward guilty of murdering ublic can gain nothing by his death from the example; for if he die as he lived, there will be more anxious to emulate his bravery.... But if he is suffered to live, he will receive the worst punishment—obscurity—and the public will have nothing to admire. We also know, and we can not consider it too much, that he has killed no man, and that if he be put to death we shall have the anomaly of the victim surviving the murderer; and that, under the laws, this man can be punished only for assault and battery with intent to kill, and, therefore, imprisoned. We know, also, that we are at the end of a civil war, a time when it is desirable there should be no farther mention or remembrance of fraternal strife. If we put this man to death, he will live forever in the hearts of his comrades, and his memory will forever keep our brethren from us. If, moreover, we put his to death, we will show that war is still in our hearts, and that we are only content to live with them because we have subdued them. Finally, we know that if we let him live and teach him better, we show the whole world that this war was carried on to undeceive a deluded people and to maintain the supremacy of the laws, so that, now that the laws are supreme, we may begin with reform; but if we put him to death we show only that we are vindictive, and use our victory only to gratify our anger. Let him, then, live. His youth asks it, fraternity asks it, the laws ask it, our own sins ask it, the public good demands it. Because you and I taught him the code of assassination in slavery; because you and I brought about a civil war, which practiced him in assassination and made him justify it; because you and I spurned him from us when he sought refuge with us, and bade him destroy himself, ignobly, by his own hand, or grandly, by

assassination; because, in short, you and I have made this boy what he is, therefore, lest we who are really ourselves guilty of this attempt at murder, should perpetrate a real murder, let him live, if not for his sake, for our own. Take from the refugee his desperation, and you have the cavalryman; take from the cavalryman his hate, and you have the soldier of Hill; take from the soldier his martial habits, and you have the slave-holder; take from the slaveholder his slavery, and you have again the pure and simple child, who, four years ago, went singing in innocence over the land. Before I close, one word from myself. I have heretofore spoken of the prisoner as his counsel; I may also speak of him in my character as a man; and I can testify that in the four weeks' acquaintance I have had, hearing him converse with freedom and explain all his secret thoughts, in spite of the odious crime with which he is charged, I have formed an estimate of him little short of admiration, for his honesty of purpose, freedom from deception and malice, and courageous resolution to abide by the principles to which he was reared. I find in him none of that obstinacy which perseveres in crime because it is committed, and hopes to secure admiration in a feigned consistency. Neither is there about him a false desire of notoriety, nor a cowardly effort to screen himself from punishment; only one prominent anxiety—that is, lest people should think him a hired assassin, or a brute; an aversion to being made a public spectacle of, and a desire to be tried at the hands of his fellow-citizens. Altogether, I think we may safely apply to him, without spurious sympathy or exaggeration, the words which were said of Brutus—
"This was the noblest Roman of them all
All the conspirators, gave only he,
Did that they did in envy of great Caesar;
He only, in a general honest thought,
And common good to all, made one of them.
So mixed in him, that nature might stand up
And say to all the world, "This was a man!"
I commit him, then, without hesitation, to your charge. You have fought on the same fields, and as you have never been wanting in mercy to the defeated, so I know you will not be wanting in mercy to him. You have all commanded private soldiers, and as you could estimate the enthusiasm of your own men, so you will know how to estimate the enthusiasm of those who fought against you. The lives of all of you have shown that you were guided in all perplexities by the stern and infallible dictates of conscience and duty, and I know that you will understand and weigh in your judgment of the prisoner, dictates and duties so kindred to your own".

He must have hesitated a full half an hour on this fanciful rubbish. Doster must have stolen a march on Baker. Both were obsessed with Caesar and Brutus. Perhaps they were already dreaming of a new Roman Empire. The prosecution themselves could not have made out a more damning summing up, not just in destroying his character but with a patronising, political, demonizing satire of his entire background and culture in one foul, boring swoop. If this is not blatant malignant racism turned inwards, then what are these kinds of warped minds conditioned to think about other peoples. The only single none useless thing about this defence is they allowed Mrs. Grant to say Powell had saved the lives of two Union soldiers. And this may have been solely due to her own advocacy and clemency. This trial made far more than a mockery of justice. The defendants would have retained more honour and dignity had they been lynched. It also gives the lie to Baker's account that Powell (also known as Payne) was one of three Kentucky outlawed brothers and a professional murderer.

Chapter 7

The Master's of Illusion

Lafayette Curry Baker

1826- 1868
The Froth Rises To The Top

Born 1826 in upstate New York from farming stock moving to Michigan as a young man. In 1849 he went to join the gold rush but instead became a vigilante in San Francisco and along the bars of the Barbary Coast. He learnt how to bully people as a professional security man, come bouncer come doorman, relating many 'colourful' accounts of beatings and lynching; often as an informer to the police and developed his street qualities there, becoming devious and cunning.

He returned east to offer his services as a spy for the Union in 1861 and after failing before an officer's board, he later managed to gain access to General Winfield Scott (1886-1866), the enormous and aging General, who had once fought the British. He was in his tent and preparing a campaign when Scott was impressed and easily taken in by the fast talker . Baker wanted a commission and Scott agreed with Baker's plan to spy, not in Richmond but in the southern field and would only pay him expenses. He was dispatched to infiltrate the Confederate army posing as a photographer; but was gaoled as a spy and escaped living as a vagrant in the countryside but recounted many famous deeds on his return to the Union. Scott believed his intelligence work was useful and recommended him to Stanton who immediately engaged him as his secretary knowing his talents coincided with his own special requirements.

If you read his book it is all there and boldly written full of lurid details and many secret service adventures, like a fiction novel written typical of the Victorian idiom, widely inaccurate, luridly embellished in its blatant and wickedly exaggerated gothic style, reminiscent at times, of the macabre fiction of Bram Stoker or Edgar Allen Poe; but certainly a pathological liar with a morbid taste for the suffering of others. He loved describing death and the instruments of death with the sadistic flair of an executioner, in exquisite detail. Thus in describing the tragic death of dear Mary Surratt:

"Mrs. Surratt cast her eyes upward upon the scaffold, for a few moments, with a look of curiosity, combined with dread. One glimpse, and her eyes fell to the ground, and she walked along mechanically, her head drooping, and if she had not been supported would have fallen. She ascended the scaffold, and was led to an arm-chair, in which she was seated. An umbrella was held over her by the two holy fathers, to protect her from the sun, who's rays shot down like the blasts from a fiery furnace. She was attired in a black bombazine dress, black alpaca bonnet, with black veil, which she wore over her face till she was seated on the chair. During the reading for the execution, by General Hartranft, the priests held a small crucifix before her, which she kissed fervently several times. She first looked round the scene before her, then closed her eyes and seemed engaged in silent prayer. The reading and the announcement of the clergymen on behalf of the other prisoners having been made, Colonel McCall assisted by the other officers, proceeded to remove her bonnet, pinion her elbows, and tie strips of cotton stuff around her dress below the knees. This done the rope was placed around her neck and her face covered with a white cap reaching down to the shoulders.
When they were pinioning her arms, she turned her head, and made some remarks to the officers in a low tone which could not be heard. It appeared they had tied her elbows too tight, for they slackened the bandage slightly, and then awaited the final order. All the prisoners were prepared thus at the same time, so that when she was thus pinioned, she stood scarcely ten seconds, supported by those standing near her, when the General gave the signal, by clapping his hands twice, for both drops to fall, as soon as the second and last signal was given, both fell, and Mrs. Surratt with a jerk, fell the full length of the rope. She was leaning over when the drop fell, and this gave a swinging motion to her body, which lasted several minutes before she assumed a perpendicular position. Her death was instantaneous; she died without a struggle. The only muscular movement discernable was a slight contraction of the left arm, which she seemed to disengage from behind her as the drop fell. After being suspended thirty minutes, she was cut down, and placed in a coffin, in the clothes in which she died, and was interred in the prison yard. The rope made a clean cut around her neck, fully an inch in diameter, which was black and discoloured with bruised blood. The cap was not taken off her face, and she was laid in the coffin with it on, and thus passed away from the face of the earth Mary E. Surratt."

This from the false mouth of someone who is getting his joy from writing about, in his cognisance, of this innocent woman's torturous death. Indeed even the executioner Christian Rath had been expecting Mrs. Surratt would get a reprieve; because he had had prepared three nooses fully, with seven hitches the night before, leaving Mary's till last. He had to make do with five for her as he was tired, thinking it would not be necessary. He then used it and found it still worked perfectly well.
At the same time Baker was profiteering certain amounts of money from the cotton embargo deals, from the criminal arrests and the contraband. He had even offered 10,000 dollars of his own money on the wanted posters, which he never honoured but instead moaned about getting only 17,500 dollars out of killing, executing and imprisoning innocent American soldiers and citizens, including the President.

Mary's parents were Archibald Jenkins and Elizabeth Anne and she was born in Southern Maryland. Her father died when she was two years old. Mary was enrolled in a private girls boarding school Academy for Young Ladies in Alexandra, Virginia. She married John Harrison Surratt in 1839, when she was sixteen and he was twenty-seven. They had three children, Isaac (1841), Elizabeth Anna (1843-1904), and John (1844). Together they ran the post office that gave the town its name- Surrattsville. In effect the town's postmaster general. That Mrs. Surratt was really of good stock is practically admitted by Baker himself in his book. Thus:

1823-65
Her Faith In God Did Not Falter
Though Man's Little Mercy Died

"Southwest of Washington stretches a tapering peninsula, composed of four fertile counties, which at the remote tip make Point Lookout, and do not contain any town within them of more than a few hundred inhabitants. Tobacco has ruined the land of these, and slavery has ruined the people. Yet in the beginning they were of that splendid stock of Calvert Lord Baltimore, but retain to-day only the religion of that peaceful founder. I mention as an exceptional and remarkable fact, that every conspirator in custody is by education a Catholic. These are loyal citizens elsewhere, but the western shore of Maryland is a noxious and pestilential place for patriotism.
The country immediately outside of the District of Columbia, to the south, is named Prince George's, and the pleasantest village of this county is Surratsville . This consists of a few cabins at a cross-road surrounding a fine old hotel, the master whereof, giving the settlement his name, left the property to his wife, who for a long time carried it on with indifferent success. Having a son and several daughters, she moved to Washington soon after the beginning of the war, and left the tavern to a trusty friend- one John Lloyd. Surrattsville has gained nothing in patronage or business from the war, except that it became, at an early date, a rebel post office. The great secret mail from Mathias Creek, Virginia, to Port Tobacco, struck Surrattsville, and thence headed off to the east of Washington, going meanderingly north. Of this post route Mrs. Surratt was manageress; and John Lloyd, when he rented her hotel, assumed the responsibility of looking out for the mail, as well as the duty of making Mrs.Surratt at home when she chose to visit him".

Yes, the trusted friend turned informer, helping to send her straight to the gallows.
The Execution General, Thomas Harris made out in a letter to the New York Times on

4th August 1901 that the evidence of Louis Weichmann was irrelevant, but that it was Lloyd's testimony that sent her to the gallows. Lloyd died in 1892.Thus:

"It must be remembered that on the night of 17th April (1865) Payne returned to her house, with pick-axe on the shoulder and cap made from his shirt sleeve on his head. The very act of this red-handed murderer fleeing to her home at such a time, was in itself, the strongest and most damning evidence against her. Take away these two items of evidence - the terrible story of the shooting irons and Payne's return, wipe them out, remove them for the record, and Mr. Weichmann's evidence as to what he saw and heard in Mrs. Surratt's house falls harmlessly to the ground."

Yes and so does 'The Fall of the House of Usher' by Edgar Allen Poe.

So, 36 years later this stupid old executioner has decided that he can now protect Weichmann's name and put it all onto Lloyd, now that Lloyd was 9 years dead. And as you will see below from Baker's account of the fleeing assassins, whiskey was needed for 'Herold' to give to 'Booth' because he was in serious pain from his injured leg. Indeed they only took one carbine because Booth could not manage to carry the other one on his horse, such was his injury. It is also bizarre that Mary accompanied by Weichmann, should have to take whiskey to John Minchin Lloyd's tavern, in addition to a number of revolvers and two carbines (short lightweight cavalry weapons) and field glasses. Sounds like a military General's kit. Indeed it's even more bizarre to imagine that Mary must have been thinking ahead of everyone, in knowing that 'Booth' would need whiskey to ease the pain of a broken leg.

OK getting back to Baker, he is making out that Catholics in this area were unpatriotic. However Mrs. Surratt was herself a Presbyterian but her husband was a Catholic who, before he died, had been a long time postmaster and the pillar of the community, being honoured with his name, which now goes in the honour of Clinton (ex-President, no doubt), even if pro-southern. Yet, Baker has granted that Surrattsville itself was a pleasant village of good character and nothing like his descriptions of Port Tobacco. Of course he infers that it was a rebel post office, yet Lloyd who turned it into a tavern was granted immunity at the trial. This is because he testified against Mrs. Surratt and even got out of that, by telling everyone he was drunk at the time. Talk about double talk and treachery, this man John Lloyd takes the cake, or his whiskey by the jar. And Lloyd and Jenkins (Mary's maiden name) are both of ancient Welsh stock. Baker himself probably came from good stock but turned rotten along the Barbary Coast. Thus, perhaps exaggerated in the manner reminiscent of a Victorian writer:

"The Barbary Coast is the haunt of the low and the vile of every kind. The petty thief, the house burglar, the tramp, the whoremonger, lewd women, cutthroats, murderers, all are found here. Dance-halls and concert-saloons, where blear-eyed men and faded women drink vile liquor, smoke offensive tobacco, engage in vulgar conduct, sing obscene songs and say and do everything to heap upon themselves more degradation, are numerous. Low gambling houses, thronged with riot-loving rowdies, in all stages of intoxication, are there. Opium dens, where

heathen Chinese and God-forsaken men and women are sprawled in miscellaneous confusion, disgustingly drowsy or completely overcome, are there. Licentiousness, debauchery, pollution, loathsome disease, insanity from dissipation, misery, poverty, wealth, profanity, blasphemy, and death, are there. And Hell, yawning to receive the putrid mass, is there also.
The Barbary Coast rose from the massive infusion of treasure seeking Argonauts during the Gold Rush. Men from Europe, Asia, South America, and the eastern United States sailed into San Francisco Bay bound for the Mother Lode, many only staying in the gold fields briefly before returning to San Francisco broke or with tiny leather sacks of nuggets and gold dust. At the end of 1849 out of a population of between 20,000 and 25,000, only about 300 were women and an estimated almost two-thirds of those were prostitutes. miners, sailors, and sojourners hungry for female companionship and bawdy entertainment continued to stream into San Francisco in the 1850s and 60s becoming the Barbary Coast's primary clientele. As The City exploded with the new arrivals, some with shady pasts, soon a wide variety of land sharks, con artists, pimps, and prostitutes staked out an area designed to pluck the gold and silver from the pockets of men through liquor, lust, laudanum-laced libations, or just a hard knock on the head. Sailors in particular had cause to dread the area because the art of shanghaiing was perfected. Many a sailor woke up after a night's leave to find himself unexpectedly on another ship bound for some faraway port. When there was a shortage of sailors for departing ships any able-bodied man who wandered into the wrong saloon, or drank with the wrong companion, could wake up with a mysterious hangover onboard a ship. Crime in the streets and corruption in the government offices plagued San Francisco in the 1850s. Nearly all drinking and dancing establishments in the area were destroyed in the fire that followed the 1906 earthquake, but within months a dozen or so were rebuilt and back in business. Upon the ouster of Eugine Schmitz from the mayor's office and following the P. H. McCarthy administration, the election of James Rolph jr. the demise of the Barbary coast as a vice zone picked up steam. Between the 1913 anti-vice campaigns led by the San Francisco Examiner and the passage of the 1917 Red-Light Abatement Act the Barbary Coast was effectively diminished and vice activities hidden from view. In 1917 the San Francisco Police blockaded the neighbourhood and evicted the prostitutes."

And all seemingly caused by the lust for gold, which had caused Baker to emigrate there in the first place. And there are none more earnest and oft more gullible in this endeavour and of mixed blessings, than these kinds of people themselves. Baker also had a lustful and imaginative eye for anatomical detail as the following descriptions of the other three hangings show:

"Payne died as he had lived, at least as he has done since his arrest, bold, calm and thoroughly composed. The only tremor exhibited by this extraordinary young man during the terrible ordeal of the execution was an involuntary vibration of the muscles of his legs after the fatal drop fell. He walked erect and upright, and retained the peculiar piercing expression of the eye that has ever characterised him. He was dressed in a blue flannel shirt, and pants of the same material. His brawny neck was entirely exposed, and he wore a new straw hat. He ascended the scaffold with the greatest of ease, and took his seat on the drop with as much sang froid as though he was sitting down to dinner. Payne stood as a statue when the drop fell. Although next to 'Harold,' who died the hardest, he exhibited more bodily contortions than the others while suspended. While the noose was being adjusted to is neck, Payne raised his head, and evidently desired to assist the executioner in that delicate operation."

Here we see in Baker his admiration and almost homosexual feelings towards a very brave young soldier, perhaps something that he wished he had been instead of a deviant and treacherous spy; in order to gain rapid backdoor promotion to the officer class. He was not so admiring of the others though as we see his sadistic emotions towards the supposed Herold, in fact an innocent scapegoat Confederate soldier:

"Probably no one of the criminals felt as great a dread of the terrible ordeal through which they were to pass as young 'Harold.' From the time he left his cell until his soul was sent to the Almighty, he exhibited the greatest emotion, and seemed to realize thoroughly his wretched condition His face wore an indefinable expression of anguish, and at times he trembled violently. He seemed to desire to engage in conversation with those around him while sitting in the chair awaiting execution, and his spiritual adviser, Rev. Mr. Old, was assiduous in his attentions to the wretched man. At times he looked wildly around, and his face had a haggard, anxious, inquiring expression. When the drop fell, he exhibited more tenacity of life than any of the others, and he endeavoured several times to draw himself up as if for the purpose of relieving himself from the rope from which he was suspended."

Yes, perhaps this innocent young man was still fighting against this ghastly miss carriage of justice, because all he had done was to help a fellow lame soldier on his way home from the war. Baker new this but it didn't stop him enjoying the horrid deaths of those he had engineered with careless perversion. That brilliant horror actor Vincent Price gives an excellent cameo of this kind of visual perversion when he takes a long moment to look back, at the priest and young woman he has had tortured and barbarically hung, before leading his horse off to his next village marked out for rampant witch burning. Appointing himself 'Witch Burner General' of the realm in 17th century England, with lucrative payments in the proverbial bag of Judas's pieces of silver.

As for Adzerodt he was even more contemptuous. George was born in Thurlingen, a state in central Germany, 12th June 1835 and his family emigrated to America in 1843, although other sources say he was of Austrian descent. He owned a business jointly with his brother, in Port Tobacco as a carriage repairer (garage owner and mechanic) but was 'officially arrested' in Montgomery County. The arresting officer was an NDP detective called Officer Lee (see Chapter 11) at the home of his cousin Hartman Richer on the 20th April, in Germantown. But this is very unlikely because Lee was operating in the area of Southern Maryland around Leonardstown and Port Tobacco, with Major O'Bierne, according to Baker. In fact Baker said that O'Bierne had telegraphed Montgomery County for Adzerodt to be arrested there, whilst Lee was still with him at Chapel Point, Port Tobacco. You will see this to be true because Baker had sent this squad under Major O'Bierne, on the 18th April, to remote Southern Maryland and they did not return until five or six days later, well after the 20th April. The only

George Adzerodt

1835-65
My English was not perfect,
So they forked my tongue

uncertainty about this is it might have been another arresting officer called Lee. The implication of this is that Germantown is a lot closer, with faster travel connections, to Washington than to Port Tobacco. It is also another deception. So, how could Lee be in two places at the same time, unless he moved at the speed of light? The only connection George had with the conspirators was that he had stayed at Mary Surratts house at some earlier stage, but had been asked to leave because he had been drinking in his room. There are also stories that he had been a blockade runner, or at least ferrying Confederates across the Potomac as a business side line. But with all these rumours, how can the truth be known, particularly when the NDP and informers and 'historians' now, are still manufacturing false evidence.

It is very unlikely that George was arrested where they said he was, so this deception is then not without malevolent purpose. You will also see another deception in Chapter 11 where they went into his home, or the home of his girlfriend and checked it out. This is where they collected their 'evidence'. And indeed this is where Lee must have arrested him because Lee was in that area operating with Major O'Bierne. The spin offs and particle debris are limitless with the illuminati. To continue with Baker's account:

" During the reading of the sentence, he kept perfectly quiet, but his face bore an expression of unutterable woe, as he listened attentively. He wore a thin moustache and small goatee, and his face was pale and sallow. Once , and once only, he glanced round at the assembled throng, and occasionally muttered incoherent sentences, but he talked, while on the scaffold, to no one immediately around him. He then stood up , facing the assembled audience, directly alongside the instrument of his death. His knees slightly trembled, and his legs were bent forward. He stood for a few moments the very embodiment of wretchedness, and then spoke a few words with an undertone to General Hartranft, after which he shook hands with his spiritual adviser and a few others near him; while he was being secured with bands, tied round his legs and arms, he kept muttering to himself as if in silent prayer. Suddenly he broke forth with the words, 'Gentlemen, beware who you-' and then stopped, as if with emotion; as the white cap being placed over his head he said, 'Goodbye gentlemen ; may we all meet in the other world. God take me now.' He died without apparent pain and his neck must have been instantly broken. After hanging a few seconds, his stomach heaved considerably, and subsequently his legs quivered a little. His death appeared to be the easiest of any of the criminals, with the exception of Mrs. Surratt, who did not apparently suffer at all."

This man's English was not so good being of German or Austrian descent and perhaps the true inspiration for the Austrian writer Otto Eisenschiml, an Industrial Chemist with a degree from Vienna University, and President of the Scientific Oil Compounding Comp any in the US; and the inventor of the contact sealed envelope, when writing his book 'Why was Lincoln Murdered'. Adzerodt was no doubt was trying to say something against the infamy, with perhaps an open threat. However whether he finished it or not, Baker made out that in the end, he thanked the General and all his staff for their kindness. This was a speciality of Baker turning truthful words around.
Above all else Baker wanted fame and his greed and ambition were relentless for which he was prepared to take on all risks. He pretended to care about the plight of the slaves and black people in general but some of his more racy remarks showed he was a practicing false hypocrite. It was a political game to reinforce the patriotism of the North and the treachery of the South. He did petition Lincoln about the atrocities being committed against blacks in Maryland, and even against freed slaves, but to what ends? He was far worse than Victor Hugo's police chief in Les Miserable and was prepared to go to any lengths to destroy anyone who transgressed the law or the patriotic code, or even if they were innocent civilians, to suit his own ends. He was perfectly loyal to Stanton but this did not last, and he then became the hunted man after he fell out of favour with Andrew Johnson, who threatened to throw Baker into his own dingy cells and release the prisoners instead. In fact Johnson granted amnesty to all Confederates by Christmas (1868). In his book Baker vilified every supposed member of the conspiracy plot portraying them as traitors, without any scruples whatsoever. Mary Surratt did not stand a chance:

"Treason never found a better agent than Mrs. Surratt. She was a large, masculine, self possessed female, mistress of her house, and as lithe a rebel as Belle Boyd or Mrs. Greensborough. She had not the flippancy and menace of the first, nor the social power of the second; but the rebellion has found no fitter agent."

His powers of exaggerated lying are unmatched and quite phenomenal. And in trying to illustrate how the army captured Booth he described it like a biblical epic, greater than any march during the war. Thus:

The Hanging of An Innocent Woman, Two Innocent Soldiers and An Innocent German-American Citizen at The Old Arsenal Penitentiary, Fort McNair on the Anacostia River. (Other accounts say it was the Old Capitol Prison- another deception).

" The military forces deputed to pursue the fugitives were 700 men of the of the 8th Illinois Cavalry, 600 men of the 22nd Colored Troops, and 100 men of the 16th New York. These swept the swamps by detachments, the mass of them dismounted , with cavalry at the belts of clearings, interspersed with detectives at frequent intervals in the rear. They first formed a strong picket cordon entirely around the swamps, and then drawn up in two orders of battle, advanced boldly into the bog in two lines of march. One party swept the swamps longitudinally , the other pushed straight across their smallest diameter.
A similar march has not been made during the war; the soldiers were only a few paces apart, and in steady order they took the ground as it came, now plunging to their armpits in foul sluices, now attacked by legions of wood-ticks, now tempting some unfaithful log or greenish solid morass, and plunging to the tip of the skull in poisonous stagnation; the tree boughs rent their uniforms; they came out upon dry land many of them without a rag of garment, scratched, and gashed, and spent, repugnant to themselves, and disgusting to those who saw them; but not one trace of Booth or Harold was anywhere found. Wherever they might be the swamps did not contain them."

This adventure into literature sounds just an inkling like the style of the 17th century poet, John Milton, when describing Satan's flight in "Paradise Lost", but without the classic literature and word power. Baker used a ghost writer named Phineas Camp Headley, a New England writer, who was no doubt steeped in the classic genre. He wrote a biography of the Marquis General Lafeyette and a novel of 'The Life of Empress Josephine' in the time of the French revolution. He detailed doomed accounts of the aristocrats and their macabre executions on the avenging instrument of death, through Robespierre's tool and inspiration, 'Madam La Guillotine.' Indeed all writers can see the influence of the earlier classic writers. A good example is Daniel Defoe's perfect English novel Robinson Crusoe, where its descriptive effects come through clear in many parts of Abraham (Bram) Stoker's, Dracula.
Milton was a born a Catholic (but later became an Anglican) and was England's greatest poet and survived the English Civil War throwing his sympathies in with the Parliamentarians and Oliver Cromwell. But had to keep a low profile when Charles II was restored to the throne, and was imprisoned, but influential friends saved him. Milton's works have affected every great romantic poet/author.. Blake, Keats, Wordsworth. Pope and so on, and statesmen including Winston Churchill…it's in the stanzas. Milton gradually became blind in old age but it did not stop his prolific output like 'Paradise Lost' then 'Paradise Regained'.
A long time ago when the writer lived in Indiana in a trailer, whilst building yet another gigantic oil storage tank another of 21 States. Yes, with later memories of R. Dean Taylor's haunting: 'bee, baa, bee, baa, eeeeeow, eeeeeeow, bee, baa, bee, baa …..'Indiana Wants Me':

Mmmm, mmmm
Indiana wants me, Lord I can't go back there
Indiana wants me, Lord I can't go back there
I wish I had you, to talk to

If a man ever needed dyin' he did
No one had the right to say what he said about you
And it's so cold and lonely here without you
Out there the laws are coming
I'm scared and so tired of running (Refrain)

It hurts to see the man that I've become
And to know I'll never see the morning sunshine on the land
I'll never see your smiling face, or touch your hand
If just once more I could see
You, our home, and our little baby (Refrain)

I hope this letter finds its way to you
Forgive me love for the shame I put you through
And all the tears
Hang on love to the memories of those happy years
Red lights are flashin' around me
Yea love it looks like they found me (Refrain)

Indiana wants me, Lord I can't go back there
("This is the police, you are surrounded, give yourself up")
Indiana wants me, Lord I can't go back there
("This is the police, give yourself up, you are surrounded") (Refrain)
(c) Copyright 1970 by Jobete Music Co., Inc.

And with further memories of Kent Lavoie with his enchanting, 'Me and You and a dog named Boo':

Dee, daa, dee dah:
I remember to this day
The bright red Georgia clay
How it stuck to the tires
After the summer rain
Will power made that old car go
A woman's mind told me that's so
Oh how I wish we were
Back on the road again

Me and you and a dog named Boo
Travelin' and a livin' off the land
Me and you and a dog named Boo
How I love being a free man

I can still recall
The wheat fields of Saint Paul
And the morning we got caught
Robbing from an old hen
Old McDonald, he made us work,
But then he paid us for what it was worth
Another tank of gas and
Back on the road again (Refrain)

I'll never forget the day
We motored stately into big L.A.
The lights of the city
Put settlin' down in my brain
Though it's only been a month or so
That old car's buggin' us to go
We gotta get away and
Get back on the road again (Refrain)

The writer then happened to lay my hand on Paradise Lost (1669) and since I was missing England just a bit, and a bit bored, I decided to go back in time to John Milton's England. I read and memorised a passage or two from John's epic saga of God versus the Devil. Thus I have always remembered this brilliant passage as being as close to heaven or hell, or as good as it ever gets, in describing Satan's flight from Heaven. 'Old Nick' had somehow called God, the creator's bluff:

Meanwhile, the adversary of God and Man,
Satan, with thoughts inflamed of highest Design,
Puts on swift wings, and towards the gates of Hell
Explores his solitary flight; sometimes
He scours the right hand coast, sometimes the left,
Now shaves with level wings the deep, then soars
Up to the fiery concave towering high,
As when far off at sea, a fleet descried
Hangs in the clouds, by equinoctial winds
Close sailing from Bengala, or the isles
Of Ternate and Tidore, whence merchants bring
Their spicy drugs; they on the trading flood
Through the wide Ethiopian to the Cape
Ply, stemming nightly towards the pole, so seemed
The far off flying fiend. At last appear
Hell bounds high, reaching to the horrid roof;
And thrice threefold the gates; three folds were brass,
Three iron, three of adamantine rock,
Impenetrable, impaled with circling fire,
Yet unconsumed, before the gates their sat
On either side, a formidable shape;*
The one seemed woman to the waste, and fair,
But ended foul in many a scaly fold,
Voluminous and vast, a serpent arm'd
With mortal sting: about her middle round
A cry of hell hounds never ceasing bark'd
With wide Cerberean* full mouths aloud, and rung
A hideous peel: yet, when they list, would creep,
If aught disturb'd their noise, into her womb,
And kennel there: yet still bark'd and howl'd
Within unseen. Far less abhorred than these
Vex'd Scylla bathing in the sea that parts
Calabria from the hoarse Trinacrian* shore:
Nor uglier followed the Night-hag, when call'd
In secret riding through the air she comes,
Lured with the smell of infant blood, to dance
With Lapland witches, while the labouring moon
Eclipses at their charms. The other shape,
If shape it might be call'd, that shape had none
Distinguishable in number, joint, or limb,

Or substance might be call'd that shadow seem'd,
For each seemed either; black it stood as night,
Fierce as ten furies, terrible as hell
And shook a dreadful dart; what seemed his head
The likeness of a kingly crown had on.
Satan was now at hand, and from his seat
The monster moving onwards came as fast,
With horrid strides; hell trembled as he strode.
The undaunted fiend what this might be admired;
Admired, not feared; God and his Son except'
Created thing naught valued he, nor shunn'd;
And with disdainful look thus first began.
Whence and what art thou, execrable shape,
That dar'st , though grim and terrible, advance
Thy miscreated front athwart my way
To yonder gates? through them I mean to pass,
That be assured without leave ask'd of thee,
Retire, or taste thy folly, and learn by proof,
Hell born, not to contend with spirits of heav'n.
To whom the goblin full of wrath replied,
Art thou that traitor angel, art thou he,
Who first broke peace in heav'n and faith, till then
Unbroken and in proud rebellious arms
Drew after him the third part of heaven's sons
Conjured against the Highest; for which both thou
And they, outcast from God, are here condemn'd
To waste eternal days in woe and pain?
And reckons thou thyself with spirits of heav'n,
Hell doom'd, and breath'st defiance here and scorn,
Where I reign king, and to enrage thee more,
Thy king and lord? Back to thy punishment,
False fugitive, and to thy speed add wings,
Lest with a whip of scorpions I pursue
Thy lingering, or with one stroke of this dart
Strange horror seize thee, and pangs unfelt before.
So spake the grisly terror, and in shape,
So speaking and so threatening, grew tenfold
More dreadful and deform: on th' other side
Incensed with indignation Satan stood
Un-terrified, and like a comet burn'd,
That fires the length of Orphiucus* huge
In th' arctic sky, and from his horrid hair
Shakes pestilence and war. Each at the head
Levell'd his deadly aim; their fatal hands
No second stroke intend, and such a frown
Each cast at th' other, as when two black clouds,
With heav'n's artillery fraught, come rattling on
Over the Caspian;* then stand front to front

Hovering a space, till winds the signal blow
To join their dark encounter in mid air:
So frown'd the mighty combatants, that hell
Grew darker at their frown, so match'd they stood;
For never but once more was either like
To meet so greater foe: and now great deeds
Had been achieved, whereof all hell had rung,
Had not the snaky sorceress that sat
Fast by hell gate, and kept the fatal key,
Ris'n, and with hideous outcry rush'd between.
O father, what intends thy hand, she cried,
Against thy only son? What fury, O son,
Possess thee to bend that mortal dart
Against thy father's head? And know'st for whom?
For him who sits above, and laughs the while
At thee ordain'd his drudge, to execute
Whate'er His wrath, which he calls justice, bids:
His wrath, which one day will destroy ye both.

*This line refers to the famous allegory of Milton, that paraphrases St. James:
"Thus when lust has conceived, it bringeth forth sin; and sin when it is finished, bringeth forth death."

* Cerberean of Cerberus, the dog with three heads, keeper of the gates of hell.

* Trinacria, the ancient name of Sicily. Scylla and Charybdis were the perhaps mythical whirlpools between it and Italy. On which coasts the trading of Copper, Tin and Sulphur was plied between Sardinia, Cyprus and the Levant from ancient times. And not far away Napoleon was born in rugged Corsica.

*Orphiucus or Serpentarius, of the Serpent , a northern constellation of some 40 degrees in length. Comets were supposed to threaten pestilence and war.

* The Caspian is a remarkably tempestuous sea. As indeed its sister, the Black Sea can lash the Delta of the Danube in Rumania, or the gentle shores of Bulgaria, and of Istanbul and yet further along the extensive coast of Turkey. But Moldavia is shielded and tucked away behind the Ukrainian shores at Odessa. And in the 13th Century the Kingdom of Lithuania was the largest in Europe stretching from the Black Sea and incorporating bits of Latvia, Poland, Belarus (White Russia) encroaching on Moscow, the Ukraine and the cities of Kalingrad, Minsk, Kiev and the capitol Vilnius, but not Estonia.

* Jesus Christ is here intimated, who was to destroy death, and him that has the power of death.
Within this epic poem which is 300 pages long, one might see the pre-emptive parallel allegory of the tragic assassination of Lincoln by the illuminati. And the most specific line, 'Levell'd his deadly aim; their fatal hands No second stroke intend,' and later 'against thy father's head' is an extraordinary example of a poetic cipher, within an almost divine prophetic repetition; and of his allegorical and towering genius, exactly two hundred years before the event.

But to continue now after this brief musical, poetic and geographical interlude:

In actual fact Baker, personally (after authorisation by special request to Stanton, since General Auger had told him to go to hell), only dispatched three officers, including the newly promoted Lieutenant Luther Byron Baker, (Baker's cousin) and 26 men of the 16th New York on the steamer John S Ide to Alexandria down the Potomac, and disembarked at Belle Plain, some 70 miles. From there it was 15 miles horse ride to Port Conway and Port Royal. Even for that relatively short journey the cavalry troops were knackered and were falling asleep, before reaching Bowling Green. And guided from the start by the instructions of the rebel captain William Jett whom they eventually caught up with at Goldman's Tavern (lately the Star Hotel) and boarding house in Bowling Green. He also dispatched Major O'Bierne and five officers of the NDP to southern Maryland who returned unsuccessful after five days, except they arrested many innocent civilians including Dr. Mudd and George Adzerodt.

One of the best giveaways in this book is the foul technique they used to implicate innocent people in the plot. This technique was the same one used on Dr. Mudd. Thus during the search around Leonardstown. Thus:

" Major O'Bierne started for Leonardstown with his detective force , and played off Laverty as Booth, and Hoey as Harold. These two advanced to farm-houses and gave their assumed names, asking at the same time for assistance and shelter. They were generally avoided, except by one man named Claggert, who told them they might hide in the woods behind his house. When Claggert was arrested, however, he stated that he meant to hide only to give them up. While on this adventure, a man who had heard of the reward came very near shooting Lavery. The ruse now became hazardous, and the detectives resumed their real characters."

And later Mr. Claggert stayed his tongue and forfeited his freedom. But this is highlighted here because it was the same technique used to implicate Dr. Mudd. Except that time the two leading decoy detectives played off Tyson as Booth and Hensted as Herold. In fact Tyson and Hensted were the two officers who made the dummy run from Washington over the navy bridge to Surratsville, where Lloyd was waiting with two fresh horses and carbines, then finally to Beantown, posing as Booth and Herold as described below.

There is no doubt to deal with Baker required high stakes, and treachery meant nothing to him, because he could turn anything around. He was greatly feared and although many tried to get rid of him they were not brave enough to name themselves in their petitions. He was eventually demoted having appeared before a senate committee and left the service. However the service was not done with him and he lived with the fear of a sewer rat, thinking they were after him. In the end in 1868, he was poisoned, it is said, by his brother-in-law, who was then working for the War department. The evidence for this however is sketchy although a lock of his hair, analysed years later, showed an abnormally high level of arsenic. Officially he had died from Meningitis.

And finally here is an imaginative and colourful and descriptive account of the swamps in Southern Maryland; but also of his diabolical hypocrisy and his real feelings towards bonded Afro-Americans; also taking a pathetic swipe at America's true and honourable native people while he's at it:

"Frequent deep ponds dot this wilderness place, with here and there a stretch of dry soil, but no human being inhabits the malarious extent; even a hunted murderer would shrink from hiding there. Serpents and slimy lizards are the only living denizens; sometimes the coon takes refuge in this desert from the hounds, and in the soft mud a thousand odorous muskrats delve, and now and then a tremulous otter. But not even the hunted negro dare to fathom the treacherous clay, nor make himself a fellow of the slimy reptiles which reign absolute in this terrible solitude. Here the soldiers prepared to seek for the Presidents assassins, and no search of the kind has ever been so thorough and patient. The Shawnee, in his stronghold of despair in the heart of the Okeefenokee, would have scarcely changed homes with Wilkes Booth and David Harold, hiding in this un-human country."

It is pretty clear that Afro- people have talents that would put better men than Baker to shame, even if he had grown up with moral fibre; physically, artistically and in poetry. In rhythm, dance and song they are un-equalled. And in movement in particular they have rare poetic beauty. And Africa's indiginous craftsmen carve out natural grace and beauty that goes back further in time than any other race on earth. It is a pity but necessary however, that they have now to match the white man's cunning in politics and law. And even in the field of exploration an Afro- American has achieved the highest honours. It was largely due to Mathew Henson's knowledge of the Eskimos ways and dog handling skills, and his own navigational skills, that took him and Peary close enough to the North Pole to claim it. Thus they had beaten the Grand Master himself the great Norwegian polar explorer Ammundsen, who beat Scott to the South Pole. Norway of course was the land that gave us the father of Polar Exploration, the indefatigable Nansen, the first to cross Greenland. Unless the Inuits (generic Eskimo people) had often done so. Not that Britain lagged far behind when the enduring Irishman, Shackleton got to within 97 miles of the South Pole, months before Ammundsen, thus opening it up for Scott who got their one month after Ammundsen. There was another American Arctic explorer called Cook who claimed he had got to the North Pole before Peary, but then he had also claimed Mt. McKinley in Alaska. Perhaps he was a descendant of our own Captain Cook who was the first to chart Antarctica, but said it was no place for man to live. He carried John Harrison's pocket watch to determine his longitude, his fifth clock. John was another born Yorkshire man and a carpenter turned clock maker and by far the greatest singular practical genius England ever produced. It is because of him we have Greenwich Mean Time. Sadly Captain Cook was killed on the Sandwich Islands by hostile natives. Well the natives seem friendly enough today in Hawaii with the beautiful and traditional warm greetings and Aloha. Is that where we get our hello from?

The Secretary of War was the most powerful man in the land at that time because Lincoln gave him too much freedom. Stanton was a strong Methodist, born of Quaker stock and a high ranking mason, a darkly secretive man with a quick calculating mind. A 'brilliant' barrister best suited for prosecution and without any apparent need to suffer the weakness of emotion, favouring mercy or the feelings of ordinary people. An impatient man of strong drive and divine delusions through the virtue of hard work, imagination and secret crafts, with the contempt of all who are not of the illuminati,

Edwin McMasters Stanton

1814-1869
A man of few words with a big
Stick but cowers before it

including Presidents. He seemed as Secretary of War to have had more real power than the President and wanted to control him using his twisted intellect and Lincoln's Achilles heel, obvious to Stanton by Lincoln often giving deference to him. And Baker certainly knew who is master was, being his loyal hunting dog forever trying to deliver the game into his hands. Although Stanton was not to be bribed in any way, it is said he must have been aware of the cotton profiteers, and Baker's dealings in lucrative gains from criminal convictions on the contraband circuit. There is no doubt that Stanton was a strong administrator and controlled the war effort with great diligence, as this letter concerning a diversionary effort into the Indian lands of the North West concurs. It seemed that Stanton wanted to curb this diversionary commando style expedition, that smacked of territorial expansion and lucrative gains, into Indian Territories:

"WAR DEPARTMENT, Washington, D.C., September 23, 1862.
Major-General HALLECK: - GENERAL :

The large requisition made by Major-General Pope upon the Quartermaster's Department and the Commissary and Ordnance Departments, involving as they do an immense expenditure of money and material needed elsewhere, requires that you should make some order defining the extent of operations to be carried on in the Northwest as an Indian campaign. The exigencies of the war and the state of the finances afford no superfluity, and whatever is sent to General Pope will leave a deficiency to the same extent in other branches of the service. His requisitions are now pending in the departments, and your immediate attention to the subject is requested.

Yours, truly, EDWIN M. STANTON, Secretary of War."

This indicates that some Generals in the North were quite prepared to take advantage in other spheres of enterprise, but Stanton had to rightly control these excesses, because of the enormous demands on the Quartermaster's revenue, including weapons and ammunition, that were otherwise pending. The Indian territories stretched from the Dakotas; the badlands of South Dakota had been pioneered earlier by French hunters and trappers, moving down from Canada through North Dakota, and first termed it 'Les Mauvailses le Terres a Traverser', on through Wyoming, Montana and Idaho to Oregon and Washington. They also stretched southward from here through Colorado, Utah and Nevada, merging into the Spanish colonised regions of Texas, New Mexico , Arizona and California. This was home to the illustrious and archetypal Navajo, Apache and many other great Indian tribal nations, that trace their history back to the Mayans and Aztecs of Mexico and Central America, and even to the greatest civilisation of the Americas, the majestic Incas of Peru.

It was 60 years earlier under Jefferson, in December 3rd 1805 that Captain Meriwether Lewis and Lieutenant William Clark's two year expedition opened up the Oregon Trail. They started from the Ohio River, navigating the Missouri from where it joins the Mississippi , to the Platte River in Nebraska home of the mighty Sioux Nation, through the Dakotas, on to the Yellowstone River, Montana, into the feathered Crow territory; then finally to Mount Hood near Portland, Oregon where they first saw the Pacific Ocean. Not since the crossing of the continental divide in Canada by Alexander McKenzie ten years earlier, had Euro- Americans opened up the west to the Pacific. This journey of some 2000 miles through hostile territory was a milestone in American exploration and was of great geographic importance, including some valuable botanical studies.

Returning to Stanton but on the down side, it seemed that when Lincoln was gone, Stanton also became arrogant and faithless towards his new chief; the servant became the master again, because Johnson had not yet got his measure. George Milton noted in his 'Age of Hate' (1930):

"The country could not understand why Johnson did not discharge the faithless Secretary of War. Radicals were as amazed as Conservatives. Doolittle, the senator from Wisconsin, wrote that: "For six long months, I have been urging the President to call on Grant temporarily to do the duties of the War Department. But Stanton remains, and so the report has spread all over the State, that there is something sinister at work.''

And Otto Eisenschiml in his book 'Why was Lincoln Murdered' (1937) was convinced of Stanton's treachery:

"There was one man who profited greatly by Lincoln's death; the man who was his secretary of war, Edwin M. Stanton. Brusque, insolent, cruel, Stanton was without doubt the most unpopular member of

Lincoln's administration; but the President in spite of strong pressure, had been loath to let him go while the conflict was raging; he seemed to think that no one else could do the work as well. After the war was over, however, it seemed only a question of time when Lincoln would divest himself of a secretary who was fast becoming both a personal and a political liability to him. It was to his advantage to have the President out of the way; it would mean a continuance in office, increased power over a new and supposedly weak Chief Executive and a fair prospect of replacing the latter at the next election. As secretary of war Stanton failed in his duty to protect the President's life after he was convinced that there was danger in the air. He bluntly denied Lincoln's request to be protected by Major Eckert and did not provide a proper substitute. It was probably due to the efforts of Stanton that all evidence of negligence on the part of John F. Parker was carefully suppressed. He directed the pursuit of Booth and allowed it to be conducted in a manner that, but for the assassin's accidental injury, would have allowed his escape. The actual pursuit and subsequent capture of Booth were silenced by unusual methods and were subsequently removed from contact with the public, either by infliction of the death penalty or by banishment to a desolate fortress. Other prisoners, of at least equal guilt, escaped punishment. Plausible as such an indictment may seem, it would stand no chance of surviving a legal attack. There is not one point in this summary than can be proven; it is all hypothesis. Circumstantial evidence, at best, is a dangerous foundation upon which to build."

There was no doubt that Stanton was a brusque, insolent, and calculating cruel master who took the major role in conducting certain overtures from a right wing cabal. Here is an example of Stanton's cruelty knowing no bounds, according to Samuel Arnold in 1902, when describing how he and the others were gagged in prison and on trial:

"The covering for the head was made of canvas, which covered the entire head and face, dropping down in front to the lower portion of the chest. It had cords attached, which were tied around the neck and body in such a manner that to remove it was a physical impossibility. It was frequently impossible to place food in my mouth."

Yet Stanton was also a coward because according to Edwin Bates (1864):

"Stanton believes in mere force, so long as he wields it, but cowers before it, when wielded by any other hand. If the President had a little more vim, he would either control or discharge Stanton."

We even have his own adjutant General Burnett, also from Ohio, describing how Stanton would give him an order, like using Weichmann for information and letting him go to find Surratt in Canada; then turning on Burnett a few day's later saying, 'What have you done with Weichmann'? Burnett was fortunate to run into Weichmann later near the White House ironically, and throwing his arms around him, took him to see Stanton. Then Burnett realised how flippant and dangerous Stanton could really be. He immediately resigned his commission to Stanton. Then Stanton crawled back and begged him, saying it was the country's burden on him and sometimes no one else mattered. Stanton was obviously not really up to his job, he used his office as an excuse for his own child like behaviour and failures. Also in regards to Mary Surratt the evidence is that Stanton tried to block all appeals to Johnson. Indeed Anna had tried time and time to gain Johnson's ear but was turned away by officials. Also Colonel Wood was convinced of Mary's innocence and also tried but to no avail because of Stanton. Thus:

'Col. William P. Wood, superintendent of the Old Capitol Prison while Mrs. Surratt was there, had become convinced of her innocence. Just before the execution, he rushed to the White House hoping to see President Johnson and make an appeal for mercy on her behalf. He was met there and blocked from entering by Col. Lafayette Baker, Stanton's chief detective, who held a signed order from Stanton specifically prohibiting Wood's admission to the premises. In an undated article that appeared in the Washington Gazette shortly after the death of Stanton in 1869, Wood revealed and interesting conversation with President Johnson.

"Some time after the execution of Mrs. Surratt, President Johnson sent for me and requested me to give my version of Mrs. Surratt's connection with the assassination of President Lincoln. I did so, and I believe he was thoroughly convinced that of the innocence of Mrs. Surratt. He assured me he sincerely regretted that he had not given Mrs. Surratt the benefit of Executive Clemency, and strongly expressed his detestation of what he termed 'the infamous conduct of Stanton' in keeping these facts from him. I assured him of my unchangeable friendship for Mr. Stanton...while I regretted the course adopted by the Secretary of War towards Mrs. Surratt..."

So who leaked it out that Johnson had said that she was the one that 'kept the vipers nest'? Anyone from Baker through the decades of decadent writers via corruption and vicious slander, till today and henceforth. What makes these thick people tick?

Baker himself quoted in code in Colburn's United Services Magazine that Stanton had incorporated him into the cabal to assassinate Lincoln, as the following decoded article was discovered by Roy Neff in 1960. Yet it has still not affected the general public's view of 'History' which continues to be wickedly taught to children today, instead of teaching them to think for themselves by offering them an alternative view.

"It was on the 10th April, 1865, when I first knew that the plan was in action. I did not know the identity of the assassin, but I knew most all else when I approached Edwin Stanton about it. He at once acted surprised and disbelieving. Later he said: "You are a party to it too. Let us wait and see what comes of it and then we will know better how to act in the matter." I soon discovered what he meant that I was a party to it when the following day I was shown a document that I knew to be a forgery but a clever one, which made it appear that I had been in charge of a plot to kidnap the President. Then I became a party to that deed even though I did not care to. There were at least eleven members of Congress involved in the plot, no less than twelve Army officers, three Naval officers and at least twenty-four civilians, of which one was a governor of a loyal state. Five were bankers of great repute, three were nationally known newspapermen and eleven were industrialists of great repute and wealth. Eighty-five thousand dollars were contributed by the named persons to pay for the deed. Only eight persons knew the details of the plot and the identity of the others. I fear for my life."

This account from Baker in code would have to be taken with a pinch of salt however. And it doesn't have any of the words in it that strikes an accord with Baker's own style and brevity of common touch. For example both Baker and Stanton preferred the word 'murderer' over 'assassin'. It might mean however, that he was trying to implicate Stanton as the key man and at the same time saying he himself was not involved in the hatching of the plot. He was however quick to explode the myth of the shot being fired outside the door and has given reams of literature concocting 'evidence' against all the fugitives, and had fabricated the diary. Therefore he was probably involved in the plot from the very beginning if not indeed the chief ideas man of the project. He had also been an experienced doorman in San Francisco. As for implicating Stanton, one should consult Baker's book in which he gives full praise to Stanton that contradicts this coded message, as also indicated by a specific meeting between the two after the assassination. (See below). The reason Baker, happily or stupidly, gives so much of the hidden truth way in his book, is that he is an irrepressible boaster and never misses a chance to highlight his own advocacy and controlling influence in all these events and schemes. However, as a counter measure, there are two passages in the book that go to great pains to explain his exact whereabouts and occupations at the time of Lincoln's assassination. The first is from his favourite and most active officer, and here Baker quotes Major O'Bierne thus:

"No lapse of, nor varied experience, can ever efface the memory of the hour at headquarters when the following was penned:-" The face of Lafayette Baker, Colonel and Chief of the Secret Service, overlooks me. He has played the most perilous parts of the war, and is the captor of the late President's murderer. The story that I am to tell you, as he and his trusty dependents told it to me, will be aptly commenced here, where the net was woven which took the dying life of Wilkes Booth. When the murdering occurred, Colonel Baker was absent from Washington. He returned on the third morning and was at once brought by Secretary Stanton to join the hue and cry against the escaped Booth. The sagacious detective learned that nearly ten thousand cavalry, and one-fourth as many policemen, had been meantime scouring, without plan or compass, the whole territory of Southern Maryland. They were treading on each others' heels, and mixing up the thing so badly, that the best place for the culprits to have gone would have been in the very midst of their pursuers (naturally, to suit the ruse: author). Baker at once possessed himself of the little the War Department had learned, and started immediately to take the usual detective measures, till then neglected, of offering a reward, and getting out photographs of the suspected ones. He then dispatched a few chosen detectives to certain vital points, and awaited results."

Except the photograph of John was in fact a photograph of Edwin which he gave to Lieutenant Doherty of the hunter force, but John's photograph was commissioned on the 'Wanted' posters. And Edwin was not at all like John either in looks or temperament. Yes, this officer O'Bierne, gives devoted praise to Baker and indicated how little the War Department had achieved without him. Baker reinforces this accountability of himself, the spelling un-corrected. Thus:

" I shall now proceed to give a brief official history of my connection with the arrest of the assassins of the President. For some weeks previous to the assassination I had been on duty in New York, engaged in making investigations with reference to frauds committed in the recruiting service. On Saturday morning , April 15th, while in my room at the Astor House, having just risen to dress, Lieutenant L. C. Baker, who had come on from Washington the evening previous, rushed into my room and announced the fact that President Lincoln had been assassinated. This announcement called to my mind at once the various communications containing threats of assassination that had for nearly two years had been received. The last advices from Washington, received early on Saturday morning , simply announced that the president still lived, but no hopes were entertained of his recovery. The feeling of indignation

and sadness exhibited by my whole force , then on duty in New York, when I announced to them the fact, I have never seen equaled. We had all learned to love the President as a father. Amid all the scenes of trial, through the prejudice of loyal citizens and the passion of enemies of the Republic, and of detected criminals, we had received the kindest treatment from Mr. Lincoln. Whenever he was plied with charges against the bureau, he vindicated his character, and affirmed it to be one of the necessary institutions of the civil war. (Note: Such a pity that Lincoln was so kind).
He never hastily accepted the opinion of the highest in position, nor in a single instance arrainged the national police for its action, however loud the clamour of the victims of its argus-eyed vigilence.
At twelve o'clock on Saturday, April 15th, I received the following dispatch from the secretary of War:-

Washington, April 15th, 1865.

Colonel L. C. Baker:-
Come here immediately and see if you can find the murderer of the president.

Edwin M. Stanton, Secretary of War.

No train left New York by which I could reach Washington before the following morning. On Sunday morning, April 16th (Note: the second morning) I arrived in Washington. My interview with the Secretary of War was a sad one. As I entered the Secretary's office, and he recognised me, he turned away to hide his tears. He remarked- "Well Baker , they have now performed what they have long threatened to do; they have killed the President. You must go to work. My whole dependence is upon you."

So Baker's account here might well contradict his later coded message implicating Stanton, if the coded message is genuine. It would therefore appear that Baker was not in Washington till the 16th and had made out a good case for not being there.
The later coded revelations by Baker implicating Stanton shows a different slant altogether. At the above meeting with Stanton on the 16th April, it would have logically been the time for Stanton to have relayed to him that there was a plot and he was now involved, because he had a document cleverly prepared, that would implicate Baker to such an extent, that he could not renege from it. Except that Baker in his 'coded message' said he had first learned of the plot from Stanton on the 10th April, when he also had meeting with him. That is if we are to believe anything Baker might say or swear to, especially since Baker had been in New York for some time prior to the 16th April, according to his book account. But if Baker was in Washington on the 10th then it implicates him right up to the hilt, otherwise why would he try to cover it up?
So this might be thin ground to work on in this area, and cannot be proven one way or the other, that might implicate either of them directly, in this manner. Unless of course we can find another source of evidence to prove that he was in Washington on the 10th April. In other words if we are to believe his account in his book then the decoded message is probably false. If however the decoded message is true, then both of them are totally implicated directly in the plot. At best these two differing accounts prove either (a) Baker is up to his usual brinkmanship or (b) the decoded message in Colby's magazine is not genuine. The problem with intelligent bigots like Stanton is they are generally bullies and racist. It appears to be a lack of integrity or morality. Every person's brain is capable of academic intelligence, if interested. Often women are more

intelligent than men unless they race in a man's world, where they compete at the same level or play dumb to win the male. This doesn't increase their intelligence but often reverses it in order to further serve their culture in its bigotry, its hypocrisy or its morality.

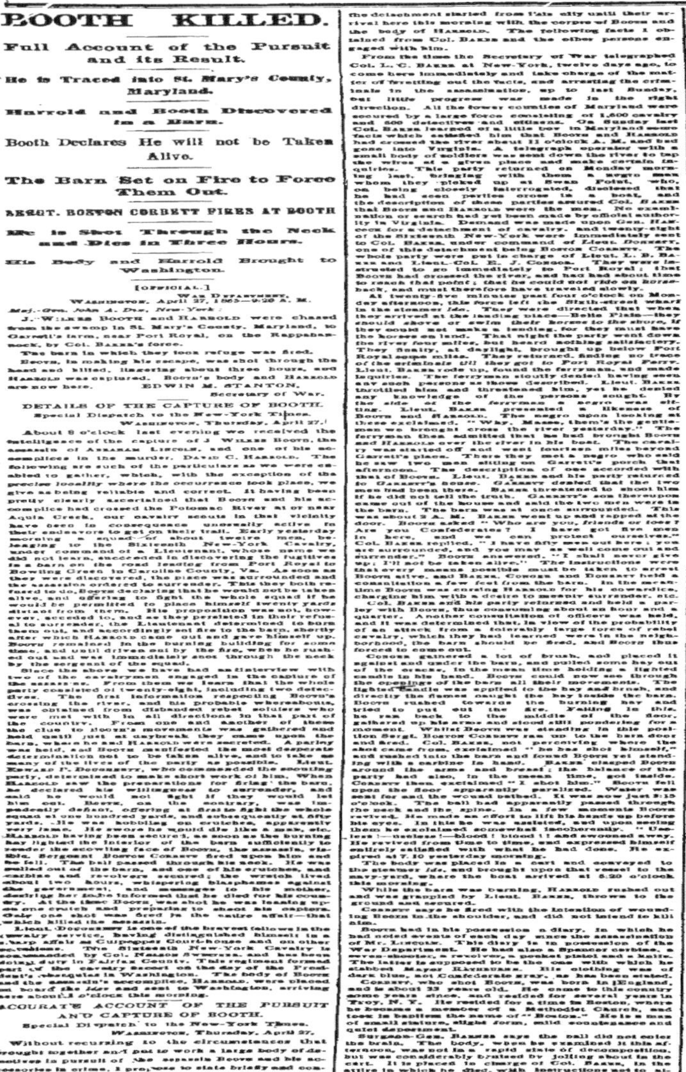

BOOTH KILLED.

Full Account of the Pursuit and its Result.

He is Traced into St. Mary's County, Maryland.

Harrold and Booth Discovered in a Barn.

Booth Declares He will not be Taken Alive.

The Barn Set on Fire to Force Them Out.

SERGT. BOSTON CORBETT FIRES AT BOOTH

He is Shot Through the Neck and Dies in Three Hours.

His Body and Harrold Brought to Washington.

[OFFICIAL.]

WAR DEPARTMENT,
WASHINGTON, April 27, 1865—9:20 A. M.

Maj.-Gen. John A. Dix, New-York:

J. WILKES BOOTH and HARROLD were chased from the swamp in St. Mary's County, Maryland, to Garrett's farm, near Port Royal, on the Rappahannock, by Col. BAKER's force.

The barn in which they took refuge was fired.

BOOTH, in making his escape, was shot through the head and killed, lingering about three hours, and HARROLD was captured. BOOTH's body and HARROLD are now here.

EDWIN M. STANTON,
Secretary of War.

DETAILS OF THE CAPTURE OF BOOTH.

Special Dispatch to the New-York Times.

WASHINGTON, Thursday, April 27.

About 8 o'clock last evening we received the intelligence of the capture of J. WILKES BOOTH, the assassin of ABRAHAM LINCOLN, and one of his accomplices in the murder, DAVID C. HARROLD. The following are such of the particulars as we were enabled to gather, which, with the exception of the precise locality where the occurrence took place, we give as being reliable and correct. It having been pretty clearly ascertained that BOOTH and his accomplice had crossed the Potomac River at or near Aquia Creek, our cavalry scouts in that vicinity have been in consequence unusually active in their endeavors to get on their trail. Early yesterday morning a squad of about twelve men, belonging to the Sixteenth New-York Cavalry, under command of a Lieutenant, whose name we did not learn, succeeded in discovering the fugitives in a barn on the road leading from Port Royal to Bowling Green in Caroline County, Va. As soon as they were discovered, the place was surrounded and the assassins ordered to surrender. This they both refused to do, BOOTH declaring that he would not be taken alive, and offering to fight the whole squad if he would be permitted to place himself twenty yards distant from them. His proposition was not, however, acceded to, and as they persisted in their refusal to surrender, the Lieutenant determined to burn them out, and accordingly set fire to the barn, shortly after which HARROLD came out and gave himself up. BOOTH remained in the burning building for some time, and until driven out by the fire, when he rushed out and was immediately shot through the neck by the sergeant of the squad.

Since the above we have had an interview with two of the cavalrymen engaged in the capture of the assassins. From them we learn that the whole party consisted of twenty-eight, including two detectives. The first information respecting BOOTH's crossing the river, and his probable whereabouts, was obtained from disbanded rebel soldiers who were met with in all directions in that part of the country. From one and another of these the clue to BOOTH's movements was gathered and held until just at daybreak they came upon the barn, where he and HARROLD were secreted. A parley was held, and BOOTH manifested the most desperate determination not to be taken alive, and to take as many of the lives of the party as possible. Lieut. EDWARD P. DOHERTY, who commanded the scouting party, determined to make short work of him. When HARROLD saw the preparations for firing the barn, he declared his willingness to surrender, and said he would not fight if they would let him out. BOOTH, on the contrary, was impudently defiant, offering at first to fight the whole squad at one hundred yards, and subsequently at fifty yards. He was hobbling on crutches, apparently very lame. He swore he would die like a man, etc. HARROLD having been secured, as soon as the burning hay lighted the interior of the barn sufficiently to render the scowling face of BOOTH, the assassin, visible, Sergeant BOSTON CORBETT fired upon him and he fell. The ball passed through his neck. He was pulled out of the barn, and one of his crutches, and carbine and revolvers secured; the wretch lived about two hours, whispering blasphemies against the government, and messages to his mother, desiring her to be informed that he died for his country. At the time BOOTH was shot he was leaning upon one crutch and preparing to shoot his captors. Only one shot was fired in the entire affair—that which killed the assassin.

Lieut. DOHERTY is one of the bravest fellows in the cavalry service, having distinguished himself in a sharp affair at Culpepper Court-house and on other occasions. The Sixteenth New-York Cavalry is commanded by Col. NELSON SWEITZER, and has been doing duty in Fairfax County. This regiment formed part of the cavalry escort on the day of the President's obsequies in Washington. The body of BOOTH and the assassin's accomplice, HARROLD, were placed on board the *Ide* and sent to Washington, arriving here about 1 o'clock this morning.

ACCURATE ACCOUNT OF THE PURSUIT AND CAPTURE OF BOOTH.

Special Dispatch to the New-York Times.

WASHINGTON, Thursday, April 27.

Without recurring to the circumstances that brought together and put to work a large body of detectives in pursuit of the assassin BOOTH and his accessories in crime, I propose to state briefly and consecutively the incidents in the pursuit from the time the detachment started from this city until their arrival here this morning with the corpse of BOOTH and the body of HARROLD. The following facts I obtained from Col. BAKER and the other persons engaged with him.

From the time the Secretary of War telegraphed Col. L. C. BAKER at New-York, twelve days ago, to come here immediately and take charge of the matter of ferretting out the facts, and arresting the criminals in the assassination, up to last Sunday, but little progress was made in the right direction. All the lower counties of Maryland were scoured by a large force consisting of 1,600 cavalry and 600 detectives and citizens. On Sunday last Col. BAKER learned of a little boy in Maryland some facts which satisfied him that BOOTH and HARROLD had crossed the river about 11 o'clock A. M. and had gone into Virginia. A telegraph operator with a small body of soldiers was sent down the river to tap the wires at a given place and make certain inquiries. This party returned on Monday morning last, bringing with them a negro man whom they picked up at Swan Point, who, on being closely interrogated, disclosed that he had seen parties cross in a boat, and the description of these parties assured Col. BAKER that BOOTH and HARROLD were the men. No examination or search had yet been made by official authority in Virginia. Demand was made upon Gen. HANCOCK for a detachment of cavalry, and twenty-eight of the Sixteenth New-York were immediately sent to Col. BAKER, under command of Lieut. DOHERTY, one of this detachment being BOSTON CORBETT. The whole party were put in charge of Lieut. L. B. BAKER and Lieut.-Col. E. J. CONGER. They were instructed to go immediately to Port Royal; that BOOTH had crossed the river, and had had about time to reach that point; that he could not ride on horseback, and must therefore have traveled slowly.

At twenty-five minutes past four o'clock on Monday afternoon, this force left the Sixth-street wharf in the steamer *Ide*. They were directed that when they arrived at the landing place—Belle Plain—they should shove or swim their horses to the shore, if they could not make a landing, for they must have the horses on land. That night the party went down the river four miles, but heard nothing satisfactory. They finally, at daylight, brought up below Port Royal some miles. They returned, finding no trace of the criminals till they got to Port Royal Ferry. Lieut. BAKER rode up, found the ferryman, and made inquiries. The ferryman stoutly denied having seen any such persons as those described. Lieut. BAKER throttled him and threatened him, yet he denied any knowledge of the persons sought. By the side of the ferryman a negro was sitting. Lieut. BAKER presented a likeness of BOOTH and HARROLD. The negro upon looking at these exclaimed, "Why, Massa, them's the gentlemen we brought cross the river yesterday." The ferryman then admitted that he had brought BOOTH and HARROLD over the river in his boat. The cavalry was started off and went fourteen miles beyond Garrett's place. There they met a negro who said he saw two men sitting on Garrett's porch that afternoon. The description of one accorded with that of BOOTH. Lieut. BAKER and his party returned to GARRETT's house. GARRETT denied that the two men had been there. BAKER threatened to shoot him if he did not tell the truth. GARRETT's son thereupon came out of the house and said the two men were in the barn. The barn was at once surrounded. This was about 2 A. M. BAKER went up and rapped at the door. BOOTH asked "Who are you, friends or foes? Are you Confederates? I have got five men in here, and we can protect ourselves." Col. BAKER replied, "I have fifty men out here; you are surrounded, and you may as well come out and surrender." BOOTH answered, "I shall never give up; I'll not be taken alive." The instructions were that every means possible must be taken to arrest BOOTH alive, and BAKER, CONGER and DOHERTY held a consultation a few feet from the barn. In the meantime BOOTH was cursing HARROLD for his cowardice, charging him with a desire to meanly surrender, etc.

Col. BAKER and his party returned and held a parley with BOOTH, thus consuming about an hour and a quarter. Another consultation of officers was held, and it was determined that, in view of the probability of an attack from a tolerably large force of rebel cavalry, which they had learned were in the neighborhood, the barn should be fired, and BOOTH thus forced to come out.

CONGER gathered a lot of brush, and placed it against and under the barn, and pulled some hay out of the cracks, in the mean time holding a lighted candle in his hand. BOOTH could now see through the openings of the barn all their movements. The lighted candle was applied to the hay and brush, and directly the flames caught the hay inside the barn. BOOTH rushed towards the burning hay and tried to put out the fire. Failing in this, he ran back to the middle of the floor, gathered up his arms and stood still pondering for a moment. Whilst BOOTH was standing in this position Sergt. BOSTON CORBETT ran up to the barn door and fired. Col. BAKER, not perceiving where the shot came from, exclaimed "he has shot himself," and rushed into the barn and found BOOTH yet standing with a carbine in hand. BAKER clasped BOOTH around the arms and breast; the balance of the party had also, in the mean time, got inside. CORBETT then exclaimed "I shot him." BOOTH fell upon the floor apparently paralized. Water was sent for and the wound bathed. It was now just 3:15 o'clock. The ball had apparently passed through the neck and the spine. In a few moments BOOTH revived. He made an effort to lift his hands up before his eyes. In this he was assisted, and upon seeing them he exclaimed somewhat incoherently, "Useless!—useless!—blood! blood!! and swooned away. He revived from time to time, and expressed himself entirely satisfied with what he had done. He expired at 7.10 yesterday morning.

The body was placed in a cart and conveyed to the steamer *Ide*, and brought upon that vessel to the navy-yard, where the boat arrived at 5:20 o'clock this morning.

While the barn was burning, HARROLD rushed out and was grappled by Lieut. BAKER, thrown to the ground and secured.

CORBETT says he fired with the intention of wounding BOOTH in the shoulder, and did not intend to kill him.

BOOTH had in his possession a diary, in which he had noted events of each day since the assassination of Mr. LINCOLN. This diary is in possession of the War Department. He had also a Spencer carbine, a seven-shooter, a revolver, a pocket pistol and a knife. The latter is supposed to be the one with which he stabbed Major RATHBURNE. His clothing was of dark blue, not Confederate gray, as has been stated.

CORBETT, who shot BOOTH, was born in England, and is about 33 years old. He came to this country some years since, and resided for several years in Troy, N. Y. He resided for a time in Boston, where he became a member of a Methodist Church, and took in baptism the name of "Boston." He is a man of small stature, slight form, mild countenance and quiet deportment.

Surgeon-Gen. BARNES says the ball did not enter the brain. The body, when he examined it this afternoon, was not in a rapid state of decomposition, but was considerably bruised by jolting about in the cart. It is placed in charge of Col. BAKER, in the attire in which he died, with instructions not to allow any one to approach it, nor to take from it any

Stanton's version of the news still gives Daniel C. Harrold on 27th April. And Boston is now a Lieutenant. It's beyond stupidity. And proves it didn't matter what they said, they still got away with it. But it does show that Thomas P Corbett was already Stanton's 'Pet'.

Chapter 8

A Scenario of Strange Circumstances

The following is a summary of many of the strange occurrences in relation to the assassination of Abraham Lincoln on Good Friday the 14th April 1865. There was much withholding of suspects true identities and falsification of evidence. e.g. photographs tampered with, lost evidence recovered, some corpses dug up and a hidden macabre burial. There was malevolent implication of innocent civilians and convictions with immediate death penalties, life sentences to hard labour or some were just simply murdered and many other innocent victims. There is evidence being held even today by the FBI but never investigated properly eg tracing the story behind the letter connected with JWB's boot sent in years after he had died indicating that Booth had indeed survived, had children but possibly died in 1903. And the propagation of myth in relation to the '18' consecutive missing pages in 'Booth's' purloined diary which if they exist are not in the public realm and probably never will be, but may have been 'seen' in 1976 though restricted.(Ref: A certain Mr. Lynch).

The killing of the 'perpetrators' at the scene or shortly afterwards by the army e.g. a barn is burned down and 'Booth' is shot and killed and 'Herold' taken prisoner but was hooded as much as possible with umbrella cover on hanging day in public. And a little later 'Herold's' grave is dug up and his head removed, in which his skull is eventually exhibited in a museum. Indeed, it is said also that the body of 'Booth' had decayed so badly that his head had become detached, during the post mortem. The actual limited amount of decay in such a short time, is not a convincing reason for decapitation.

There is ample glorification and multiple stories totally exaggerated and unrelated to the real facts retold to school children and disguised as history. This entails over embellishment of the true events usually with colourful details or theatrical histrionics combined with false patriotic fervour and male bravado. The purpose of this is to aid multiple red herring effects besides raising the stakes of motivation and political intrigue to enhance the reasons and fanatical sense of political and deviant purpose of the supposed assassins.

There were informers who were members of the plot but were eventually set free. These were certain key people who supplied the vital details and when implicated, testified against their fellow conspirators. In this case the three main informers were Louis Weichmann (Wiechman from his German father) and John Lloyd (publican) and later in this book however you will see the possibility of a very secret informer indeed, one whom no one would ever suspect. Also there were odd characters that appeared to be involved in assisting the plotters but were never implicated seriously e.g. the role of Joseph 'Peanuts' Burroughs who supposedly had the horse ready for JWB's escape. Then there are unusual slight's of hand such as the President's messenger Charles

Forbes, being either stood down, or otherwise strangely allowing the assassin to go into Lincoln's box because he showed his calling card.

The amazing lapses in security at the critical hour of assassination e.g. the policeman John F Parker was not at his post with Lincoln or even nearby. Parker in fact disappeared at the intermission and did not return. He was cautioned later but did not loose his job, even though Mrs. Lincoln challenged him and blamed him directly for causing her husband's death, by his neglect of duty. It's as if Edwin McMasters Stanton, the Secretary of War (today the Secretary of Defence) had said to Lincoln, OK go to the theatre but I will not protect you if you do. In fact Lincoln's personal bodyguard and friend Ward Laman was away in Richmond, Virginia on other business. This man had constantly protected the President during his travels even to the point of sleeping next to his sleeping quarters when travelling. Again it is amazing how all protection is equated to zero at the exact time of the assassination. This cannot be pure coincidence but neither can this tremendous scale of negligence be convincingly possible without malevolent purpose. Was this to teach Lincoln a lesson by Stanton who had tried to impose his will against the chief yet again, or a pre-arranged gambit?

It is a fact that Lincoln's official bodyguard around the clock when he was out was on a roster between 5 or 6 policemen. That night Crooke was his guard up until arriving at the theatre when Parker was to take over. The military guard at the Whitehouse had recently been changed from the Pennsylvania 150th to the Ohio Light Cavalry (Stanton's state). The officer commanding this guard Lieutenant George Ashum even stated, echoing Stanton and Baker, that Lincoln would often avoid being guarded but in any case nothing could have stopped a determined assassin like Booth. Yet Ashum was detailed to protect the President and General Ulysses Grant but it was not considered necessary, when Grant was replaced by the effeminate Major Rathbone as an escort at the last minute. General Grant and his wife declined an evening with the President in public to visit relatives, his two sons, in Burlington, New Jersey.

Lincoln had asked for Major Eckert to be his personal bodyguard but Stanton told Lincoln the Major was assigned other duties. In fact Eckert had spent his evening at home but turned up at the theatre afterwards, to attend the dying President. And apparently Grant didn't need much persuading to stay away either. Remember this is the most famous American General in history, winning the civil war for Lincoln, yet not prepared to be in the public eye as guest of honour with the President. The only other personal explanation given was that Grant's wife had a prior engagement with relatives in New Jersey. The official line is that there had been a long cabinet meeting that Good Friday morning from 11am till 2.30pm on 14th April with Stanton and Lincoln and even Grant included. Afterwards Grant turned down an open invitation for the same evening at the theatre when personally invited by the President himself.

However, this story is not quite plausible because several witnesses including Harry Clay Ford brother of John T Ford the theatre owner, and the builder and manager James Gifford, were already informed and preparing the theatre, to include the Lincoln and

Grant parties, that very morning. The three Ford brothers and Gifford were later to be implicated and thrown in gaol for 39 days before being released without charge, yet John T Ford was ex-mayor of Baltimore - part of the Union. Even the restaurant owner Tavatul had been told that his favourite, General Grant, would be there and he was the third witness that gave the most graphic details of the assassination, as he was sitting directly opposite, in the other VIP booth above the stage, supposedly. Except James Ford and Harry, who were in charge of ticket office that day, said no other VIP box tickets had been purchased. Joseph J. Sessford the ticket clerk confirmed this, in his statement. And Tavatul had also stated it was he who had served Booth whiskey instead of his usual brandy, at the intermission in the Star bar.

John Surratt's fellow southerner Louis Weichman had informed Gleason weeks before of the plot to kidnap the President. Weichman himself had been arrested at Mary Surratt's boarding house and it appeared at first that he was one of the plotters. As he was an experienced clerk for the federal government then it was probably unlikely. However he did volunteer a lot of information under oath in the trial which helped the prosecution to convict Mary Surratt and the others. The defence seemed trivial in a military proceeding that was arbitrary and no better than a kangaroo court. The presiding judge was a certain General Joseph Holt a man of extreme and twisted vigour. Indeed, the atrocities he had committed in the South warranted his reputation as a war criminal in burning down a capitol building and rampant fratricide. The South had sworn if they had caught him he would be hung as a common criminal. He tried to disguise the fact that their were two plots to be considered: 1) a kidnap and 2) an assassination, and both unconnected.

Also, it is clear how Lincoln would intercede for liberals. In 1863 Holt led the prosecution of Clement Vallandigham, the leader of the Peace Democrats, known as the Copperheads. He was arrested in May, 1863 and accused of treason. He was found guilty by a military commission, and was sentenced to imprisonment. Lincoln intervened and commuted his sentence to banishment behind the Confederate Army front lines. Now you see again it is patently clear how Lincoln was fighting against the forces of evil, that wanted the war to continue under Stanton. These same people would stop at nothing to continue the war, and would eventually remove any obstacle in their way, including the President, who had helped to save this Democrat and duly elected representative of the House. Of course the War is ideal for accusing anyone of being a traitor, unless they clearly indicate they will back carnage and fratricide to the hilt. There can be no better definition of evil than this. And the men that run it are of small intellect, and all but insane in their lust for power and wealth. In fact, worse than serial killers because they are also cowards, getting others to carry out their dirty deeds, under the name of patriotism. And of course Lincoln became ruthlessly undone, paying the price for his moderation in trying to preserve the fabric of the Union.

Judge Holt Master
Of War Criminals

The North's concentration camps were no better than the South's either. It is clear that wars are not caused by people but the old aristocracy and today-right wing governments. And they are directly influenced by the illuminati in the cause of greed. Except to each new generation it's invisible and couched in illusions. People think themselves as human but the illuminati think of them as human resources, and can be used, controlled or wasted at any time. Eg. 9/11 and OK city are the most tragic examples of modern American fratricides, and in their sublime hypocrisy they deem to judge others, feigning economic growth under the Greek name of Democracy. But its not just happening in America , the same effects are occurring globally, particularly where there is weakness and instability. And today it's 'Al-kieda' but then it was the mythical and military genius of Booth linked to the Confederacy; but today Booth is Osama Bin Laden. Except the latter has been dead for over two years now, according to French intelligence, but hopefully is now going through another process of Resurrection. As indeed Booth died at least twice before he finally he got too old, but his notoriety lives forever in infamy. And who can argue otherwise, when in what we thought was the Enlightenment had happened long ago, in the days of Roger Bacon at the end of the middle ages. Suddenly people are in the dark again because learning has to be rekindled in every generation, not shrouded in mystery for the want of a little intelligence, as indeed the sun should hopefully rise every day.

The authorities quickly found out where the suspects were located. This is at Mary Surratt's boarding house and the names of Booth and his brother fellow actor Edwin, who had previously saved the life of Lincoln's son Robert, and John Surratt were immediately released to the press. Yet soon after no further mention is made of Booth's acting family because they were totally unconnected and politically pro- union, except they were all arrested, although Edwin and Asia were not imprisoned. Their father who died when John was only 13 was the great English actor Junius Brutus Booth and no doubt the family were relatively rich, because of both John and Edwin, and brother Junius was also well known. Evidence of this press release is given by John Surratt

when he over-hears the news that very day in a telegraph office on his way to Canada.
The arresting party knew exactly where to go in Washington, just along the High St., now a Chinese Take Away, to arrest Mary and take her away, because they had been informed by her lodger. In fact the NDP of which the notorious Laffayette Baker headed were able to locate Payne and O'Laughlin at the Surratt boarding house, three days later on Easter Monday. The German-American, Adzerodt who's English was not so astute, was arrested at his home in Southern Maryland, by Officer Lee directed by Major O'Bierne of the NDP. Except Baker later said he was arrested in Montgomery County close to Washington on instructions by telegraph from Major O' Bierne, then operating in Southern Maryland.
The NDP knew exactly where to pick them up; at the modest, tidy and kind hearted lady's lodging house, with beautiful pictures and not a tavern as many stories would have it. The tavern so mentioned was the family property located 2 hours or 13 miles carriage drive away in the country (then in Surrattsville County now Clinton) and originally the Surratt farmhouse which she had rented to a certain John Lloyd a publican, ex-police officer and drunkard. This publican's testimony was a tissue of lies and many witnesses including himself, all stated he was drunk at the time. A story no doubt from his own colourful repertoire was that he was strung up by his thumbs, until he confessed all he knew about the plotters.
The boarding house is where the National Detective Police arrested three of the 'conspirators', except Booth, Arnold, Spangler, Herold and Adzerodt. Payne was digging a ditch for the landlady and had a pickaxe in his hand. When they examined him his hands were that of the texture of a lady, otherwise he carried a few innocent belongings but had been a Confederate soldier from Florida, serving in northern Virginia, but had by now sworn the oath of allegiance to the Union. They asked her if she knew this man which she immediately denied out of shear dread no doubt. Of course it did not help her case. The press do not question the official story but keep on repeating it at first and then changing it as time went by to suit the plot. Eg the first story is Lincoln and half the cabinet have been assassinated by only two or three men, Booth and Surratt- then changed it later to Booth and Payne. There are incredible details of last minute plans, motivations and actions of the assassin. These included extraordinary human feats and daredevil acts with combined Blondini and Houdini like qualities. This is after shooting Lincoln in the head, then fighting hand to hand, like Jim Bowie, to 'stab' a Major. He then rides down Tenth street and Pennsylvania Avenue and on past the Mint and Capitol Hill, to the navy bridge checkpoint and escapes to Virginia......the most incredible escape artist of all time. Yet 'Booth' also foretold what he was going to do by writing an account in his diary and then penning a letter like Shakespeare to the Washington Intelligencer, the same morning.
Meanwhile, at exactly the same time starting at 10.15 pm 'Payne' tries to assassinate Seward, not far away in his house with family members, including household staff on duty. But Payne boldly knocks on the front door feigning he is delivering medicine and

one of the staff lets him in. This is incredible, what kind of medicine would the injured man need to a physical injury that no one had ordered, particularly that late at night? This story is so poor it is obviously untrue. And being untrue the exaggerations are many fold. Into the house Payne goes alone leaving his mate 'Herold' outside, where he encounters then bludgeons two grown men, to finally grapple with Seward in his bed on the second or third floor who is also guarded by a young soldier, acting as a nurse. Apparently Herold hears screams from the house, panics and then leaves Payne to his own devices. Yet Payne still 'needed' Herold, even just to escape, because Herold new the country and where to meet up with Booth. Except Baker said they had rendezvoused outside the theatre, right from the start. But Payne knew exactly where the theatre was because Booth had, less than an hour beforehand, despatched him from there. So that 'brilliant' reason is now clearly undone.
The staff allows a total stranger inside on the pretence of delivering medicine- what kind of medicine from a total stranger- bad medicine ? Then Payne has to locate Seward inside a large house on the second or third floor. He does this by threatening the servant with a 44 revolver then battles with Seward's two fully grown sons. And on making it to the room instead of shooting Seward instantly he opts for the much more difficult task of using his knife, preferring the more ritual act of repeatedly stabbing him in the face and throat. Both of Seward's sons try to stop Payne but are savagely beaten back ... this indeed beggars belief because for some reason the servants are unable to raise the alarm immediately, in the middle of Washington. And even more incredible there is a male nurse and soldier, Edward F. Robinson, tending Seward who is also attacked but offered sterling resistance. In fact this young soldier from Ohio, was later in 1871, on leaving the army finally rewarded for this specific act of bravery, to the enormous sum of 5,000 dollars plus a gold medal and a signature commending his 'valour' from the state department. Awards of valour are rarely accompanied by cash rewards in almost any other army under any circumstances. And this was after Andrew Johnson had left office. Presumably he was fully aware by then of the treachery and while he was President he would not pay the Judas money.
It is on record that Stanton had visited Seward that same night amazingly, and had a bedside discussion with him which was obviously extremely important, with Seward being in a very poor condition. Even to an average policeman this would be very incriminating unless we assume the timing was pure coincidence or that Stanton was responding to the emergency call. This simply defies all the laws of probability. In effect Stanton truly wasn't bothered about Lincoln since he had more important business with the Secretary of State that same night, who was in fact, just recovering from an overturned carriage injury at his home in Washington. It seems Stanton was never too far from the action however because he finally got back in the very early morning to accompany the dying Lincoln. In effect he must have been very busy all night.
Payne was supposed to have carried out his attack at the same time as Booth's...pre-arranged for 10.15 pm. This indicates that Stanton's visit to Seward is only a short time

before or after Payne's visit with the bad medicine. However if it was after the attack then Seward could have been in no condition for a bedside chat, and indeed it was around 12 till 1 am. according to the New York Times.

Seward in 1861

1801-1872

Seward's house near Lafayette Square, Washington

Seward after his carriage injury:

1865

Judge Elijah Miller's House, in Auburn, New York. Father of Frances and Seward's married abode.

It would be much simpler to adopt the line of intrigue that Stanton's visit was to update Seward with his plans. Then Seward could simply claim his carriage disfigurement was actually made worse by a knife attack. It is said it was 'no secret that Seward was a very rich man and desired to be President, since he also thought that Lincoln was a buffoon, yet he himself was the right stuff out of shear self righteous arrogance and being very rich'. Except he always spoke well of Lincoln and was seemingly very loyal too him. In addition, these rumours about Seward seem to contradict his many great achievements including his courageous and successful defence of a large group of conspirators in Michigan in 1851, getting 38 of them acquitted; and his un-successful defence of an Afro- American man, William Freeman in 1841 having gotten him a re-trial but he died in prison, probably innocent of killing a white farmer. (?). He was also a very strong Christian believing in the greater good of God's providence and did not falter in his anti-slavery campaign. It seems odd then that he should have been coerced into a plot with Stanton, a strong Methodist. However he was on the list for assassination and according to Hall and Maione, it was to ensure the elimination of several Presidential contenders next in line. Thus:

'If Andrew Johnson had also been assassinated as planned, Senate President Pro Tempore Lafayette S. Foster of Connecticut would have become Acting President pending an election of a new president (the process of electing a new president could only be set in motion by the Secretary of State; thus Seward's assassination would throw the Union government into "electoral chaos"). A Presidential Succession law passed on March 1, 1792, was still in effect in 1865. It provided that the President Pro Tempore of the Senate was third in line to the presidency and the Speaker of the House was fourth. This law didn't make any succession provisions beyond the Speaker. For much more information see the article entitled "Why Seward?" by Michael Maione and James O. Hall in the Spring, 1998, edition of the *Lincoln Herald*.'

Except the author has just removed the name of Booth (only) from the above account whom of course the historians clearly implicate as both the plotter and assassin, like changing the characters in a play, but hopefully not to detract from their genuine research.

One has to assume that Seward was in no condition to argue with Stanton and simply went along with him probably unaware of the real plot at the time. Without a doubt the family were stricken with fear and grief because his wife Francis died two months later, and Fanny the nurse died the following year. And it was Robinson that supplied all the details of 'Payne's' attack. So Seward and his family probably became unwilling victims, in their innocence. The stories afterwards would of course spin off in all directions of magnitude and descriptive power. And Seward was basically a good man but should have fought back, but his carriage injury had no doubt weakened him both physically and mentally.

It is easy to cover up a scar on the throat and even easier to cover no scar on the throat. Seward's face and lips were swollen and twisted down, that were so clearly disfigured by his carriage accident the week beforehand, but the so called knife scar is only faintly visible on his cheek. And since Seward was only just recovering from his accident he would still be confined to bed giving him some time for his 'throat scar' to heal. The accounts vary but Payne is generally supposed to have injured Seward badly using a knife by stabbing him in the face and throat in his bed. There must have been a good reason that he didn't shoot Seward instead of knifing him. The story is that he had a revolver and that's how he kept all the household at bay and had to fight them off, because the Colt revolver didn't actually work! The consensus is that the revolver was damaged during the bludgeoning of Major Frederick Seward and his brother, so he used his knife instead....another list of incredulities that stretches the imagination beyond all known horizons. Payne then escapes alone on his horse after trotting off quietly around the houses and after yelling at Tom Bell the house man, 'I'm mad. I'm mad'.

Another account said he yelled this to Robinson. Yes be prepared, all the stories in this

Booth saga have more variations than a whole battalion of live and progressive jazzmen, a tribute to the man from Belgium who invented the saxaphone, Adolphe Sax (1814-1894). He then heads off down the East Branch turnpike like a bat out of hell but takes a fall from his horse and gives up. He then disguises himself using mud and returns to his lodgings. As for 'Herold', he has long 'scarpered' and supposedly meets up with 'Booth' just outside the theatre. They evade capture in Washington by freely crossing the Navy bridge, only recently barricaded with gates and sentries. By now there is an even greater problem of separating fact from fiction. Nevertheless, the official line is that Booth and Herold made it to Virginia but were caught up with at Garrett's barn, 90 miles from Washington in Virginia. On the way they stopped at Surrattsville and then at Dr. Mudd's farm house near Bryantown, to fix Booth's injured leg with a splint ready made from cabinet wood and gypsum. The account by Baker begins by saying that after meeting up outside the theatre, they rode past the Mint and Capitol Hill to Uniontown. Then they were both challenged separately by a sentry at the Navy bridge over the Anacostia River but allowed to pass. In Herold's case he gave a false name of Smith but Booth told the truth and still got by, including his destination of Beantown. Payne was actually picked up at Mary Surratt's boarding house so he did not think it necessary to escape to Virginia, to try to avoid the hangman's noose. However even according to Baker, Payne did indeed try to flee north along the Baltimore turnpike, from the Capitol on his horse at a killing pace but then gave up, as you will see below.

There was convenient evidence left behind in the theatre e g the pistol is supposedly dropped by Booth, on the carpet in the President's box. This is .44 German silver plated derringer, but the 'knife' was still in Booth's hand as he retreated across the stage and 'flourished' it towards the audience. Is he still acting out a scene or showing bravado as he cries out in Latin 'sic semper tyrranis.'? And some accounts say he had in fact cried out this motto for Virginia that was conveniently hung on the wall of poor Mary Surratt's boarding house, along with pin up photographs of Booth kept by her daughter. Why should he cry out in Latin, as if he was acting? People don't understand Latin and even now there are many translations and variations of these lines.

There are amazing coincidences of time and place. E.g. Booth only found out that Lincoln would be there that day because he happened to go and pick up his mail at the theatre that very morning. Yet he was supposed to have planned to kill not just the President but also General Grant, with only a small single shot derringer and a dirk knife? In fact this derringer was a pistol commonly used by officers in the military and often sold in matching pairs. This was because the single shot was not always successful and a second weapon was desirable. This particular pistol was rare because of its ornate German silver plating and its barrel was rifled in an anti-clockwise direction (a one off). Obviously 'Booth' thought a knife would be just as useful as a back up weapon, rather than two pistols.

It was stated that Adzerodt stayed in the Star tavern next door instead of going to kill vice president Andrew Johnson at 10.15 pm., as both were staying at the Kirkwood Hotel, (so Adzerodt must have been well off). The NDP found convenient evidence under his bed- a pistol and a knife. Now, why would a man leave weapons under his bed where they could be found easily- he may as well leave them in his draw or on top of the bed to be free of dust? This extraordinarily complex plot must have required meticulous planning and timing on the day and a great deal of fast thinking and action and mostly by 'Booth' himself. It was indeed provident that General Grant had cried off and Parker was not on duty and no other bodyguards to bother about. And where were the rest of the assassins? A sergeant outside the front of the Ford theatre recorded that a posh gentlemen seemed to be constantly walking about and checking the time giving instructions to two others, including a ruffian. The two walked of briskly and the gentleman with a moustache walked into the tavern at just before 10 pm. We are to take this as evidence that 'Booth' was calculating the time to send Payne and Herold off to kill Seward. He then goes for a quick whiskey, instead of his usual brandy, into the Star tavern next door. Then he goes into the theatre between 10 and 10.15pm. This was timed for the 3rd act in 'Our American Cousin' that gave the biggest laughter line. The diminutive actor Harry Hawk playing Asa Trenchard was delivering this maximum laughter line to Mrs. Mountchessington, and included the famous actress Laura Keene, at 10.15 pm and this is when the assassin struck.

In Walt Whitman's poem he says in one line the pistol sound was heard by less than 100th of the audience (the estimated audience varied between 1500 to 2000 people that night). Booth was in the tavern at 10 pm according to the owner Taltavul, who said it was he who served him, but Taltavul's evidence is more than questionable, as you will see later. Another obvious point is that contrary to their being any protection for the President he was surrounded by at least 8 army officers which included 3 medical doctors, and the mysterious doorman, who all played vital roles such as prime witnesses with backup duties, surveillance and first aid, and indeed two of them even tried to capture the assassin but to no avail. Both Major Rathbone and Colonel Stewart used the same phrase in tackling Booth. … 'Stop that man', as did Clara Harris. Indeed Stewart said it three times and almost caught the reigns of the assassin's horse and Rathbone who was badly wounded in the arm by the knife almost stopped 'Booth' from going over the balcony, such was there immediate reactions and bravery.

Booth was an actor not a soldier yet no soldier of any rank could stop him. These two senior army officers and Clara Harris were the prime witnesses and gave statements. Except years later their lives proved to be very murky indeed. Stewart became an attorney and had a law firm and had a partner called Clarke who had left under a cloud. Later, Stewart made a sworn statement that was found to be suspect before the Kansas Senate, relating to the Ross v Pomeroy case in the Clarke letter forgery affair. Clarke in fact had not written a letter in 1862 for Pomeroy intending to swindle Indian lands, it was proven Pomeroy himself had written it to Ross, and that as a Senator he had swindled many other land and railway deals. Rathbone became a consulate in Hanover,

Germany where he murdered his wife Clara Harris and tried to kill his three children and tried to commit suicide. He was sent to a German insane asylum for the criminally insane for the rest of his life, and continued to become increasingly paranoid and demented, by his imagination and delusions.

There are of course different explanations of how Booth prepared his entrance into the box with Lincoln. One account gives he bored a hole to spy into the President's box to check the scene. Who actually bored this hole? Apparently Booth or possibly Spangler as the army prosecutors later tried to establish. In addition they gave details of how he got passed the doorman into the vestibule leading to the box, and how he used a pre-prepared method of fixing the door from the inside using a wooden brace, exhibited in the trial with blood on it. In fact Rathbone used the word 'plank' in his statement so this would rule out it being a music stand as stated elsewhere. No doubt the 'plank' or brace had not been noticed by any of the staff, if it had already been located in the tiny vestibule. And then after bracing the outer door behind him he then looked through the spy hole of the box door, box no. 7, which was supposed to be locked but the lock had been sprung, or indeed already open according to Rathbone. In fact it was the second door no.8 which was open, the entry door for the party; the lock on this door had been broken on the '7th March' by Mr. Raybold, a member of staff.

Then, supposedly he very quietly opened this door and crept up behind the President without being heard or seen or even sensed in such a small room, before shooting him in the head, like a silent and invisible assassin. Rathbone was sitting on the sofa facing this door obliquely, and 8 feet from the President in relation to the door in such a position that it would have been highly unlikely not to see and react to someone coming through that door with a weapon in his hand. Captain Theodore McGowan gave a statement that he was seated in the circle about five feet from the President's box, when a well dressed man entered the row behind him, and then halted to have a good look all around the theatre. McGowan described the gentleman as well dressed in black coat of dress frock style, dark pants and a stiff rimmed, flat topped, round crowned felt hat and a moderate moustache with smooth face, black hair, dark eyes he thought and 5ft 91/2" tall and no obdurate body markings. Note his precise estimation of height.

Could it be that the derringer was concealed inside the top hat where he also carried the knife? But what about the wooden brace? It is easily possible to carry such a length of a thin stick of about 3 feet or so inside loose pants and coat without it being noticed.

However it would have been too easily discovered if a simple body search was carried out by anyone on the door, even in the absence of the policeman John F Parker. But the assassin could not assume Parker would not be there or that the doorman would not search him. If a small hand gun such as a derringer was concealed inside a false bottom in the hat and he carried no knife and no brace he would have been at least a bit safer from a quick body search. The Victorians were clever in all and sundry having invented most things including top hats that magicians still use to hide live rabbits, inside linings of felt and false bottoms .

McGowan was convinced it was the same man who ran across the stage minutes later brandishing a knife except by then the assassin was bareheaded according to McGowan. He had also assumed that the assassin had jumped from the box balcony but McGowan had been in no position to observe this act, because he was not seated in the front row of the dress circle. In fact admitted in his statement, and being located only five feet back from the wall and door of the box vestibule which would be totally blind to the box balcony, but not the stage. The question is, what happened to the assassin's hat as there were few reports of a hat being found, yet all the other items, derringer, knife, kid glove and piece of wood covered with blood spots, were all recovered for the military trial. He must have lost his hat easily in the fight or in the jump. However the adjutant or advocate at the trial Colonel Burnett stated later that the hat was also 'found' along with the kid glove.

The assassin had spoken to the doorman and gave him his calling card from a selection of cards according to the eagle eyed McGowan. Then he permitted him to enter the passageway leading to the inner door of the presidential box. Another interesting observation by McGowan was that another gentleman whom he did not recognize, had previously gone by him and spoke to the doorman carrying an envelope intended for General Grant he thought, but he couldn't actually read the printed title. Then the gentleman returned and departed. This is interesting because it suggests this person was unaware that General Grant was not with the President. This might imply that useful information was obtained by this visit in confirming the General's absence to the would be assassin(s). However Booth had been with Maddox, Spangler and Burroughs in the tavern at around 6.30pm according Gifford and indeed several prosecution witnesses (and including Spangler's own statement found after his death) and would surely have gathered this fact by then, that Grant would not be there that night.

Ed Spangler, known as Ned the stage carpenter, had been responsible for setting up the box and removing the partition in the box, normally designed for separate parties, that same day. In fact he had been accused by 'Peanuts' Burroughs the stable boy, of saying bad things about the President when they were working in the box.. this had come out in the trial. (Except Mr. Sleichman said Ed was clapping his hands <u>and</u> stomping his feet when the President arrived). If so, the letter probably had nothing to do with the supposed assassin Booth, but then who was the sender and why send it at such a coincidental time and why to General Grant who wasn't there? However it is not inconceivable that McGowan who was a non-active but very observant army officer, together with his friend Colonel Crawford in support, might have used this statement to the effect that an assassin would never have dared to carry out a combined assassination, if he had known that the formidable and victorious General Grant was in the box with Lincoln. This of course would be contrary to the illuminati's view that Booth was plotting to kill both Lincoln and Grant and would not be put off anyway, so what matter!

On the other hand there may well have been a much more sinister reason for this letter.

Was it a last minute final instruction for the assassin to carry out his deed, stating that all was ready and with the exact time now synchronised for the assassin to strike? In other words was this the final decision and order for the assassin to carry on with the pre-determined plan? It is interesting that boring of holes is a true spying technique which goes back a long way and is today a highly sophisticated tool used by all intelligence agencies eg it was used in the Iranian embassy siege in London to good effect. And literature abounds in spy holes even going back to peeping Tom spying on Lady Godiva in Coventry. However a spy hole can also serve as a deadly accurate killing hole. Or indeed a perfectly round hole can be created by a near hyper-velocity bullet of whose accuracy can be pre-arranged by fixing a chalk or graphite mark on the door. (In the recent 1990 film called Dick Tracy, the never break a government law crime buster and never tell a lie -even when looking death in the face, a gimlet is used to bore a hole in the ceiling for a 30's style bugging device).

It turned out that the so called spy hole was exactly in line with the upper back outline, including head and shoulders, of an adult sitting in the President's chair. This 'coincidence' was actually confirmed by Clara Harris the fiancé of Rathbone, when she and Judge Olin (of the Supreme Court) returned on Easter Sunday to examine the scene, prior to her making a full statement on Easter Monday. The judge had asked her to show him the exact position of the chair, thereby fixing the President within only two to five feet from the spy hole, in exact line with the President's back when looking through the hole. And any geometrical diagram will show that it is impossible to miss from this range even if the weapon is pointed at an angle of up to 20 degrees from the centre of the body. The only proviso is the target has to remain fairly stationary for a few seconds within a latitude of several inches. In other words the President would have had to make a sudden involuntary and extreme movement of his head and shoulders to the left or right. Baker refers to this hole in a give away sentence thus:

" I have not adverted to the hole bored with a gimlet in the entry door of Mr. Lincoln's box,
cut out with a penknife. The theory that the pistol-ball of Booth passed through this hole is now exploded."

Yes, this is his only reference to it yet he does not even bother to explain how the myth was exploded, but nearly and naively infers through poetic justice that, 'the now exploded pistol-ball of Booth passed through this hole.'

However, when Booth's trunk was seized at the National Hotel a gimlet with a metal handle and 3/16" drill, was found by the clerk Mr. G.W. Bunker who handed it in to Mr. Hall. This man was supposedly looking after Mr. Ford's business, except Mr. Hall in fact was reporting to the NDP. Another question is, was the hole bored by the assassin or did the assassin's bullet bore the hole? In fact the bullet likely bored out a larger hole from the smaller spy hole. What is certain is that someone came back to make a bevel round the hole with a knife afterwards, according to Gifford, that caused scratch marks.

There is no point in carving out a bevel to a spy hole which would simply draw attention to the hole, yet do nothing to improve the spying area. If the bullet was shot through the hole, then the powder stains would have to be removed to make it look like a spy hole, in order to disguise the fact that the President was shot from outside the door. This would make the assassins task infinitely easier by a) not having anything remotely near the same risk b) not being identified and c) even a coward could do it. This puzzle is solved later, below.

The whole charade seemed to befit an act in another theatre where the supposed assassin (Marc Antony) and his bother's Edwin (Brutus) and Junius(Cassius), had once acted out Julius Caesar. Indeed a brilliant allegory of acting and real life. In other words Booth knew the theatre inside out (having spent the previous two winter seasons acting there and often visiting it) but also how convenient of Lincoln being there so unprotected that night. After the event, the theatre was compulsorily purchased by the government . Indeed this was after it tried to illegally possess it lock, stock and barrel until John T Ford threatened court action. Only then did the government agree to pay him $100,000 by settling for a compulsory purchase order instead. After all why should the government have to hang its dirty linen out yet again to the public for the sake of a few bob. Nevertheless it became the ministry of pensions but in 1889 whilst undergoing reconstruction in the basement they still managed to cause a mini 9/11, whilst Kepler and Newton looked on in total disbelief. The whole building including three floors collapsed killing 22 clerks and injuring 68 others.

The original plan by Booth was to kidnap the president- not to kill him- in order to force an exchange of Confederate prisoners. And the informer, Louis Weichmann knew this intimately from his Catholic friend and erstwhile fellow divinity student John Surratt. Surratt later told the true story about his own role and how the informant and friend had double-crossed him and helped send his innocent mother to the gallows. The reason for the double-cross was probably two fold. Weichmann had a government job as low grade clerk for the Commissary General of Prisons; but still pretended he wanted to be in with Surratt in the kidnap plot and must also have known about Surratt's blockade running for the Confederates. Surratt did not think he was suitable because he could not ride a horse or use a weapon and told him so. In in any case Booth had met him once or twice and rightly did not trust him at all. The other reason was that Weichmann was under suspicion himself unless he would come to testify against the plotters to save himself, or so it might have seemed if he was not a spy. It turned out he was the informer of the gang having already told Gleason, a government clerk, of the kidnap plot. At the trial Gleason denied fore- knowledge of the plot or that he had not taken it seriously and did not inform his superiors. Of course he hadn't officially, since their were very good reasons.

On Good Friday 14th April at the theatre Booth met, at 6.30pm in the Star saloon, the stagehand in charge of the left-stage Ed Spangler, who sometimes looked after Booth's horse and carriage in the theatre stables for occasional payments. Booth had asked him to sell them at a given price in public auction four days before. Spangler couldn't get the price and Booth had then asked him to sell them privately and then got the price, and settled up with him. And Gifford confirmed this in his statement. Thus:

'On Monday evening of the week previous to the assassination, I heard Booth tell Spangler to take his horse and buggy down to Tattersall's, the horse-market, and sell it. I presume Spangler sold it. He brought the man up with him, and asked me to count the money and give him a receipt. I took the money and handed it over to Booth.'

Booth had hired another horse that final day from Mr. Pumphrey's stable on 'C' street and went for his usual evening ride returning at 9.30 pm. He had been told that 'Crystal City'? was a good place to visit. When he came back at 9.30 pm, he asked to stable his horse but Ed was busy with scene shifting and Ed asked Burroughs to do it instead. John Surratt went to trial two years later but the jury were unable to convict him because he proved with the help of four witnesses, including a hotel ledger signature, he was half way to Canada that day and had never plotted to assassinate the President but was aware of the kidnapping plan and had written to Booth finally telling him to desist from this exercise.

There are multiple stories about Booth's career after the assassination. One story indicates he survived and changed his name. On his death bed he confessed that he was not John St. Helen, a man in Enid, Oklahoma but J.W. Booth, but he then recovered. Another alias of Booth's was David E. George. It is interesting that this name is a combination of David E Herold the man supposedly caught in Garrett's barn with Booth and that of George Aderholt the one assigned to kill Andrew Johnson the vice president. Are these stories simply interesting coincidences or just more red herrings to follow up? You will find out later. There were some amazing events that were to follow those three who had witnessed at close range the killing of Lincoln. His dear wife Mary was hit with immediate depression and later entered a rest hospital for a short while after the swift military trial. She finally retired to her home town of Springfield, Illinois and became a bit of a recluse, after visiting Europe.

Major Rathbone the son of a rich merchant had inherited the family fortune as a young army officer (having tried to take on his father's business) by 1865 and then suddenly became promoted, he later became a Consulate in Germany. However he proves to have been inherently unstable and haunted by the past and murders his wife Clara in 1889 (his step-sister in law, the daughter of Judge Ira Harris who had married his mother on the death of his father). Do these acts and conditions suggest how un-stable they really were or were they driven insane by the really terrible knowledge and guilt connected with or resulting from the hidden agenda of the illuminates? Indeed the owner of the house across the street where Lincoln died, William Peterson (of Sweden -Petersen) later committed suicide on the grounds of the Smithsonian Institute, and the fact it happened to be government property was just another sinister coincidence. The President had no finer nemesis than Booth for his death and aftermath. Lincoln's elevation to a great literary and poetic statesman, indeed a popular legend, for future Americans to look up to, like Jack Kennedy or the tragic Marilyn Monroe. As Stanton prophesised when he witnessed Lincoln's last dying breath. 'Now he belongs to the Ages'.

The illumini imbibe or totally replace every fact with fiction, which simply magnifies itself for the sake of it, even amongst the most well meaning, exaggeration is second nature; and truth means nothing for the sake of artistic impression, and so history is forged like a biblical epic and even the English language is corrupted for the sake of journalistic sensationalism. This is quite apart from the indigenous colonial licentious nature in exaggerating events, into false heroics or diametrically opposite villainous acts, so that nearly everything relating to the truth is buried. Who needs truth when you can make the story fit to suit the cause? Indeed the President had been very un-popular presiding over a civil war which was in the control of the War Secretary, the devious Edwin McMasters Stanton a man from Steuberville, Ohio; once a 'brilliant attorney' to whom Lincoln, himself a mere self taught Kentucky country boy, had once deferred to in fellow counsel as the better man. Lincoln had also become a lawyer. It seemed Lincoln had deferred to Stanton in a trial years before saying that Stanton would be the better defence attorney of the two. No doubt Lincoln would have really been the better in the defence of the Union. Stanton seemed indispensable to Lincoln and told him to countermand any decision that Stanton felt was wrong .

These decisions may have been in Lincolns mind, only strategic in relation to the war but not politically important and that Stanton's fast calculating mind and devious methods would help win the war. (In fact Stanton or anyone would have made no real difference, since even Baker could fool him). But Stanton may have had alternative plans to ensure his position of controlling influence over the President whoever, and at whatever the cost. However when the war the was over Lincoln wanted the South to be in civil control with no loss of status. Stanton wanted total subjectivity with loss of property to the gentry and landowners and military control, as if conquering a foreign country especially relating to the spoils of war, if not total dependence.

There was a radical republican policy that included the Wade-Davis bill, yet Stanton was a Democrat (but later turned Republican) as was vice President Andrew Johnson, who eventually got rid of Stanton. But not before Stanton had Lorenzo Thomas arrested, the man Johnson had appointed to take over the as War Secretary (see the cartoon in Harper's magazine). The final decision was clearly to be a political one and Lincoln would never allow Stanton to over-rule him on this one. Lincoln was a caring and considerate man if obdurate and Ahab like when it came to policy, yet able to take criticism, but when his mind was made up nobody not even Stanton could change it. You can imagine the War secretary wanting to continue the war at any cost till he got his way ' total control of the South.' In retrospect Stanton had little respect for Lincoln the baboon he had fashioned, yet arranged his funeral and after life was propagated to be the biggest giant of a President who ever lived.

The Lincoln memorial is a 20 foot giant man sitting in a giant chair the allegory of the one he was assassinated in. Did that mean Lincoln was a great thinker or that he was a slow man, sitting down un-protected in a theatre, and so easily copped an actor's bullet? But perhaps Lincoln's true weakness was that he also was suffering from a mute form of arrogance which surely must afflict all rulers of state, not towards their people, but towards their close and immediate inferiors. Stanton would have picked it up right away and thought this man thinks he is a Christian God and acts as if he is perfectly just and righteous, yet allows me to do the dirty work for his ends; but I have another agenda and will show him that a sublime man is a fool and he has to reckon with the real powers behind the throne, or face destruction.

The implications of Booth's political sympathies and esoteric motivations and detailed plans and liaisons were all crammed into that very day of action on 14th April 1865. Even all this busy thinking schedule did not stop him visiting the Star tavern, next to the theatre twice, and Gautier's theatre restaurant where he wrote a letter (supposedly). He also popped into his old friend Andrew Johnson at the Kirkwood Hotel, but he was out so Booth left his calling card. Of course he also had to liaise with his band of rag-taggle assassins, of which it seems only by conjecture that George Adzerodt was near at hand to kill vice-President Andrew Johnson; as both were staying at the Kirkwood Hotel. It was stated that Booth popped into the hotel around 3 pm to see Johnson, but both he and his secretary Browning were out so Booth left his calling card, like any gentleman would do, with the desk clerk Robert Jones. Perhaps Booth wanted to talk to his old friend Johnson, knowing that he was intending to get George to assassinate him at 10.15 pm that night, and thereby confirm his movements. Or perhaps just to meet for a drink and catch up on old times, since George was really miles away. Yes, he was managing to supervise everything alright. There is later evidence from Hamilton Howard (1907) that Booth and Johnson were once good friends having met in Nashville in Feb. 1864. Indeed they had shared two sisters as mistresses, when Johnson was governor of Tennessee and Booth was performing at the premier opening at the Wood's theatre.

Now, according to the evidence at the trial, Raybold a senior member of staff met Booth and gave him a letter, and Booth read it sitting on the front steps surrounded by friends. It was a long letter of several pages and he seemed happy, laughing to his friends. Booth often collected his mail their, kept in Mr. John T. Ford's office. This was around 11.30 am to midday outside the Ford theatre, and he was informed about the President coming in that evening. Booth was a perfectly dressed and well mannered gentleman, with a foppish air, dressed in coat and tail, dark clothes with a tall silk hat, kid gloves and a cane as he later walked away towards Pennsylvania Avenue. And, James Ford said in his statement that he saw Booth near Pennsylvania Ave. around 12.30 pm. Yet Raybold had actually met Booth to give him the letter, and Raybold had only come in for an hour between 10 and 11 am,, he said. But Harry Ford said he was still there at 12, because Raybold had neuralgia in his face, so Harry had relieved him, but asked Raybold to help him put up the flags, before he went home. And Raybold himself placed the rocking chair according to his own statement. And Harry himself was not aware of the spy-hole, under oath. He said it was always dark in the vestibule until a door was opened throwing daylight in. So the hole would go un-noticed by anyone. This then throws into question the letter from Frank Ford years later that his father drilled the hole. This letter must be yet another forgery. And the hole was therefore probably drilled by Raybold, and he had also got his instructions from the treasury man for the location of the flags.

Raybold certainly knew when to be there, and when not to be there, and he was a rash and brash, unreliable character. It was he and the treasury man that gave Harry instructions for the decorations in the box. He had previously resigned his commission in the 6th Infantry Maryland Volunteers, as a Captain on August 16th 1862, after joining in December 21 1861, promoted 2ndLieutenant in April 3rd , 1862 and promoted Captain July 16th, 1862. Thus he resigned after holding a Captain's rank for only one month and having served less than eight months. This indicates a very wilful and unstable character indeed.

Now for 'Booth', so suddenly updated, it would be a case of fast action and even faster thinking. Also, according to Baker and the New York Times a kid glove was found on the stage after the assassination. As it turned out Harry and John T Ford and brother James, got 39 days in prison. It was also stated but not confirmed that Booth met a fellow actor called John Mathews around 5 p.m. and handed him a sealed letter, to be given to the National Intelligencer the very next day. Indeed some modern media biographies outline not just what he did but a chronology of his movements hour by hour throughout the day. It would appear that Booth was not just another actor he was the greatest criminal and military genius of all time. He had even managed to telegraph all his plans just before he successfully carried them out in front of 1700 or so people including actors, stage-hands, lawyers, two army captains, two army majors, two army colonels, two army doctors, a naval officer, another doctor, actors, musicians, doormen and policemen and under the noses of the whole Union defence establishment, including the NDP. This is of course is familiar history today as it was then, and the war department (today the pentagon and defence) indicate they were totally unprepared for a strike (whenever the all seeing eye is looking the other way). However, as a saving grace, Stanton and Major Lamon had repeatedly tried to stop Lincoln's innocent visit to the theatre. There can be no other logical reason for this total lack of security, beyond the political intrigue of how and why the assassination was set up that night.

Booth had often visited the Ford theatre and everyone knew him there as he was most popular. He spoke to everyone and lifted their spirits. He kept his horses in the stables there, whenever he was in Washington. The previous two winters he had been acting there . According to Spangler he would often take his horse out riding in the afternoon usually alone but always came back by about 8 or 9 o'clock. This time he had already reneged on his plot to kidnap the President but the illuminati insists that he was involved in a far bigger plot to kill Grant, Seward at his home not far away, and at the same time Andrew Johnson and the President in the theatre. Any sane person must ask for God's sake…Why? Except the abstract reason being cognizant in the minds of the illuminati that they had included Johnson on the assassination list, in addition to Lincoln and Seward. Well, that's nearly half of the cabinet, that was the rumour put about before the assassination. As a cover later, they tried to implicate Johnson as being involved in the plot with Booth. These right wing radicals were extreme and violent creationists. In Chemistry they would be known as free radicals or spontaneous catalytic reagents, that initiate or accelerate a reaction. The very opposite of true nobility or indeed morality, that is chaos personified and pure evil.

This new scheme would defy Faust himself and catapult this fine actor and gentleman into the realm of total character assassination imbibed with Machiavellian evil, pointless oblivion and useless suicide. This sort of thinking falls in line with the style of the decadent, secretive, sadistic world of the illuminati, and they even managed to project his dying words to the world for him Useless, Useless. That was the final insult they should get him to say this in his dying breath if ordinary people are nieve enough, wicked enough or just plain stupid enough to believe it. It would be beyond madness in every direction in its method in its planning, in its motivation and most importantly in its political objective.

It certainly would not gain him the exchange of prisoners that was is only hope and fervent purpose, in one great humanitarian act. They were suffering badly in Northern prisons and it was more than politics it was his passion to help them in some grand manner. But being an actor was not good enough for this brilliant, warm and passionate man; he wanted to help the Confederate cause not rest on an actor's laurels and above all he wanted a fair justice, not revenge. He was already famous and earning good money. Kidnap is not assassination, which would at best only make for more bad blood and re-kindle the war in a revenge mafia style back lash, and certainly would not be in the interest of Jefferson Davis who was hoping to secure a good deal with Lincoln, who was above all was an honourable man. Davis and Booth might not have been fully aware of Stanton's policy for the South ie complete and utter ruthless domination and subjection, subservience and total dependence of all southerners their lands and property.

At the same time Lincoln was offering them a return to civility and local government provided the overt and apparent cause of the war, the abolition of slavery, was made law in every state. In the end Stanton's policy did not happen since instead of manipulating the democratic incumbent, and perhaps not so decadent Andrew Johnson, whom Stanton thought he could control, Johnson wisely out manoeuvred him, instead. He pulled rank and sacked him but not before Stanton and the Radicals but I think <u>not</u> including Secretary of State Seward (the man who bought Alaska from Russia and his name mapped Seward Peninsula) had just narrowly avoided impeaching him, before he got rid of Stanton. So in fact Andrew Johnson should be credited as the man who really saved the Union; after Lincoln had been eliminated for trying to save it by being ruthlessly undone, as lightning strikes the mighty oak. America has Johnson to thank also for purchasing Alaska with all it's oil and gold then unknown and possibly the most strategic move ever made on the world's global chess board. And they still try to undo him to this day. Well that's politics and dirty business for you. The mafia has far more honour and intelligence.

The man Booth was far too intelligent and refined to carry out such a black hand style vendetta, in such a risky enterprise and doomed to political failure from all sides unless he was a part of the illuminati himself. This meant he would not be destined for physical death, but settle for character assassination, total alienation and loss of a fine acting career. In short total oblivion living in fear for the rest of his life without a home or safe harbour and to never live a normal life of love, happiness and the pursuit of justice but to have to hide like a hunted animal, as a criminal guilty of murder.

That is unless he had been deceived by them, in a classic double cross set up, in which Booth could not have failed to have realised all of the inevitable consequences. If he had been liaising with them, as is purported in the missing '18' pages of the diary, he must have quickly assessed he was dealing with treachery itself and reneged immediately. To follow through with any of the illuminati's plans would indeed be the mark of insanity or sublime martyrdom to the Southern cause. And Booth was certainly no fool. In addition none of his motley crew, a mediocre gang of rank amateurs would be up to a fraction of this madness, let alone a professional syndicate associated or affiliated to the confederacy, that would need to be of a much higher calibre in both training, skill and ruthlessness. In the outcome what a truly great American anti-hero Booth, of ultimate fiendish bravery against all odds, became, even though vilified as an assassin with style and brilliance not to mention his good looks and undoubted great acting ability, obvious charm, passion, influence and all the girls had pin ups of him. This is not the sort of man that would fire a bullet into the back of a man's head through a spy hole, nor indeed creep up behind a man even if entailing brave deeds that involved this one cowardly act. The act itself pre-supposes a coward and therefore could not make such a leap. And a self-made man with fine clothes and earned 20,000 dollars a year he himself had said.

In the words of John F Parker when Lincoln's wife Mary accused him of being responsible through idle neglect he answered with rhetoric 'would I stoop so low as to murder the president'. Here is an indication of uncertainty suggesting the possibility of a third party in addition to or instead of Booth, who had been 'identified' as the assassin a little while after the deed was done. This is because Parker's answer seemingly implies that there is some doubt as to who the real assassin was, but he certainly was not involved because he would never 'stoop so low'. There seems no indication in this reply that he was sorry or prepared to bear any of the responsibility of his negligence in order to secure the safety of the most important man in the land. He was later to face trial and reprimanded but never lost his job. In fact the official story is that Lincoln himself probably asked him to stand down. It is now absolutely certain that someone else

ordered him to stand down. It was stated that Lincoln had asked Stanton if Major Eckert, a physically powerful man in high office in charge of the federal telegraph network, would be his bodyguard that night so its on record that he had requested that he needed someone.
As it turned out he needed Parker like a hole in the head. It was quoted by more than one source that Parker went to the Star tavern next door at the intermission before the final act in the play and never returned till he showed up at the police station in the morning, having arrested a prostitute. This would indicate that he had indeed been ordered to return to police duties by the army, or someone in higher authority.
Lieutenant George Ashum was in charge of the Union Light Cavalry, an Ohio regiment known as the 7 th Independent Regiment, that had recently taken over from the Pennsylvania 150th division with direct responsibility of guarding the President. General Christopher Auger was in overall charge of Washington DC's Defence and Security. Two of Auger's reserve officers that he was responsible for- Captain Theodore McGowan and the higher ranking Lieutenant- Colonel Crawford were stationed 5 feet from the Presidential box that night and monitored all visitors.
It is also believed that Charles Forbes was stood down, but this does not tie in with Captain McGowan's statement that it was the President's messenger sitting outside the door, that allowed the assassin in to see the President. That is unless he did not realise it was a different presidential aide to Charles Forbes, or perhaps a security government officer. This was corroborated at the trial by another witness sitting in the circle called Dr. Leale and he saw a man being admitted by the Presidential aide at the door. And also by a Mr Sam Koonzle. All three gave corroborating evidence on this particular point. This evidence then does not necessarily over rule the story that both Charles Forbes and John F Parker were seen together in the Star saloon at the intermission, indicating that both gentlemen had been stood down by this time.
This would have been not too long after 9.30 pm at which time Booth was asking Ed Spangler to look after his horse. Later the owner of the Star tavern said Booth came in and ordered whiskey and water around 10 pm instead of his usual brandy and then left quickly. Another report said Booth was with his girlfriend Lucy Hale at the front of the theatre around this time i.e. between 9.30 and 10 pm that is at the intermission. If this is true then Booth would have found it impossible to accommodate such a complex operation to even contemplate meeting and chatting to his girlfriend, of whom he must have arranged to meet beforehand. Its just to many distractions to an already military style operation fraught with such extreme danger and difficulties that only a modern, crack specialist commando unit would have a chance of success at cracking, unless aided by extensive inside help.

Chapter 9

Events in the Theatre

The tell tale signs of spying and the tools of the trade were well documented in the Ford theatre that Easter in 1865. It is on the record that a hole had been mortised (drilled) by a gimlet into the door of the President's booth. It was said that it was used to spy on the party inside. One speculative story has it that Booth himself had drilled this hole in the afternoon since he had free access to the theatre. Perhaps he had asked Ed Spangler to lend him a gimlet, or better told Ed to do it, as he needed to spy on the President but Ed would have done it for him anyway. Gifford had said Ned was always a drudge for Booth. Now how could Booth possibly know that Parker would be stood down from this door, unless he was in league with the illuminati. However the author of this story is unknown, except it came from the prosecution at the trial.

It is said that Frank Ford the son of Harry Clay Ford admitted years later, in a letter (Ref : National Parks Service), that it his father had drilled this hole, to facilitate the security of the President by allowing him to be observed without disturbing him. But this letter has to be seriously questioned for authenticity, since Harry Ford swore under oath that he didn't even know about this hole. And it was Raybold that had placed the rocking chair in the box, according to his own statement. It is indeed true, the hole was there, because Mr. Gifford the maintenance manager of the theatre had to accompany Stanton himself to examine this hole and the crime scene, including the passage door, on Saturday 15th April. Stanton also asked Gifford to effect a wooden strut to this outer vestibule door that had supposedly been used by the assassin to prevent intrusion. This is because the supposed original strut was missing at this point, though later recovered for the trial with blood stains on it. Mr. Gifford noted that there was a groove in the opposite wall gouged out to receive the strut and anchor it. There was no plaster debris on the carpet so it had been cleaned up by someone afterwards. The blood on the wooden strut would have belonged to the supposedly wounded Major Rathbone, as he described removing it with difficulty, whilst people were trying to get in after the assassination. In fact the strut had supposedly been picked up that night by a certain Isaac Jacquelle, who had taken it home with him to his boarding house. Then an officer had asked him to saw a piece off it for evidence, but it is not certain if he did this or not, and eventually it was recovered by the prosecution as evidence all in one piece it seems. The mystery of the bloody strut and its initial disappearance might be easier solved if it never existed in the first place. It would certainly have made the assassins job easier if he didn't have to bother finding a piece of wood about three and a half feet long and smuggling it in with him. On the other hand there is always a good explanation to fill the gap. It is that Booth had found a music stand earlier and left it in the passage way, to use its leg as a brace, and when he returned later that night to complete his task it was fortunately still there. But the really big question is why would the Secretary of War be

interested in measuring the space for a brace that probably didn't really exist, until it was discovered later at a boarding house covered in spots of blood?
Stanton instructed Gifford to find a make-piece brace instead, to reconstruct the barring of the door. On doing so it was found that anyone applying steady pressure from outside would not force the door to open. However by shaking and rattling the door the brace fell down and thus entry might be gained this way if anyone was really determined to gain entry. The spy hole in the inner door was also examined and it was found that a bevel around the hole from the outside had been freshly gouged out, using a knife, and there were scratch marks extending radially from around this hole, particularly on one side. According to Gifford who had not noticed this hole before, it had seemed the scratch marks were very fresh (he was once a carpenter himself), and probably the result of using a knife that had occasionally slipped in the bevelling of the hole. He assumed it was a knife rather than a hammer and chisel because it would have been a more silent process (for an assassin, or indeed after the deed later on). He must have been assuming that the approx. 5/16" diameter hole had been made just before the assassination, but the bevel had probably been made even more recently. And Gifford admitted to Stanton that the last time he had examined the area was a week before and he would have noticed it (he had helped to build the theatre and was responsible for its maintenance).
There was also the business of the lock to the President's box door to be examined. It appeared that the two screws fixing the clasp had been loosened, such that the door could be opened by just inserting an index finger into the key hole and gently pushing the door open, ipso facto. The aide or doorman would have heard the shot go off immediately and thus alerted would have entered the vestibule if the brace was not there; otherwise the assassin had only seconds to make his exit, unless the assassin and the doorman were both one and the same. Otherwise this would have been the only risky part of the operation unless the aide had been otherwise distracted, or was directly involved. After all Charles Forbes might have been purposely stood down for some reason, perhaps to serve this very purpose. The other question is why would anyone go to the bother of bevelling a hole which was perfectly adequate for spying and less likely to be noticed without a bevel? The time required to drill a hole at the time of the assassination would not allow any extra time to bevel it and the noise would be noticed anyway.
There was once a famous Victorian cat burglar called Charlie Piece from Sheffield and supposed killer of Arthur Dyson, according to a 'confession' to a policeman, who was an expert at drilling holes and gaining entrances to houses in London. No doubt he would have such tools and expertise to quickly and silently accomplish this task in seconds. It was said he could gain entrance to any house in less than a minute. However there might be a perfectly good reason to bevel and scratch around a spy hole, if in fact, it had been used as a combined spy and killing hole. The reason being in order to remove gun powder stains afterwards, at the point where the shot was fired through the hole, for the purpose of deception. Consider the advantage of using this method:1) the

assassin need not enter the box at all. 2) If the sitting target is in line with the hole by spying then within a matter of seconds, the weapon can be inserted parallel in the spy hole and immediately fired. The target would have to move suddenly by more than several inches to the left or right to avoid being hit. Even if the President was leaning forward, the assassin would have made allowance for this by angling the line of sight only a few degrees lower, to hit his upper back or neck. As it happened the bullet entered under his left ear and parallel to the neck. This means the back or upper shoulders was the original target and the bullet was off bulls eye laterally by only 2 or 3 inches at maximum. It was said that the preparations for the President's box was supervised by Henry Clay Ford, including the flags, because the usual manager was off work that day with a stiff neck. Perhaps what he was really suffering from that day was the gift of extra-sensory perception. In fact it was Thomas J. Raybold and he was at work for two hours that morning and Harry let him go home sick, taking over his duties. However not before Raybold had placed Lincoln's chair in the box and handed a letter over to Booth. See his own sworn statement in the appendix at the end of this book.

The target distance is variously quoted from 3 to 5 feet depending on which eye witness account was the most accurate. This has to be Clara Harris or Rathbone, and Clara remembered the exact position of Lincoln's chair in relation to the door which she and the judge estimated to be about two or three feet. Even so, heavy powder burns were seen by the doctor's attending the dying Lincoln and were said to be 'forensically proven' on his head but this evidence would have been challenged in a civil court. The chances of the President not being hit would have been extremely low, from such a close range. The President was not a young man and a slow, deliberate person who enjoyed relaxing and would have been absorbed in the play by this time. And according to Rathbone, the President remained in his chair throughout the play getting up only once early on, to remove his coat. Indeed most people in a theatre seldom move there heads when absorbed if they are in a good position. It is an excellent form of relaxation where mind and body are calmly distracted from real life.

And finally 3) the assassin could immediately retire because the element of surprise is still to his advantage. In seconds he would have disappeared, exiting directly from the second floor exit stairs from the south circle to the rear of Taltavul's saloon, the Star tavern. The shot was designed to go off at the moment of 10.15 pm when Harry Hawk was delivering his punch line to the famous actress Laura Keene, for maximum laughter and loud reports in a theatre can often be mistook for a part of the act. In a poem penned by Walt Whitman about the assassination, America's favourite poet at the time, one line mentions the sound of the shot was heard by only one hundredth of the audience. How the hell did he know since he wasn't even there, perhaps from the illuminati? However Captain Theodore McGowan had indeed corroborated this by saying there were a number of loud noises that interpolated the play, and that the shot he first mistook for a report in the play.

This indeed was brilliant strategy on the part of the assassin to time his shot in order to minimise its own noise. However this reasoning could not have been used by Booth, since it would not have mattered a pile of beans to him how loud the shot was because he then had to show himself, first to the three live people in the box then fight with Rathbone. Then he had to jump over the balcony in full view of the audience to land on the stage and cry out 'thus to all tyrants' and adding possibly 'the south is avenged' very loudly in Latin; because he had planned to act out his final act on the stage and broadcast it to the world saving 'Don't cry for me Argentina'. And indeed his words were supposedly heard loud and clear by a few false witnesses because he was indeed a brilliant actor. But one witness said he saw the whole thing and never heard these words at all and never saw any one jump from the balcony either. In fact if you even consider for a moment the shot going off in the box, the whole theatre would have been alerted immediately, thus making his escape IMPOSSIBLE.

The actions and reactions in the presidential box took only 30 seconds according to Rathbone, so 'Booth' was also a very fast worker for an amateur assassin. Nevertheless this surely would have given someone ample time to react and indeed one person did react immediately. It was Colonel Joseph B. Stewart who was sitting right up front stage at the right hand side (left stage), inside the orchestra pit along with the musicians, and just below the President's box at the closest point to where Booth landed on the stage. Stewart stood 6 foot 6 inches and had a black moustache with black receding hair and a grey suit just like Booth, according to the many drawings of him chasing 'Booth' in the alley. Another artist's drawing shows the 'assassin' running across the stage with a big knife aloft, and even this drawing indicates a tall man. In his statement Stewart said that he clearly heard the pistol go off inside the President's box and looked up to see 'Booth' fighting with Rathbone, and then leapt onto the stage and turned his face towards him and the audience, with the dagger in his hand 'gleaming in the gas light' and calling out in Latin 'sic semper tyrranis.' In two bounds Stewart was chasing Booth across the stage but was slightly impeded by the exit door beyond the wings and way back stage, as he cried 'Stop that man, Stop that man, Stop that man' and followed Booth into the alley. By then 'Booth' was on his waiting horse but 'the horse kept turning and turning on him as the rider was slumped to one side, and the horses hooves were clattering on the rocks and he could see the assassin above him in the moonlight.' He nearly caught the horses reins but it gained on him again but he still ran after the fleeing assassin. Yet William R Smith an actor said it was two or three minutes before a tall gentleman in a moustache ran across the stage 'after Booth'. Not only this, Stewart saw a woman nearby and told her what had happened then he returned to the theatre. Shortly after this he went straight to the police station to report all he had witnessed. No doubt he did not get time to see if the President was alright, as he had to get the facts straight to the police as soon as possible, in case he forgot all the details. Ed Spangler said in his statement found after his death, that he could not use to defend himself in a

A tall man ran across the stage immediately after the shot rang out

military trial, that he was behind the centre stage door, preparing his scene shift when he heard the pistol go off, and then almost immediately a man whom he did not recognise came running across the stage. He also said he did not see this man or anyone exit into the alley, from his vantage point, directly in line with the exit to the alley leading off from back stage. He said that that particular door did not shut properly and was nearly always slightly ajar. The key for the stable door outside was kept on a hook in this door, that he could see there. So which way did the running man disappear? Stewart himself stated that he went through this door to chase the assassin, but when he came back into the theatre everyone was in a state of pandemonium, over excited and milling about on the stage; except he noticed that Ed Spangler was behaving oddly, that he was just standing about and acting suspiciously. However according to Ned himself he was very scared as he had just heard someone shout ‘burn the place down’ and he later slept in the stables convinced that someone would burn the theatre that very night.

The assassin and his twin pursuer Stewart, both tall men with moustaches in this artistic impression. Burroughs 'waited an hour' for 'Booth' to return but was 'struck on the head when he did'.

Another witness however said Ned was holding a handkerchief to his face as if crying. Yet another witness called Jake Ritterspaugh, assistant stage hand, said that he had climbed on the stage to chase the assassin but was stopped by Ned Spangler, who hit him in the face and then said to him 'Don't say which way he went'. Note the singular pronoun referring to only one person that had run across the stage. However little Harry Hawk, the actor on stage, stated later that it was he who made this remark because he was upset and confused by the shock of it all, at the time. Perhaps Harry thought it was a line that he might not wished to have said to help the assassin get away but at the same time improving the issue later by appearing to have helped Stewart, the pursuer, to disappear instead. If Stewart had gone out through that door as he said and nearly caught Booth fleeing on his horse then Spangler did not notice him exit that way. However if no-one including Stewart went out that door then Stewart, or the assassin must have disappeared somewhere else behind the scenes or possibly through another door. However we also have the testimony of Joseph Burroughs (colloquially known as 'Peanuts' because he sold peanuts outside the theatre, aside to his duties as a stable boy and extra hand). He said that a man he recognised as Booth came out the alley way door and struck him on the head with the butt of his knife then jumped on the horse, that he was holding for him, and then kicked him out of the way. Now why would Booth have to do that since the boy had been waiting nearly an hour patiently holding his horse for him? Booth had treated him, Ned and Maddox to a drink earlier in the Star tavern so there was no need for this extreme action. Unless in fact Peanuts thought that it wasn't Booth, whom he knew very well being the stable boy, but a complete stranger and naturally would not let him steal Booth's horse.

Another point always kept coming up in court in reference to Ed Spangler's case. Was the defendant wearing a moustache? Well all witnesses for the prosecution and defence agreed on this point that they had never seen Spangler with a moustache. However Colonel Stewart did have a black moustache just like Booth and both were well dressed gentlemen in dark or grey clothes bearing a similar likeness (except for height in fact) as can be seen in the artist's drawing. This dilemma can now be resolved if we tie it in with the weapon being fired, not in the box, but in the corridor entrance enclosed by the door to the circle, known as the vestibule. In a statement given by a witness called Taltavul, a restaurant owner for the prosecution he said that Gifford had reprimanded him the next day. The witness was sitting opposite the box in the opposite circle and had seen the flash of the pistol go off. Gifford then said to him and the witness repeated it in court.

"That was a hell of a statement you gave last night. How the hell did you see the flash when the gun went off outside the box."

It seemed at the time that it was self- evident to Gifford the shot was fired through the door from outside of the presidential box. This same witness then said to Gifford:

"Where is the union flag and why is it not on the pole above the theatre ?"

To which Gifford clipped dryly,

"He had thought there was a flag somewhere but anyway there's a rope up there on the pole, wasn't that good enough."

To which the witness then replied,

"Hey Gifford you should be up there on Old Capitol Hill" and

"Gifford had never liked me anyway."

If the shot had been fired through the spy hole then the job would have been much easier, not having to risk jumping over the balcony into a free fall of 11feet hitting the stage at 20 mph.. Even a trained paratrooper would have to land with both feet together and go into a parachute roll to prevent certain injury. In addition they said Booth's boot spur was momentarily caught in the union flag that was draped over the balcony that Lincoln was still 'clutching' . They also said it twisted Washington's picture skew- wiff but fortunately it didn't fall down. This catch would effect a sudden pull, levering the leg of his body and would undoubtedly have catapulted the assassin into a wild fall, flipping his body from which he would hardly recover to land on his feet. This kind of twisting fall would defy any human feat from which only a cat could recover.

The final point about Taltavul's testimony is in fact, the very proof of the pudding. The whole idea of the plot was to strike from the vestibule through the spy hole, when at maximum noise level from the audience. The muffled sound, if heard, being mistaken for an interpolation in the play, as McGowan rightly observed. If the assassin had fired the weapon in the Presidential Box however, the whole of the theatre would have been alerted by the shot and the 'flash', so it would have been impossible for the assassin to fight for 30 seconds, then jump and escape across the stage. So, Taltavul's lie again proves the truth of what Gifford found obvious and self-evident. Indeed the audience would have caught him and lynched him right there and then, as Baker observed when the angry element shouted 'Hang him, Hang him'. But of course there was no one to hang, since the assassin had already disappeared within 30 seconds of the strike, since he didn't even have to use this time to fight Rathbone, either.

If the assassin had drilled the hole some time earlier that day, it might have gone unnoticed, particularly if he had not bothered with scratching an extensive bevel around it. To what purpose would this bevel serve ? It would not increase the area of view when spying through it and conversely would make it more conspicuous to a casual observer, thereby increasing the risk of compromise to the assassination plot. The army officer in the circle who observed the assassin gain entry to the presidential booth was a military captain under the jurisdiction of General Auger. In his statement Captain Theodore McGowan of the Veteran Reserve Corps made it clear that he couldn't help noticing a person go in to the vestibule, after presenting his credentials to the presidential aide. At the same time the police bodyguard John F Parker had disappeared at the intermission around 9.30 to 10 pm, and was not seen again until he reported back at the police station early in the morning, having arrested a prostitute. The location and position of the policeman should have been inside the vestibule, by the inner door that contained the spy hole to the presidential box (known as the prosynium). It was said that Parker wanted to look at the play at one stage, and may have taken up a place in the circle not far from the aide and the army officers, before finally retiring at the intermission. The only explanation for this, other than a deliberate act of dereliction of duty, is that he was replaced by someone else in higher authority.

Captain McGowan was sitting with his colleague, Colonel Crawford, only 5 feet from the President's booth. He saw one man arrive and stoop down to deliver a message to the President's aide sitting in the circle on seat 300 by the vestibule door, and even noted that it was an envelope for General Grant (who had declined to be there) and it was not delivered so he departed. If this first man happened to be a part of the plot he may have used a letter to determine if Grant was with the President. However, the prosecution said that Booth was planning to kill Grant as well, but a moments reflection

would over-rule this, because he did not carry a revolver but a single shot derringer, so often lucky to go off that they were usually carried as matching pairs by military officers. Perhaps the letter was for another purpose altogether.
Then shortly after this event McGowan saw another man, of which he gave a complete description, down to 5ft 9 ½ inches tall in dark grey attire, with a felt hat and dark eyes and black moustache. This man he observed well because he stood in his line of sight looking around the theatre before speaking to the President's messenger, seated outside the door of the passage leading to the inner door of the presidential box. McGowan then saw the man giving his calling card and was allowed entry. The President's box is located directly above the stage from whence Booth is supposed to have jumped down from. So anybody outside the box wall sitting in the circle would be able to see the play. However the location and proper post of Parker was inside this vestibule, that gained access to the doors of the presidential box. Parker of course was excused duties at the intermission but the two Army officers happened to be at hand nearby in the circle. The passage or vestibule would provide ideal cover for the assassin, having two doors to the box inside but one was locked for security (the spy hole door on the immediate left).
In fact the passage-way door of the South Circle was the door which had been strongly braced, according to Major Rathbone, when he tried to open it after the assassination . 'Wounded' as he was, he removed the 'heavy piece of plank' with great difficulty, as he noted in his statement that people were trying to force the door from without but it stood firm. Rathbone then requested Colonel Crawford to prevent other persons from entering the box, after allowing the two army surgeons and a medical doctor in. The highest calibre of medical aid was close at hand. Clara and Judge Odit went back to the theatre on Easter Sunday 16th April to check the scene, before she gave her statement. However, in Rathbone's statement he said:

"The distance between the President, as he sat, and the door, was about four or five feet. The door, according to the recollection of this deponent, was not closed during the evening. When the second scene of the third act was being performed, and while this deponent was intently observing the proceedings upon the stage, with his back toward the door, he heard the discharge of a pistol behind him, and looking around saw, through the smoke , a man between the door and the President. At the same time, deponent heard him shout some word, which the deponent thinks was "Freedom!" This deponent instantly sprang toward him and seized him; he wrested himself from the grasp, and made a violent thrust at the breast of deponent with a large knife. Deponent parried the blow by striking it up, and received a wound several inches deep in his left arm, between the elbow and the shoulder. The orifice of the wound is about an inch and a half in length, and extends upward toward the shoulder several inches. The man rushed towards the front of the box, and deponent endeavoured to seize him again, but only caught his clothes, as he was leaping over the railing of the box. The clothes as deponent believes, were torn in this attempt to seize him. As he went over upon the stage, deponent cried out, with a loud voice, "Stop that man!" Deponent then turned to the President; his position was not changed; his head was slightly bent forward, and his eyes were closed,. Deponent saw that he was unconscious , and supposing him mortally wounded , rushed to the door for the purpose of calling medical aid. On reaching the outer door of the passageway, as above described , deponent found it barred by a heavy piece of plank, one end of which was secured in the wall, and the other resting

against the door. It had been so securely fastened , that it required considerable force to remove it. The wedge or bar was about four feet from the floor . Persons upon the outside were beating against the door, for the purpose of entering. Deponent removed the bar, and the door was opened.
Several persons, who represented themselves to be surgeons, were allowed to enter. Deponent saw there Colonel Crawford, and requested him to prevent other persons entering the box. Deponent then returned to the box , and found the surgeons examining the President's person. They had not yet discovered the wound. As soon as it was discovered , it was determined to remove him from the theater. He was carried out, and the deponent then proceeded to assist Mrs. Lincoln, who was intensely excited, to leave the theater. On reaching the head of the stairs, deponent requested Major Potter to aid him in assisting Mrs. Lincoln across the street, to the house to which the President was being conveyed. The wound which had deponent had received was bleeding very profusely , and on reaching the house, feeling very faint from the loss of blood, he seated himself in the hall, and soon after fainted away, and was laid upon the floor. Upon the return of consciousness, deponent was taken in a carriage to his residence. In review of the transaction, it is the confident belief that the time which elapsed between the discharge of the pistol and the time which elapsed between the discharge of the pistol and the time when the assassin leaped from the box, did not exceed thirty seconds. Neither Mrs. Lincoln or Miss Harris had left their seats.

H R Rathbone

Subscribed and sworn before me , this 17th day of April, 1865.

A B Olin

Justice of Supreme Court, District of Columbia."

Apart from the legal dressage of using the third person to help make lying easier, this failed specimen of a human being uses a refinement of language that would make a sailor blush. He is trying so hard to remember his lines about being wounded, that it sounds as if he was the one nearly assassinated and not the President. Seriously, it shows how easy it was to manufacture any kind of un-convincing statement in the ease of knowing he would get the full support of the illuminati, no matter what he said. Except he had to remember a few details of how the door was to be braced and so on. However it was a little more difficult for Clara's statement, as we shall see below.
The description of the imaginary thick plank, wedge or bar, comes straight from the horses mouth and thus kills the myth of the music stand. So where have the historians been searching? Note also the assistance of Major Potter, yet another army officer close at hand. Or, could this be Andrew Potter the Detective, later dispatched to track 'Booth' as far as the mountains of West Virginia and Tennessee and into Oklahoma? Baker often promoted his officers into military rank.
The most striking thing about this false statement is there is no description of the assassin, not even a moustache or the wearing of kid gloves or a hat. Yet he fought hand to hand at close quarters with the man. All we have is a man with a pistol and a knife who shoots the President and whom he thinks the man called out "Freedom". The decision to move the President was made as soon as they had located the wound.
The object of this was to get him out of the theatre right away instead of waiting for a stretcher to take him to hospital. This criminal decision was made under the pretext that he was in safe hands, because the greatest President had two senior army surgeons and a

doctor with him. These were later joined by the Surgeon General Joseph B. Barnes, across the road at Petersen House. And finally his estimation of the duel with 'Booth' took 30 seconds. This was the same exact time quoted by the New York Times at 11.16 pm , exactly one hour after the assassin struck the President, yet Rathbone could never have deliberated or even spoke to the press that night. The back up statement from Clara Harris is even more mysterious, because no doubt she had been in a state of shock and could not remember anything about the assassin, because of the smoke from the pistol. However, her imagination recovered a little when she saw him disappear over the parapet:

District of Columbia, City of Washington, ss.:

"Clara H. Harris, being duly sworn, says that she has read the foregoing affidavit of Major Rathbone, and knows the contents thereof; that she was present at Ford's Theater with the President and Mrs. Lincoln, and Major Rathbone, on the evening of the 14th of April instant; that at the time she heard the discharge of the pistol she was attentively engaged in observing what was transpiring upon the stage, and looking round, she saw Major Rathbone spring from his seat and advance to the opposite side of the box; that she saw him engaged as if in a struggle, with another man, but the smoke which he was enveloped prevented this deponent from seeing distinctly the other man; that the first time she saw him distinctly was when he leaped from the box upon the stage; that she heard Major Rathbone cry out." stop that man!" and this deponent then immediately repeated the cry "Stop that man Won't somebody stop that man?" A moment later someone from the stage asked, "What is it?" or "What is the matter?" and deponent replied, "The President is shot. Very soon after, two persons, one wearing the uniform of a naval surgeon, and the other that of a soldier of the Veteran Reserve Corps, came upon the stage, and the deponent assisted them in climbing up to the box. And this deponent further says, that the facts stated in the foregoing affidavit, so far as the same came to knowledge or notice of this deponent, are accurately stated therein.

Clara H. Harris

Subscribed and sworn before me, this 17th day of April, 1865.

A. B. Olin.

Justice of Supreme Court, District of Columbia.

So, now it is clear why this Judge of the Supreme Court accompanied Clara to the scene of the crime the day before on Easter Sunday. It was to ensure that she would indeed get her facts right. OK, lets be kind to her and say from her first words that she was given the opportunity to see the statement of Major Rathbone beforehand. One then has to assume she was assisted in a manner, not to deviate too much from him. Indeed, like a bird of paradise she imitates his very words but does manage to add another line. Of course allowing for the fact she is a Victorian women she would have been in a state of shock and did not even see the assassin, till he was nearly gone. So that's a time frame of 30 seconds during which the assassin was INVISIBLE. However, she did see her boyfriend immediately spring at this invisible assassin.

Also, it is true that she was intently watching the play and had no idea what was going to happen. Mainly because she was seated on a chair with her back to the spy hole door. However Rathbone was sitting, not in the chair next to her but on the sofa, almost facing that door, and slightly further away out of the firing line. It is also cute that after the assassin has jumped onto the stage with a dirk in hand shouting out in Latin, despite this, two military gentlemen are gently inquiring, up from the same stage -"What is the matter?". Well, talk about a 'Brian Rix' farce it could not be funnier, if it wasn't so wicked. However, in the context of the subdued shot being fired outside the door and therefore no assassin on the stage, this part of the affidavit would be true. Indeed there were two army surgeons there -Dr. Leale and Dr. Sabin Taft. (One should read his father's diary since: The Library of Congress presents these documents as part of the record of the past. These primary historical documents reflect the attitudes, perspectives, and beliefs of different times. The Library of Congress does not endorse the views expressed in these collections, which may contain materials offensive to some readers). This suggests Dr. Taft has provided an alternative account which may ring out the truth. Unfortunately for her she would slowly become undone, and cruelly by her parasitic crustacean of a boyfriend; and she would have been better to have become a heroine, but even so she must have lived in considerable fear as it was.

A good example of the perpetuation of the myth is the book 'Blood on the Moon' by J Steers 2001. The author introduces by saying that he has thoroughly researched from all original sources from various authorities and includes the trial testimonies and the legal authorities involved up to date, quoting University of Ken…., University of…ad nausium.. However his description of events paraphrases much of the old myths, and elaborates further in a typically colourful and overly descriptive manner, with all the gory details. He intimates the exact path of the bullet through Lincolns head with a full description of the organs and tissues it passes through, that would match a modern forensic examination. What use is this if the author can't figure out exactly where the bullet started its journey and the true location of the weapon?

This work is purely for effect and is not bereft of recurring lucid imaginative passages and detailed observations of minutiae, that no one not even 'Booth' himself could have possibly remembered, as if someone was recording his every move. It even matches the Victorian accounts in its artistic licence. It is more like the illuminate's description of the character in a play produced and directed by them. Which indeed it was. If he qualifies or raises questions he explains them in such away as to reinforce the myths. For example he mentions the fact of Frank Ford's statement saying his father had drilled the hole, and that Booth conveniently uses this hole to spy, after barricading the outer door with his even more conveniently placed music stand. He does not explain how this stand happened to be still standing about in a small passage way, as an eye sore for the President's party, except that Booth had put it there earlier; at the same time not having to drill the hole himself because it was already done. He does suggest however, as a counter explanation, that the hole was meant for John F Parker to especially keep an eye on the President. Of course the hole turned out to not to have been used for this purpose since Parker himself disappeared. If anybody, even a child, had been in that passage at the time the assassin could not have carried out the deed. So much for Lieutenant George Ashum, in charge of Ohio's Union Light Guard- Lincoln's home and White

The Beautiful Picture in Mary's home, of three generations, behind which her daughter Anna kept a pin up picture of the handsome and charismatic actor John Wilkes Booth.

House personal guard, that no one could have stopped a man as determined as Booth. It's literally out of the mouths of the illuminati into the mouths of babes and sucklings. The more obvious and truly Machiavellian reason for the hole was to kill the President, since Lincoln's head and shoulders were in direct line of sight. The reason for the bevel in the hole was to clean up the gunpowder and carbon deposits around the hole afterwards. This had to be accomplished fairly soon, probably the following morning when the theatre was closed, after the dying President had been carried over the road to Petersen house.

They said they could not transport him over rough cobbles to a hospital, yet they manoeuvred this giant up and down tall flights of stairs that must have reduced his chances of surviving even more considerably, notwithstanding that the three medical doctors Dr. Leale, Dr. King and Dr. Taft should have known better, except Taft was otherwise innocent and did his best. They could have laid him out on the carpet and wrapped him in the enormous patriotic Union flag, he had been clutching when he was shot, to keep him warm then waited for his condition to stabilise. And there was cushions on the sofa nearby to put under his precious and noble head. By then a stretcher would have arrived to take him to hospital and when nature judged the time was right. In fact it was all a cover, another illusion. They needed to get him out quickly for someone to 'doctor' the spy-hole in the door, before too many genuine people arrived.

It's a strange, mystic and obscure title 'Blood on the Moon' but perhaps not so for the initiated. At first one might guess it could have some strange esoteric connection to the beautiful picture of three generations and the family dog, in a restful garden setting at the home of poor Mary Surratt, which was used as evidence in the trial. This simply because they found a picture of Booth behind this picture, it belonged to Mary's daughter Anna who was a fan of the handsome and popular actor. This, a pin up picture much as a modern teenager has of a pop artist would naturally have. Yet they were used to help condemn an innocent hard working women of kind heart and good character, to suit the swift and ruthless ends of the illuminati. This title is not even that imaginative, as it was used for a tired plot-less western, starring Robert Mitchum in 1948, full of the usual guileless diet of gun slinging violence, and Mitchum was a good actor. It however relates in one of his chapters to remove the 'stain of innocent blood from the land' and not from Mary Surratt's innocent blood.

Mary was the first women to be hung in the US. This was one of the first malignant stains in its recent history and an eternal mark of shame upon this freedom land's all seeing paranoia and its popular claim to be a just and fair democracy. This democracy has always prided that the defendant is innocent until proven guilty. Even today many cover up her innocence because they cannot go back on myths which are ingrained, and have a strange and deep pathological effect on their culture, to such an extent that an expression of true belief antagonises their sub-conscious inability to come to terms with their fundamental feelings of inferiority, relating to the natural truths of the world, which for example their own native Indians were once blessed with in abundance. This is not withstanding their otherwise great and superlative achievements, outside of widespread Republican support for right wing cabals in politics, perhaps materially justifying the devil's alternative at a heavy price.

This psychological scar is particularly reinforced by the illuminati such that the average honest, big hearted and generous American is gradually assimilated through false male bravado, rampant patriotic fervour and fear of demonization, try as he or she might to seek truth and justice for all, or to understand the outside world. This over excites them when they have to pull a trigger on a weapon. (This criticism could equally be applied to some of our own poorly trained special police force, or of the wrong substance). By far the best virtue of the people is that the democratic majority once aroused, will try to oppose and depose flagrant bullies in the hierarchy, when the time is right , and the mood of Congress and the Senate concords with stemming of the miss-use of power by the State, to restore justice. The problem is its often far too late, before sudden episodes of rampant carnage and violent national fratricide on thousands of innocent hard working victims, has been brutally carried out. It was not just Mary Surratt and Mr. Lincoln but Dr. Mudd, Mary Lincoln, Ed Spangler, Samuel Arnold, Boyd and the Unknown Soldier amongst many other unfortunate victims of this atrocious deed and this should be forever remembered, on this occasion. Dr. Mudd himself was a true hero to his calling when imprisoned for four years and pardoned by Johnson, in the disease ravaged Fort Jefferson, took over the work of the prison doctor who had died of disease. They suffered years of agony and Lincoln did not suffer too long, but was raised by these same villains of the illuminatti to immortality, as one of the greatest loved of Presidents of the people, yet severely mocked and hated during his tenure by these same cloned inferiors.

Ironically Lafayette Baker who as head of the NDP, or Baker's 'Secret Service', had arrested the conspirators was foisted on his own petard in the end, and slowly poisoned by arsenic. This was four years later after he had revealed (post-humus but in code and therefore questionable) the numbers of bankers, congressmen, judges and even a state governor loyal to the union and not forgetting elements of the press, involved in this diabolical plot that can have no scruples whatsoever, on an enormous scale inside the government. This all inclusive cabal, were ambitiously involved in this treasonous deed of cowardly murdering the President in cold blood. Baker was their greatest tool, but to give him credit, if true, he later tried to expose them all, but it was too late for him and he had been their knave of diamonds. And the trump of all the suits in these ruthless games was the demonic worker and master craftsman Stanton, the ace of spades. If not the Ace then he was the Joker and irrevocably miss-played.

The unfortunate Confederate soldier was accompanied by another rebel soldier travelling from Southern Maryland whom he had met and helped him. It was reported in the local paper the 'Herald', that these men were captured wearing Confederate uniforms. These were henceforth to be forever personified as Booth and Herold trapped in Garratt's barn with the pre-meditated murder of one by Boston Corbett (himself having the death penalty hanging over him for supposed desertion); under the innocent command of Lieutenant Doherty, but controlled by Conger and Baker working for Lafayette Baker. This is why the 'Booth's' body was hidden away in a top secret burial in a concrete prisoner's grave at the Washington Fort arsenal and why the conspirators were hooded and why the picture of 'Herold's' face on the scaffold was blanked out and later his body dug up and decapitated.

The fact was that Booth never did jump from the balcony and injure his leg was an accidental master stroke of the illuminati. The story of his injured leg would seem to have been 'pre-prepared', and not without good reason, but see below. They were a) to mark him as an easily identifiable assassin and b) to give credit to his 11 foot leap onto the stage. Most people and the world would even come to believe that he caught his foot in the union flag in an impossible fall. Why are people so gullible? And the reason for this line of the play is it would give more credence to the act that the jump was not an illusion, because their was the evidence of a torn flag and a twisted picture of President Washington. Its not difficult to work out this kind of reasoning, if you have a limited number of options, as to how Booth could make his escape that only a madman would even contemplate. However the wanted posters that were issued on the 20th April by Stanton do not mention a lame Booth. They mentioned John H Surratt and Daniel C Harrold and neither did Baker's posters, that do however mention Booth. It would seem from this, the illuminatti did not even 'plan' the lame leg at all. The explanation for this is given elsewhere. And Stanton got Herold's name totally wrong from the start, it should have been David E. Herold.

In fact apart from mentioning John Surratt their was nothing useful on the posters at all, except a warning that if you harboured them you would be hung. The rest of the poster was plastered with dollar signs, a measure of the limits of Stanton's intelligence. The later reason he became lame was that this man could easily be tracked down and captured, even if it happened to be a Confederate soldier returning home, or on the run. There must have been many injured soldiers returning home as the war was only just finished and many skirmishes were still going on, not to mention a selection from a wide choice of candidate prisoners. Indeed according to Guttridge and Neff, a certain Captain James William Boyd of the 6th Tennessee Infantry had appealed yet again for his early release from prison in February 1865, after his wife Caroline had died in December 1863, to look after his seven motherless children in Jackson, Tennessee. His release was granted inside 24 hours after finally writing again, this time to Stanton according to the War department records in the National Archives. Steers however challenges this and suggests it was yet another man called J. Waters Boyd. G&N then counter this by checking this man's grave and say he was killed in a shoot out, in some town. But in any case all of this hypothesis is unnecessary because the lame leg came about as a ruse in the field by a detective decoy called Tyson. Only then did they look for and find a soldier, as it happened with a lame leg, a tattoo and a diary. The JWB of the soldier's tattoo, came from Baker's imagination. Baker himself explains how the Unknown Soldier became injured on his journey in his diary, perhaps adding his own romantic flair to the soldier's account. Thus:

"The diary kept by Booth after the murder of the President, to which I referred in connection with the giving of the personal effects of Booth to the Secretary of War, recorded the adventures of the fugitive; on one of those was the killing of his horse in the tangle of the forest to avoid detection, and then sleeping between the animals legs to get the warmth while it remained in the dead body, during the long hours of the horrible night. With the dawn, he dragged his own painful limbs along the un-trodden path of flight from the apparently slow, but certain, grasp of avenging justice."

Well, indeed it must have been a 'horrible night' for Baker to register it. Thus, Baker tries to imply that the soldier killed his horse to avoid detection but had to then drag his painful limbs along. However the truth is more obvious. The rider must have taken a fall in the forest and injured both himself and the horse, forcing him to kill it for mercy's sake, as is usual for a horse that cannot get back on its feet in the wilderness. It also indicates that this man had a diary and it was returned to Baker intact. So when Baker appeared before the Senate committee and swore that the diary was intact when he handed it over to Stanton, then to whose diary was he referring to?

More tellingly it also gives the lie that explains the truth. Baker has stupidly forgotten about Booth's companion Herold altogether. He himself stated that he teamed up with Herold outside the theatre and they galloped off together past Capitol Hill to Lloyd's and Dr. Mudd's houses, and of course they were caught together at Garratt's farm. Then how come the above account is in the singular? If Booth was with Herold then he wouldn't have had to drag his own painful limbs along that un-trodden path. Herold would have been able to give him a lift on his horse. However, in the context of the soldier's diary it would be true because he was on his own until just before he reached the Rappahannock River, when he met up with another Confederate soldier, whom he had then asked for assistance. Both soldiers were probably from Moseby's command, that had very recently disbanded.

It also contradicts Baker's alternative account that both Booth and Herold together had shot their horses, on the lame excuse that it would help avoid detection. It is unlikely however that this injured man was Captain JW Boyd for the reasons stated elsewhere, apart from the coincidence of him having the same initials as JW Booth. In any case the myth and mystery of Booth's boot does not require another lame man with these initials. Also in the story of Ruggles' own account, he said that the man called 'Boyd' was the comrade of the lame soldier (in the wagon), and the one he first spoke too at the river.

Now, returning to the theatre after this digression, the plan also required an amateur fake actor -an extra or stunt man, dressed as Booth in grey clothes and a dark moustache, sitting conveniently with special permission in the orchestra close to stage where Booth would supposedly land. Colonel Joseph B. Stewart was such a man but being overly tall at 6ft 6ins as it happened, and with an even larger moustache. This would reinforce the image of Booth on stage which, like a movie, can create an illusion of height in the lime-light, particularly in peoples memory of a man suddenly running across the stage in a time frame of a few seconds, as if it was an act in the play. In any case who could possibly remember afterwards that it was not Booth unless they knew him well and had been close up to him. Or worse, who would dare say otherwise. Ned Spangler knew Booth very well and did not recognise this man as Booth, and said no one left by the back door into Baptist Alley . He was the scene shifter and would have been aware of everything that was happening on stage and backstage. He could see from his location (centre back stage) both the front and back stage and the back door and the trap door to the secret passage under the stage.

The only other place apart from the actors main dressing room door , where he could have disappeared from the wings, was into or near the Prompter's box and thence back into the audience or possibly to the secret passage under the stage, if obstructed from Spangler's view, which it wasn't by all accounts. And in his statement, Stewart did in fact return into the theatre within a minute or so of his vivid and overly descriptive account of chasing the assassin into the alley, as 'the horse veered and clattered on the rocks and the assassin above him in the moonlight.' By this time Stewart knew of course the theatre would be in pandemonium, as he described it with fervent detail, when in fact he had simply hidden away beyond the wings in the shadows of the Prompter's box for a few moments, then reappeared (or disappeared) into the final scene of bedlam in the theatre. It is quite possible that his large moustache was a false one so he simply removed it there. This would tally when you consider the number of times the witnesses in the trial were asked. 'Did he have a dark moustache'? That is why Harry Hawk claimed that it was he who said to Jake Ritterspaugh as he rushed onto the stage, ' Don't say which way he went'. This might infer that Harry himself did have an idea of which way he went but it was not out the back door. To have gone out the back door risked compromise since others may have identified him better, especially Ned Spangler. In fact the prosecution made a big thing out of their not be any scenery blocking this exit, as there usually was. This was to imply that Ned had made sure this was clear to allow the assassin to escape more easily. In fact the true reason was the illuminatti wanted scenery and dark shadows there, so that Stuart would have a more convenient place to hide for a few seconds. Even John T Ford stated that this play did not require much scenery and in any case, that passageway was always kept as clear as possible for safe and free access from the dressing room to the stage, and to the exit door.

Rathbone had said, despite his distraction of fighting Booth and being seriously wounded, that it took only 30 seconds for Booth to shoot the President, fight with him and then leap onto the stage. However, Spangler said he saw someone running across the stage immediately after the shot rang out. It would not matter if it was one second or 30seconds however regards to the fictional jump of Booth; but it would have been to the advantage of Stewart to climb onto the stage the very moment he heard the shot go off (he was the closest person to the President's box and only a couple of feet from Booth's supposed landing position). This is because a) it's his cue for action and b) it would be still considered as an act in the play before the alarmed ladies could possibly ring out a scream, from the dying President's side. To have to wait 30 seconds would easily risk some sort of compromise. As McGowan had said their were several interpolations like this in the play . And Walt Whitman had said in his poem not 1/100 of the audience heard the shot. This is another indication that the weapon was not fired inside the open box but outside of it, in the closed vestibule; as Gifford the maintenance manager had himself first stated the very next day. The reason Rathbone quoted 30 seconds was that it was the very minimum he could give, to account for all the action after Booth had shot the President; in order to tie in as close as possible with Stewart (otherwise Booth) running across the stage. In this brief appearance Booth (Stewart) turned to the audience brandishing the knife in the air (supposedly) for all to see crying out the much vaunted line in Latin 'Sic Semper Tyrannis'(supposedly). This also designed, but probably only retrospectively, to be part of the act- a cunning conundrum to keep people guessing, but with the ulterior motive of implicating Booth the actor and his conspirators. However this acting line might not have been quite so true at the time, since the motto for Virginia was only later discovered at Mary Surratt's house. That is unless the illuminati had fore-knowledge of this motto being there, which they could easily have gained from their inside man Louis Weichmann, who lived there.

Navy Bridge that Tyson crossed

Ford Theatre circa 1869

Ford Theatre Location on 10th St.

Chapter 10

Probability versus Illusion

Washington was built on swamp land with radial roads leading out from the capital as designed by the great French architect Pierre Charles L'Enfante, a freemason, in 1791. It is said the design was according to the goat's head (in Greek mythology, a Satyr like Pan, son of Zeus of the pasture, forests and lonely places, chaser of the wood nymph Syrinx, who reached the river and changed into reeds -hence the pipes of Pan), capped by the US five pointed star, of Babylonian origins, of Iraq and Mesopotamia. Its main economy is government and people commute from as far as Baltimore and Richmond and the surrounding counties of Maryland, Virginia and Pennsylvania. Like many US cities, the centres are overwhelmed with neglect, the unnecessary product of infinite waste and consumerism. Washington is particularly bad with a very high crime rate per capita and where over 50% black people live. They give the city its vibrancy and its soul, adding to the otherwise mainly tourist attractions - the Capitol building, Lincoln memorial, Library of Congress, Jefferson monument by the Potomic, Washington monument, Smithsonian Institute and a liberal sprinkling of art galleries and museums.

The navy bridge where Booth supposedly passed confidently using his real name is well east of Arlington, with its tomb of the unknown soldier, lit by its eternal flame and guarded, dedicated by President Kennedy. Then further down past the ugly compact structure of the Pentagon set on a hill. This structure reflects a five pointed star when drawn point to point, and is symbolic of its ancient and mystical origins. Its ugliness is not from its shape designed as a mathematically perfect or pythagorian fortress but its internal prison like windows of shut out light frames. There is however the natural beauty of the Indiana limestone blocks, but too polished with little relief from sharp edges and straight lines with inner endless red brick walls (Rings A to E). And could never match the Egyptian or Greek masters in not using cement or concrete, even this low. It was supposed to be impregnable like the Titanic was unsinkable, a structure designed from arrogance and power, yet vulnerable from the real terror within and not the self created fear of terrorism without. It is a target weakened by the eternal struggle of mini departmental empires and intrigues and the arrogance of the illuminati who control it. Its as if the whole world was assimilated within its most abstract and meaningless values, relating somehow to pseudo abstractions of freedom and democracy, under its total control but flawed with brash doctrines and paranoid agencies forever set against each other. The typical office worker is the epitome of the 60/70's dress code brightly coloured short sleeved shirts and semi-broad ties with navy pressed trousers and shiny shoes- 'civilian uniforms' and the chiefs wear suave suits when out and about. The personnel have been ground down to serve with pseudo and penultimate loyalty and give the impression of total good manners and nice guy image but under neath lurks the ripe seeds of greed and ambition, so as to follow any order or

intrigue in order to survive. In other words a total 'Yes' culture.
In Lincoln's day it would have been the War Department and Stanton would have ruled it like an iron fist and a far more possessive and wilful man than anyone in today's hierarchy. In total, Washington is flawed by the effect of such a massive and overpowering government presence which overwhelms its more natural development, such that it must always have generated conspiracies and intrigues against the obdurate conditioning of central government control. That which is natural and enterprising must come from its poorer but richer in spirit and not unequal citizens, according to Jefferson. In the immortal words of James Dean 'There ain't nobody King around here' except he was referring to Texas. Yet the Washington Post is more reactionary than the New York Times by a long straw. The military presence however does present the brighter side of brass bands playing classical works of the great composers but especially their own Phillip De Sousa, combining patriotic fervour with suburban taste, like the 'Stars and Stripes Forever' and for the Confederates the more poetic and light hearted 'I wish I was in Dixie' played out free and strong to show they are at least united again. It is said that Louis Weichman had once played, as a cadet, for this band or its equivalent. And this down by the bridges of the Potomac with the 'good and sensible Republican Thomas Jefferson' looking down, on an oft sunny Sunday does lift the spirit if you're a deserving patriot, or even if you like good music, they might play you: Sam Cooke, Tina Turner, Josephine Baker, James Brown, Ella Fitzgerald, Paul Robeson, Nina Simone, Ray Charles, Pearl Baily, Duke Ellington, Dionne Warwick, Stevie Wonder, Aretha Franklin, Jackie Wilson, Billie Holiday, Billy Eckstein, Billy Daniels, Marvin Gaye, Ben E. King, Louis Armstrong, Ethel Waters, Jimmie Hendrix, Sarah Vaughan, Nat King Cole, Mahalia Jackson, Luther Van Dross, Dianna Washington, Chuck Berry, Ma Rainey, Smokey Robinson, Mamie Smith, Oscar Peterson, Riley B. King, Gladys Knight, Dianna Ross, Miles Davis, Sonny Rollins, Salena Jones, Charlie Parker, Sisters Sledge, Dizzie Gillespie, Barry White, Champion Jack Dupree. Lester Young, Little Richard, Roberta Flack, Percy Sledge, Whitney Houston, Darlene Love, Count Basie, 'Fats' Domino, Martha Vandella, Jimmy Ruffin, Bob Marley, Totlyn Jackson, Jimmie Cliff, Harry Belafonte or Andy Hamilton (except these last five great artists are from Jamaica) and so many other great, great artists, in which Washington should be a proud, proud Capitol, because Lincoln freed a lot of people. But what are her finest executive and enterprising minds' exact inner ulterior motives today? To spread democracy or chaos around the world. Does she have any intelligent brains left that are not white-washed? Or has she become so banal she can't split the joker anymore? Or is she sinking in her ship of fools? This ship is run by the ZIA and its favourite ports lie in Central and South America particularly Guatemala, Nicaragua, Costa Rica, El Salvador, Honduras, Puerto Rico, Panama, Venezuela, Columbia, Bolivia, Ecuador, Chile, The Guyana's and many other different ports of call in the Caribbean. Excepting for a Lullaby of Paraguay, a Vienna Waltz, a Hungarian or a Polish Rhapsody, or fatefully a Swedish Death Polka. President Regan launched a new

era of Democracy in order to provide economic reform to these poorer but richer in spirit countries. Unfortunately the methods they use, have been counter-productive and now the world can see that the evil empire he was talking about was not Russia, but a figment of his star like and mordant imagination. And Cuba? What will happen to her when Fidel is gone.

True Heroine

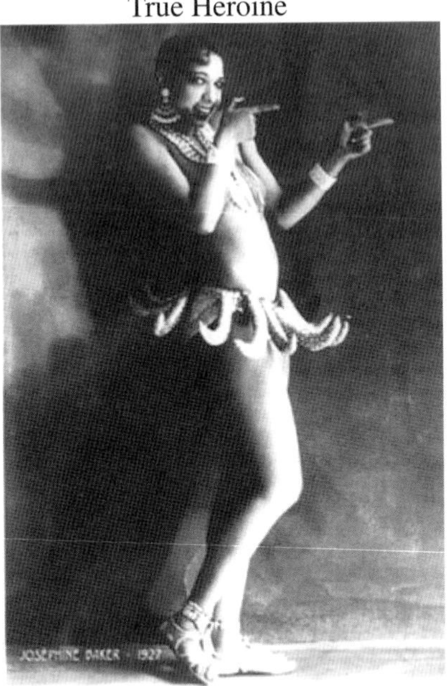

The girl with the golden eye

Will she embrace this new democracy? This gives a backdrop of sorts to an approach, as to the latter day settings of Washington, be it a mere graphical, musical or dare say, political exercise. It is fitting now to try to describe certain insights into the probable roles of the main characters that took place in the events that time in Washington. Firstly we can look at the probable details and then the make up of the main events and character roles by an evaluation of what we know about them; and by applying certain insights that graphically show how the master's of illusion crafted this ill fated scenario, its villains and its heroes and its tragic consequences.

In order to assassinate the President and set it up so that Booth could be framed required detailed planning and help from inside the theatre; someone had to drill the hole and set up the President's chair exactly in line with the hole. This person had therefore to know exactly what he was doing. He also had to come in, or stay over in the theatre late, after every one had gone and bevel this hole to remove the powder stains. He also had to fix the lock on the first box door, that had been locked during the play, by loosening two screws that fixed the clasp. He, because in those days women rarely entered the man's world of murder and mayhem, having relatively little power to abuse. This would then

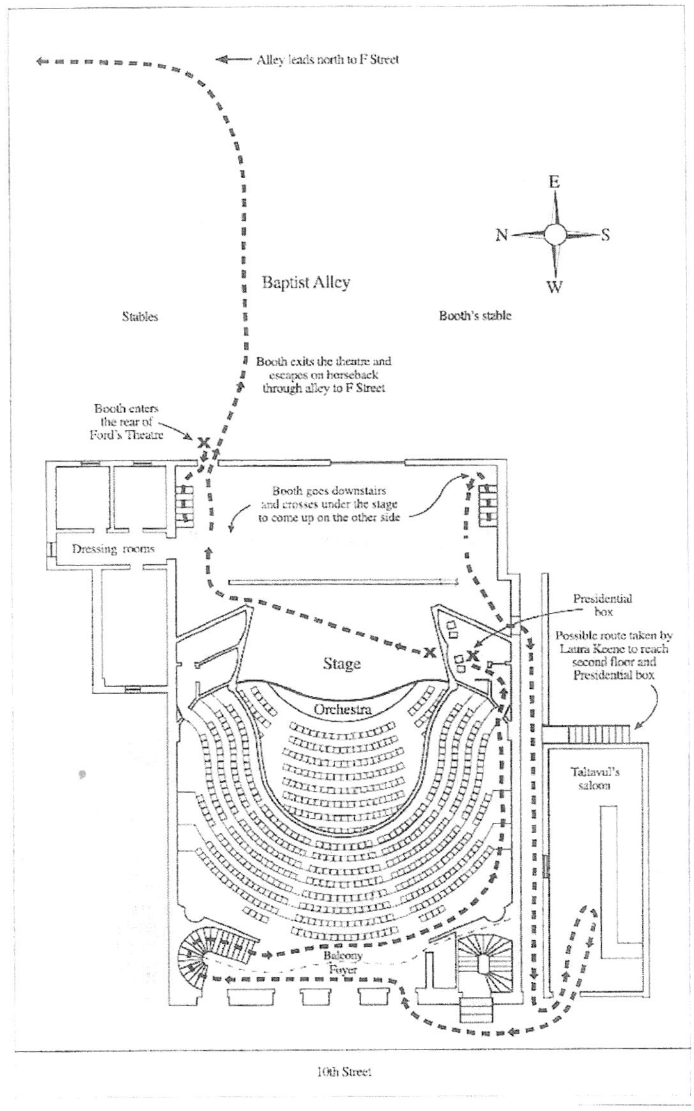

The Supposed Route of Booth to carry out his Mythical Assassination. Note the more direct route Laura Keene took direct to the South Circle make it superficially obvious afterwards, that the assassin had gained entrance into the box directly behind the President, only three to five feet away from this locked door. He also had to make a groove in the wall inside the passage way door to take the imaginary brace. As Gifford and Stanton noted the day after, the carpet was clean of plaster debris and no wood scrapings beneath the hole. Someone had been very thorough in cleaning up the debris. This person therefore had to have easy access to the theatre after hours and probably quite familiar with its layout, for example a member of the staff. This could then account for the all but impossible difficulties of the assassin having to do it. The illuminati had tried to implicate that Spangler was the inside man. However it was Mr. Raybold who had supervised the setting up of the furniture. Thus, in the trial he stated:

"When the partition was taken down, it left a triangular corner, and the rockers went into the corner at the left of the balustrade of the box; they were there out of the way. That was the only reason why I put it there. I had it so placed on two occasions before; last winter a year ago, when Mr. Hackett was playing, when the President was there. The sofa and other parts of the furniture had been used this last season, but up to that night the chair had not."

This was the same man that bust the lock on door 8 with his foot, yet never bothered to inform Mr. Gifford on March 7th, five weeks beforehand. Mary Lincoln was right, that theatre was a dreadful place. He must have been instructed to do this by the illuminati; but someone had also facilitated the bevelling of the hole, the springing of the lock and the gouging of the groove to complete the operation for them afterwards. In fact Raybold (assistant manager of only a year there) had forced and broken the lock on door no. 8, breaking the striker, because the key was not available, when Mr. Merrick and guests who had booked it, came late and the usher had gone. By all accounts he also 'discovered' later for the trial, that the lock to door no.7 had been sprung, but without such force. This was the spy-hole door. Mr. Merrick was cross examined again on this point and Merrick went into great detail to confirm that it was indeed door no. 7 that Raybold had (also?) bust by force on the 7th March. However James O'Brien the usher said:

"Some time before the assassination I noticed that the keeper of box 8 had been wrenched off. I was absent one evening, at home sick, and when I came next I found that the keeper was broken off; but, as the door shut pretty tight, I never thought of speaking about it. You might lock the door, but if you were to shove it, it would come open. The keeper on box No. 7 appeared to be all right; I always locked that box. The door of No. 8 was used when the Presidential party occupied the box; when the party occupying the Presidential box entered, the door was always left open. The door of the passage leading to the two boxes had no lock on it, or fastening of any kind."

So this appears to confirm that door no. 8 was broken at an earlier date. Yet it contradicts Merrick's statement regarding door 7, and that it was in good working after

this date. And it was locked as normal, as it happened and intended to be, for the assassin to carry out his deed. We now see why, it was convenient. It was to make sure no one else would use this door by mistake, but to use the open bust lock door instead, as instructed to the usher. This in turn implies that Merrick's statement that Raybold bust the lock to door 7, on the 7th March, is untrue. (That's why he was cross examined again). And Raybold's statement that he bust door no 8 is true, but he may not have bust it on the 7th March, but it was bust before the assassination.
The most important inference from all of this however might suggest another reason for the Lincoln party arriving late. That is that Ashum was stood down and Rathbone was instructed to pick up the President, to arrive late. The usher, when absent, always kept door 7 locked so the party would have to use the bust door 8, ensuring the spy-hole door was set up for its target. And the President's party would have been in a hurry and theatre lights dimmed with the play in progress. Leaving little time or light for small observations, such as a locked spy hole door. The assassins job was then made simple. All he had to do was enter the passage way close the door after him, then look into the spy hole, to check the President's head and shoulders were not otherwise but in line. Even if he had used a small derringer (but unlikely, for the power required) he could not miss the fatal strike from this range pre-set to be on target. He should have carried two of a matching pair of these pistols in case one did not go off which was common. Later the (fired?) derringer was 'found' inside the box which could easily have been left there by someone else tending the dying President. In fact it was a very unlikely weapon to commit this act, and was just a cover. However it is most likely that the derringer 'found' in the theatre was an illusion, so no one had to carry this weapon. Indeed the brace was an illusion, so why not the derringer? And the gimlet was later 'found' in John Wilke's trunk at the National Hotel by Mr. Bunker, with a 3/16" drill.
The assassin then quickly returned the way he came exiting in a matter of seconds from the theatre the way Laura Keene had entered i.e. down the back steps from the circle to the rear of the Star saloon. The assassin could have been the relief doorman himself since both Forbes and Parker had been stood down for this exact purpose. And after the assassination who would need a secure doorman now that the job was over and done with. The arguable question of using a derringer, a gentleman's pistol is questionable because they have to be muzzle loaded with shot. It was certainly not a gun for an assassin requiring power, speed, accuracy and repeatability. Its only advantage being that it could be carried easily in the pocket or even inside a secret pocket inside a top hat. It really was a gentleman's or lady's gun more of a threat, than a weapon.
The more likely weapon of that period was the black powder .36 calibre colt navy revolver (1861), single action, with a round 7 1/2" long barrel, for accuracy , or the compact version with a 5 1/2" barrel. There were six paper wrapped cartridges (nitrated) and it was a mass produced revolver for the Civil War, firing ball or bullet. It was automatically rammed by a lever mechanism but the percussion caps had to be placed into the cartridge nipples, on loading. It would have required a holster for all practical

purposes. It was a favourite weapon of Union officers. The assassin would have been familiar with this rank and file revolver, able to fire six rounds and much more accurate and powerful. Remember Booth was supposedly planning to kill Grant as well. Why then was he carrying only a single shot derringer and a dirk knife? Its like David against Goliath and Booth was no David, he was an actor not a warrior. And find me a stunt man, with a knife in hand, that can make such a leap onto the stage with or without practice and get caught in the union flag as evidence!!

However, since the hole was estimated by Mr. Plant the cabinet maker witness, we are guided, that the calibre of the bullet would have made at least a 5/16" hole +/- 1/16". That would give us a hole of 0.3125 +/- 0.063". The calibre that would fit this exactly is a .31 Colt matching, for example, the 'Baby Dragoon' hideout revolver (1848) and they were sold in large numbers and later modified into a Colt 34 for the police. Of Colt's belt and holster guns, this 'pocket' revolver is a fair possibility. The gun held 5 shots in its cylinder, and easily recognizable by its lack of a loading lever. Balls were forced into the chambers by dismounting the barrel and cylinder, then using the cylinder base pin as a ramrod. In 1849 the Baby Dragoon was further refined with the addition of a loading lever, similar to those found on the Dragoon and Navy models. The M1849 could be had with barrels of 4", 5" or 6". This however was probably <u>not</u> the weapon because the weight of the ball would be far too low according to the following statistics and discussion.

According to recent surgical reports from New York, the ball made a clean hole through the bone into the brain, with little secondary effects and little temporal cavitations. They imply from this that, it was a ball, and it had no oscillating yaw, otherwise it would not have been a perfect hole. Distortion will occur if the velocity of the bullet is too low and a non-spherical projectile. They estimated the velocity from E=mv^2 (kinetic energy) and found it only had the velocity of an air gun e.g. a 22. If however the velocity was approaching sub-hyper velocity speed, it would be more likely to penetrate the bone. The power of a .22 is unlikely to penetrate the bone at a distance of more than three feet. A low velocity needs a spherical ball to produce a round hole, otherwise the yaw of a bullet would produce a distorted hole. The ball or bullet was flattened on penetrating the bone, with average diameter of 12.7 mm+/-0.5 mm, but distorted, with a flattened length of 7.2 mm.

The weight of the ball is now 6.314 grams, but it lost a bit on impact plus a tiny bit more when they drilled it to mount it in a museum. Then there is corrosion. The corrosion effect would not amount to much more than 5% if that, so we can assume a 10 % or 20% loss at maximum. If the ball was a sphere, we can deduce its diameter from its volume. Thus:

V= 4/3pi R^3.

Also, density of lead = 11.35 g/cm^3.

And mass of ball = 6.314 grams.

So, V= M/D=6.314/11.35=0.556 cc.

So, 4/3piR^3 = 0556 cc.

So, R = 5.09 mm

So, Diameter of ball = 10.18 mm +/- 2 mm.= 0.4" + /- 0.1"

However, the cabinet maker said the spy-hole diameter was about 1/4" to 3/8", so a 0.41" ball would not have passed through it. So let us look at a bullet and not a ball.

In those days tapered bullets were termed conoidal or conical, having a flat bottom tapering to a conical tip like a 'fat' cone shape. Thus if we work on the equation for a cone and a cylinder we can take a look at these two results to find the length of a bullet that would correspond to 5/16" diameter exit hole in the door.
It is in fact 0.9 cm for a cylinder, and 2.7 cm for a cone.

The actual length of the bullet now, is 0.72 cm.

So, indeed the bullet would then approximate more closely to a tapered cylinder.
So the contracting of the bullet would be anywhere between 0.9+ cm flattening to 0.72 cm.

The bullet penetrated the bone, so it could not have flattened that much. This makes it near to, or less than 1 cm. long (originally).This approximates to .39 ins long, approx.= 3/8" long. So the projectile, if conoidal, had a length 3/8" and diameter of near to 0.4 +/- 0.1 ins. The M1861 Navy cap and ball revolver. 850-1000ft/sec muzzle velocity, ball or conoidal bullet, does not quite fit the criteria. The weight of this bullet should be 86 grains = 5.6 grams. However the weights were not always consistent, being hand moulded. And a round ball or bullet of .36 calibre, would have left a 5/16" to 3/8" hole in the door.

There was a .41 Southern Derringer which would fit exactly to the round ball weight of 6.3g but possibly of low velocity ball, but would have made a 3/8" to 7/16" hole in the door, and unlikely to penetrate the bone.

But the best fit would be a .38 calibre bullet = 3/8", that would leave a 3/8"hole in the door and penetrate the bone.
The volume of the bullet assuming a cylinder would be:
PiR^2 times the length(l) and this =M/D=6.314/11.35=0.556cc.
Therefore, l =V/PiR^2 = 0.556/Pi(0.476)^2 = 0.78 cm

Adding 20% for corrosion and splinter loss = 0.94 cm.= 0.368 ins.
This makes it 3/8" long.+/-0.1"

So the bullet was a 38 calibre and 3/8" long, according to the most favourable limits set by the spy-hole and weight of the shot.

In order to create the illusion of Booth entering the Presidential box and escaping over the balcony, the illuminati needed to explain how he could possibly do this without injury, whilst ripping the Union flag and disturbing Washington's picture as mock evidence. It was also convenient in retrospect, as it happened, to have an identifiable lamed man who could be easily caught, by the traditional methods of offering rewards to those providing information leading to the capture of the murderer and to bounty hunters. Thus in allowing the 'assassin' to escape they needed not to have to capture him immediately and bring him to trial, and the lame assassin myth would later be established (as it happened) but of course Booth was not the assassin. And he could also have easily proven that he was in the wrong location, with witnesses, when the shot rang out.

In fact he had probably already left the theatre after giving his horse to Spangler. Or met some people possibly Lucy out front during the intermission and then left, since he was too late and un-interested in the play. In any case John Surratt was the first suspect but he was miles away, on his way to Canada. Thus Booth had time on his side and was not even lame, had money and was well connected. The illuminati had to allow his immediate escape in order to fulfil the myth of the illusionary jump, injury and escape. They were aided in this by de-commissioning the telegraph lines so that no sentry might capture the real Booth by mistake, or too soon, or in the wrong place, or even in Washington. In addition it was mainly to aid the passage over the navy bridge of the two decoys.

When 'Booth' dropped onto the stage, Stewart said he climbed onto the stage immediately and chased after the assassin, across it. However, their were no reports of two people running across the stage at close to the same time. In fact, one witness quoted a two minute delay, and yet another a 3 seconds delay. And Harry Hawk the actor stated it was he who said to Jake Ritterspaugh, the next man on the stage-' Don't say which way he went'. Why did Harry say that, since it was obvious to escape the theatre Booth would have had to exit the nearest door into the alley, where his horse was 'waiting'? And Harry used the singular 'which way he went' but Stewart had supposedly chased Booth 'on his heels' across the stage and into the alley, so it should have been in the plural. Stewart was close on the assassin's heels as he fully described in his statement. If on the other hand Stewart's cue was to run across the stage as soon as the shot rang out, with the shot confusing the audience for a second, as Stewart suddenly stood up and climbed out of the orchestra pit to the same point where Booth supposedly landed, then in effect he would be acting out the role of the assassin following the same path. If he then disappeared behind the wings in the dark somewhere, say in or around the 'Prompters Place' (P.P.), he would have time to remove any false moustache and re-appear in seconds when the theatre was in pandemonium, with many people running onto the stage.

Note, Stewart was 6ft 6inches tall but McGowan with detailed accuracy said the assassin was only 5 feet 9 and a half inches tall. This would not matter for a few

seconds on stage because the difference in height on stage would be just another acting illusion, in anyone's memory after the event, but the close up presence of this giant immediately afterwards might not be mistaken (pre-cognisant of the deed) for a possible unknown assassin, as he might be just another actor. This may be the reason why Harry Hawk made this statement at the trial, since he was too confused to admit it at the time, to show that he was hiding Stewart instead of Booth. Whereas initially Jake, the next person running onto the stage, had attributed this remark to Ned Spangler, when Ned had supposedly struck him in the face. Jake was implying that it was Ned who was protecting the assassin and thus getting him a sentence of 6 years for the trouble.
Captain McGowan had said the assassin was bear headed when he ran across the stage but prior to this he said he was hatted when he entered the passage door, from the circle. Thus, Stewart would be very unlikely to be wearing a hat in order to more accurately mimic Booth, as he was sitting in the orchestra pit and would draw some attention as it would also be strictly against Victorian etiquette, when gentlemen should always remove their hats inside any house or theatre. This also flags the question of what happened to the supposed Booth's hat anyway (which must have supposedly fallen off in the theatre, after the struggle and leaping onto the stage). But, why then was he still wearing it 10 days later when he was met at the Rappahannock River at Port Conway, according to Ruggles, the Confederate officer who helped 'Booth' (really a soldier) cross the river and to travel to Bowling Green. Ruggles described the hat he was wearing as almost identical to McGowan's description. And why was the description of the captured men given in the local newspaper as wearing Confederate uniforms (but according to the New York Times they were dressed in blue attire)? Indeed according to Major Burnett one of the commission's junior Advocates at the trial, the hat was found on the stage with the kid glove.
Thus we can deduce the probability of Booth's later identity to being fictional, if he did lose his hat in the theatre, despite what Ruggles said, and both he and 'Herold' eventually managed to get hold of Confederate uniforms to further disguise themselves. Not an easy task for two civilians on the run, including one with a lame leg. It is more obvious than this what actually happened however as we shall see later, when all the evidence is put together. Illusions are like mirages they can easily fool the fevered mind that is easily tricked, by the glaring and bewitching lime-light of the national press, who were receiving their misinformation directly from the illuminati. Sedation is sublime.
Technically the assassin's real job in fact was easy and he had the back up of the illuminati, including look outs, nevertheless he had to have two qualifications at least 1) be a soldier or ex-policeman or agent familiar with firearms or the firing thereof and 2) be of ruthless character with un-questionable and unthinking loyalty to the illuminati.
In those days these kind of agents were rare and not so well trained as today so he was probably a soldier of the mercenary type and also possibly without any moral uncertainty whatsoever- a hired gun dedicated to the cause. There was such a soldier, an ex prisoner of war, and he was the only one not assigned to a proper regiment at the

time, having being arrested for desertion. He was soon to be specially consigned to Lieutenant Doherty's New York regiment to chase after Booth. It was he who was instructed, when Major Conger had set light to the barn, to shoot the lame soldier, which he did in the back of the neck (like the President was) through a crack in the Garrets barn door, after it was lit up in the dark, by setting the tobacco ablaze. Corbett himself stated with poetic licence that the Lord had inspired him to do it as his patriotic duty. Perhaps the Lord had indeed instructed him in a more direct manner, through the voice of the 'illuminati'.

He later became notorious as 'The man who shot Booth'. He also said that 'Booth' had never uttered a single word before dying, that it was all Victorian 'clap trap'. Later he got another door man's job at the Topeka Kansas Legislature having by then gained the highest of credentials and qualifications in doorman experienced assassinations. He was however an honest and true man and could not abide hypocrisy at any level. But he was also a born survivor and a cracking good soldier. One day he must have got truly bored because he had been more used to killing people as a doorman, through cracks and holes, than having to wet nurse them. This time however he got dangerously angry with other security men at Congress, un-holstering his revolver and began to threaten the sublimely, righteous assembly. The reason they gave was that the lead speaker was reading a prayer in such a manner that it was obvious, in its tone and sarcasm, it was a plain mockery to the Lord. Obviously, Corbett did not like hypocrites. He was sent to an insane asylum in Topeka but eventually, this agile and pro-active cavalry man, easily escaped on a spare horse tethered by the postman, in the square, to Texas or Mexico and was never heard from again. But he made sure he left the horse tethered for its owner just a little way out. Except later his name turned up on the census of those who had died in an extensive bush and forest fire in Minnesota. This end is doubtful because he was a born survivor and it would take more than a fire to catch this able soldier.

Indeed, he was a kind of born again right wing Christian fervent man who had castrated himself years before becoming a hired assassin. His name was cavalryman Corporal Thomas P. Corbett known as 'Boston'. However, a later and very credible Edwardian writer maintained that his name was then John Corbett, having visited his home and spoken to his army pal and having drawn an excellent picture of his dwelling place in Kansas. Another interesting journey in space and time where the hit man has adopted the name of the supposed assassin. Or indeed, was that his original name and the illuminati changed it to Thomas P. whatever P stands for? He must have been extra-special to Doherty because was now a Sergeant and arranged for a secret code word of 'Boston' to be used by his men creeping up in the dark when laying a silent ambush from a 50 yard stake out perimeter around the Garrett's barn.

This man's history was certainly unique. He was born in London, England in 1832 and moved to Troy, New York in 1839 with his family when he was 7 years old. He became a Methodist and worked for a hat manufacturer where he must have been effected by mercury used in the manufacture of felt, a common ailment of these workers. The

Edwardian writer mentioned nothing of this but did say he was a local eccentric character. It is also true that he threatened the local sheriff with a his trusty rifle after upsetting the local kids one day, since they were misbehaving.

Boston's Dug Out-Back To Nature

The disease and its symptoms were highlighted by Louis Carroll in some detail as quoted in reference to the Mad Hatter in Alice in Wonderland. Mercury in fact attacks bones and teeth and the nervous system. He married at barely 20 but tragically lost his wife and child when she was giving birth. He moved to Boston and worked for Morse Jr., a maker of fine hats at Dock Square and Washington St. He later became a more fervent Christian and attended the Methodist prayer meetings daily intending to become a preacher. But he was often tempted by ladies of the night and otherwise experienced much heartache and loneliness.

After one such engagement on July 16th, 1858 he decided to finish with temptation and returned to his bed and castrated himself, with a pair of scissors and a bible at hand. The doctor (Dr. Zabdiel Boylston Adams) found him bleeding badly, beside him the scissors and the bible. This was after he had calmly gone out for a walk and ate dinner, thinking no more of it and would never be so weak as to go to a saw-bones. Dr. R.M. Hodges a local surgeon performed legation surgery to heal the wounds. Then he was sent to Massachusetts General Hospital for a month. Such a baptism of fire was bound to profoundly effect the life of this strong willed and serious young man from thenceforth. He joined a volunteer regiment the 12th New York militia in the Union army and became a truly dedicated and good soldier. On June 24th 1864 his detachment was captured by Mosby's Partition Rangers and he spent several months in Andersonville prison in Georgia, one of the Confederate prisons with the highest death rate from malnutrition and disease of the civil war. Moseby's Rangers was the same outfit that Jett, Ruggles and Bainbridge had belonged to. And indeed it was probably the same one the two fugitive Confederate soldiers belonged to, considering the same locality and coincidental time events at the Rappahannock River. The command must have been disbanded, since the war was over and all skirmishes were drawing to a close.

After attempting to escape Andersonville, this indomitable great survivor was considered to be of value to someone so he was eventually exchanged and returned to the 12th NY cavalry. He later told his regimental commander not to swear against the Lord and this led him into direct conflict with the authorities, who put him on a charge of insubordination and sent him to the guardhouse with his bible. Later he went absent without leave, insisting his time was up if it included his time as a prisoner of war. They had other ideas, put him on trial and sentenced him to death since the war was still on and they implied it was desertion. However it is at this stage where we have an interesting event. He was suddenly pardoned and officially transferred to the 16th New York Cavalry by April 1865 about the time of Lincoln's assassination, since they had found a much better use for him.

It was company L detachment that corporal Boston joined and he was its only designated acting member on this occasion, since both the H and L companies were sent to capture 'Booth'. Thus H company 25 men plus L detachment 1 man plus officer in charge Lt. Edward P. Doherty plus two members of the NDP, Lieutenant (or Major?) Conger and officer Luther Baker cousin to Colonel Lafayette Baker were detailed to rendevous with an informer at Port Royal on the Rappahannock River, Virginia. There is good evidence however that Corbett was already attached to the 16th NY Cavalry on the 14th April and stationed near to Washington on guard duties, because we have Cavalryman Millington's account. Thus:

"On the morning of April 15, 1865, I was on guard, when news came that President Lincoln had been shot at Ford's theater." wrote Millington. "We were ordered to form part of a cordon to prevent the assassin from escaping. Our company was deployed through the brush. It was a chilly day and a cold rain was falling. A few days later we were ordered to Washington, where we served as an escort at Lincoln's funeral. We were held in Washington, quartered in the J street barracks. On April 24 I returned from a patrol and put my horse into the stable, leaving him saddled, and fed him and went to the barracks to get something to eat. Before I had finished eating, "boots and saddles" was sounded and there was a rush to the stables. We were ordered to fall in as fast as we led out, disregarding company formation.

As my horse was already saddled, I slipped on his bridle, led him out of the stable and mounted. I was next on the left of the sergeant. We were ordered to count off in fours. We went to Pennsylvania avenue and out 14th street about opposite the old Willard hotel. We halted just in front of the office of Colonel Baker, chief of government detectives and scouts. Our lieutenant, Dougherty, reported, and in a few moments he and two detectives, Lieutenants Conger and Baker, came out and mounted, and the order to march was given. We rode to the wharf of the navy yard, on the east branch of the Potomac, or the Anacostia River, where we took the steamer John S. Ide and started down the Potomac."

Prior to this promotion Corbett had been clearly out of line with authority and a bad example to the men, but was an excellent soldier and good with weapons, could not his loyalty have been gained by giving him a very special job for which there must have been very few candidates. The illuminati had very good bargaining powers ie death by hanging or firing squad or alternatively carry out a special assignment. What is now conjecture but highly possible is that Corbett had agreed to assassinate someone as his first task, to prevent being hung for desertion. He had all the qualifications and a highly experienced soldier who was a crack sniper. (And who is to say he would certainly know who he was killing through a locked spy-hole door?). Indeed in later years in Kansas he impressed the locals at his skills in shooting hawks and even smaller birds, such as crows in full flight. The motivation is clear and the fact is he was a highly specialised loose cannon who did not fit the mould as an average soldier and was inspired by the Lord.

Boston-Forever Amber and his trusty Lieutenant the Commendable Doherty

Another interesting observation which was the statement of Parker to Mary Lincoln when he said 'Would I stoop so low' . (To have to spy through the hole at 3 feet high.) Corbett was only just over 5 feet tall and did not need to stoop so low. Finally, there is another clue to the assassin's identity which is worth mentioning. Baker printed a lot of letters from the public after the assassination and to quote this one in particular because it's a cipher letter, the only one in his book, and the sender seems to have a nick name for the assassin. Thus:

Translation of the Cipher Letter. Washington, April 15th 1865.

Dear John,

I am happy to inform you that Pet. has done his work well. He is safe and Old Abe is in hell. Now, sir, all eyes are on you-you must bring Sherman. Grant is in the hands of Old Gray ere this. Red Shoes showed lack of nerve in this Seward's case, but fell back in good order. Johnson must come, Old Crook has him in charge. Mind well that brother's oath and you will have no difficulty; all will be safe, and enjoy the fruit of our labours. We had a large meeting last night - all were bent on carrying out the programme to the letter. The rails are set for safe exit. Old-always behind- lost the pass at City Point. Now, I say again, the lives of our brave officers, and the life of the South, depend on the carrying of this programme into effect. No. 2 will give you this. It is ordered no more letters shall be sent by mail. When you write sign no real name, and send by some of our friends who are coming home. We want you to write us how the news was received there. We received encouragement from all quarters. I hope there will be getting no weak in the knees. I was in Baltimore yesterday. Pet. has not got there yet. Your folks are well, and have heard from you. Don't loose your nerve.

O.B. No. Five.

The outstanding remark in this cipher is the phrase 'getting no weak in the knees' since this is one of Baker's own favourite expressions that you will see quite often in his literature. However it is probably a coded message from one of his agents in Washington. In fact it sounds like this 'agent,' is in fact a key man in the plot.

Now please look at the questions this coded letter might raise: Is Baker making out that he has intercepted a Confederate letter to John (Wilkes Booth or Surratt) from a confederate agent possibly with the initials O.B. , Agent No. 5 ? However there are certain phrases which characterise Baker himself , it has his common touch. E.g. 'no getting weak in the knees,' and 'lack of nerve' and again the overall brevity of expression, as expected of Baker, or his agents. This then might be another effort of Baker to implicate Booth in a coded message and further to implicate that there was a bigger plot involving the Confederacy and Richmond. The main thing however is the implication of a real assassin nicknamed Pet.. Why Pet. ? Since it was supposedly Booth who pulled the trigger. Could it be that Baker was stupidly trying to give us the real hit man? Now if you take the name Thomas P. Corbett you can get Pet. out of it, either from bett or from P.ett by removing or rearranging nulls to make the phonetic sound. An enlightened Edwardian writer, of considerable authenticity, said that Corbett called himself John Corbett, after the Victorian era, circa 1903, when he was living in a dug out in Kansas. Or the dot in Pet. might indicate a missing letter. In Morse code a dot would signify e, so that would make it Pete. Or indeed by taking his Christian initials reversed P.T. = Pet. There is no available knowledge to indicate the Christian name of P. , it could have always been a cover. Admittedly, it is thin ground and would need further research. And Corbett may well have remained in Washington with the regiment, who had also been assigned to funeral duties for the President. However, Corbett was the only single member of 'L' company under Doherty and may have at further special duties to carry out in Baltimore. Possibly to hunt again for Booth since this used to be his home at Belair. But then the letter is full of double meanings. I'm sure Edgar Allen Poe could solve it, but alas he's gone from us, but thankfully his poetry and fiction has not. Non the less, this may well have been a genuine coded letter from an agent in Washington to Baker in New York, to say the deed was done and the assassin was safe, at the same time implicating Booth or Surratt, as a cover. In fact Union ciphers like this always used nulls and covers. And the standard covers were always the addressee and the addresser. So in this case Dear John and No. 5 are covers and therefore null. So John does not mean JWB, or John Surratt, it's just a cover.

'Old Crook' or 'Old Gray' might refer to Stanton. Indeed 'Old Crook has Johnson in charge' might refer to Stanton having Andrew Johnson in hand, now that Abe was gone whom he couldn't really control properly, but see below. 'Red Shoes' might refer to an even more sinister aspect of the plot. That is they were planning to do away with Seward that night, but Red Shoes bottled out. Nevertheless, Robinson still got 5000 dollars out of it, when Grant became President. This was to insure his secrecy, no doubt, under a promise that he would have to wait over four years, till Johnson was out and the Republican, Grant, back in. In fact nick-names like these were code names for people or places. Thus, Adam was a code name for General Henry Wager Halleck (he was at Peterson House, where Lincoln died). Arabia was General Don Carlos Buell. Lincoln was Louisville, Kentucky and so on. And this type of cipher was used by the Union, that was never cracked by the Confederates, and they would have had a totally different code system. And Pet. was therefore the Union code name for the assassin. More to the point the cipher logically gives John as a cover for the assassin, who's real code name is Pet.. Also, why ask the agent not to use a real name since the sender did, as it was a standard cover which all agents would be clued up on. However, this letter, was supposedly not sent into the NDP, it was 'discovered' floating in the wet somewhere and 'turned in' to the prosecution for the trial. Or, if it had been, then this is where the prosecution got their incriminating evidence, from Baker. In fact the defence team had a devil of a job in just trying to prove that although the letter was very incriminating, it should not be considered damning evidence because it was not found in Payne's possession, although he had probably been digging the ditch in the rain, as it was wet that Easter. After considerable debate was allowed, Judge Holt, in his ultimate and all seeing twisted wisdom, finally over ruled the Defence Council. So it was yet another nail in young Payne's coffin. Even so their was much talk about "Red Shoes" being Herold; and "Old Crook" and "Pet". But the assassin was referred to as "Pet" and not "Pet.". This subtle difference would have been most important, if trying to crack the assassins real name from his code name. Perhaps the reason it had been found all wet, was that Payne had been all wet, since he was plastered in mud from 'disguising himself' before digging a ditch, but then it should also have been a little dirty as well. There seems to be a reference to the two Union Generals Sherman and Grant but it is difficult to work out in what context. We do know however that Grant was originally 'on 'Booth's list' for assassination but at the last minute Grant was ordered not to attend the theatre, intentionally to suit the arrangements. In any case the set up in the theatre was for a single fixed target and no more. However they should have code names so perhaps this is odd, yet two famous Generals mentioned together cannot be by chance. And Old Crook might also refer to Abe's private police bodyguard- Crooke that he 'seemingly favoured' and was in charge that evening till Parker took over. City Point was a big port on the River James Estuary and was occupied by Grant in the siege of Petersburg (1864-65) and the Union, built a big railway depot there. Now, it is a suburb of Hopewell in Prince George County. And General Grant's authorisation was used to issue passes to Union citizens when they travelled south. Even Wilkes Booth had one to travel freely as an actor, according to his beloved sister Asia. Finally the use of the words- 'brother's oath' might suggest there is an implied connection to a secret society.

A note purely of abstract interest: The Union Generals, Crook and Kelly, were easily captured whilst sleeping in a hotel, in Cumberland by a small band of Confederates under Lieutennant Mc Neil and taken back over 60 miles to Richmond. There is probably no connection here with 'Old Crook' however.

So, in effect the plan for the deed was basically very simple and can be outlined in a few steps, or a dirty dozen. This does not mean that Lee Marvin, Clint Walker, Charles Bronson, Ernest Borgnine, George Kennedy, Tele Savales, Donald Southerland, Trini Lopez, Jim Brown, John Cassavetes, Al Mancini and Tom Busby were involved in the plot however. Thus:

1) Set it up in the Ford Theatre whereby Booth was a frequent visitor and knowing he had planned to kidnap the President.

2) Give orders to the management as to the seating and security arrangements including a 3 foot high, dead centre 3/16" spy hole, for keeping an eye on the President.

3) Arrange the timing such that it was coincidental with maximum noise level from the audience. That is at 10.15 pm.

4) Ensure Grant would not be there and substitute Rathbone instead.

5) Incorporate a stunt man who was a gentleman somewhat similar to Booth having a dark moustache (or a false one), and have him located as close as possible to the stage below the President's box.

6) This man's job would be simple enough. All he had to do was climb onto the stage immediately the muffled shot rang out. Then run across the stage through the wings and hide for a few seconds until pandemonium broke out. Then he would have to go straight to the police station and make out the pre-planned statement.

7) Order Parker and Forbes to be stood down at the intermission and substitute the assassin as the replacement doorman.

8) The dummy run and navy bridge security arrangements had already been set up, and of course the cutting of communications.

9) Variations on a theme would come into play naturally. For example 'Booth's lameness' came from Tyson, in order to gain access to Dr. Mudd's home at four in the morning. From this also, the catching of 'Booth's' leg, the torn Union flag and the skew-wiff Washington would provide 'later' mock evidence.

10) Inform the press one hour after the event with just the basic details. A young man takes thirty seconds to shoot the President with a derringer then escapes, brandishing a dirk knife, and dropping a kid glove on the stage.

11) Ensure arrangements are made early Saturday morning to scrape the gun shot deposits from the spy-hole by scraping out a bevel. Also make a simple groove in the wall plaster inside the circle door to the vestuble. And clean up the debris from the carpet. And possibly loosen two screws in the spy-door lock.

12) The assassins job was then technically easy. He would have taken easily less than a minute to enter and close the circle door, stoop and look through the spy hole door for his target in position, draw level his revolver to the hole, fire….then immediately vacate his post down the side stairs leading to the back of the Star saloon. Then go home.

Chapter 11

The Real Scenario

The scene is set at the intermission of the play. Parker and Forbes have been stood down and Captain McGowan and Colonel Crawford are stationed five feet away from the door where the new doorman is positioned sitting at seat 300 in the circle by the passageway entrance door. Army doctor Charles Leale is also seated in the circle not too far from McGowan and also keeps an eye on this door. The doorman's duties allow him free entry to the passage and to keep an eye on the President through the locked spy hole door to the box (the first of the box entrance doors), as previously arranged under the security measures already in place, by which Parker was supposed to be stationed there all the time. The acting doorman receives a letter addressed to General Grant from a visitor who stoops down to him to give it to him then retires, as observed by Captain McGowan around 10 pm. This letter is coded for him and he opens it to read his final instructions that all is in place, confirming the exact time for him go ahead with the assassination. Then at the right time he enters the vestibule closing the circle door behind him. He is armed with a Colt revolver in its holster, and possibly in uniform and at the precise time of 10.15 pm, stationed at Parker's post he spies the President in position, then levels his revolver through the spy hole and fires one lethal shot.

Rathbone is sitting on the sofa against the wall furthest from this door and behind Clara, and so half facing it and anticipating it, from his very position and ready for the strike. Clara is sitting on one of the two chairs facing the stage and so is not prepared for the deed. This exact time coincides with maximum laughter in the show. The assassin then immediately retires via the same passage way door and out of the circle via the south side circle door down the steps to the rear of the Star saloon and disappears.

As soon as the shot goes off Colonel Stewart immediately climbs onto the left-stage from his seat in the orchestra, causing another distraction. He then runs across the stage and disappears into the wings going into the right stage corner by the Prompter's box. As he charges through the wings he collides with Withers the band leader on his way back to the orchestra, and knocks him flying out of the way, mainly due to Stewart's enormous size. Withers in turn falls against the wings and bumps into Miss Jenny Gourlay another actress, who is startled. Stewart remains in the shadows of the Prompter's box and quickly removes his false moustache (if at all, he conveniently needed to use one); and then after waiting only seconds for pandemonium to break out, he then observes the scene. Then knowing the President is shot, he leaves for the police station and makes his statement describing how he chased Booth into the alley, and nearly caught the reigns of Booth's horse, flowered with many extra details. He also includes the line of Ed Spangler behaving oddly on stage whilst everyone else were excited or in distress. The recently qualified army doctor Charles Leal (who had majored in gun shot wounds at Bellevue Hospital Medical College) probably in uniform and Dr. Albert Freeman Africanus King (1841- 1941- English born gynaecologist & paediatrician from Virginia) together with Dr. Charles Sabin Taft (army surgeon, son of Horatio Nelson Taft) attend the dying President. Leale pokes his finger into the wound intending to locate and possibly withdraw the bullet. They also administer resuscitation by chest and arm massage. King and Taft manipulate the president's arms to stimulate his heart.

Then Laura Keen arrives from the stage via the under stage route and part of the route of the assassin i.e. the short cut to the circle from the back of the Star saloon using the fire exit staircase. It is said that this famous and tragic actress with a heart as big as the moon, cradles her dear President's head into her lap to give him the love he might still be gratefully conscious of, since his dearest, gracious Mary is too overcome with grief and shock. As soon as they have located the projectile in the President's brain, the doctors decide to remove the President manually from the theatre down its stairways into the street for propriety reasons. The Victorians were very strict in the realms of correctness of behaviour. King takes hold of Lincoln's left shoulder to rest it for the journey because it's immobile. They then look perchance to a suitable house over the road which is a boarding house (Petersen House-of Sweden) with yet another big flight of steps to negotiate. For some reason they could not leave him in the theatre safely and without having a stretcher or waiting for him to be taken to hospital. They make this incredible decision to manhandle a critically wounded giant over this fearsome obstacle course which certainly reduced his chances of recovery. Even this is not enough when the Surgeon General, Joseph K. Barnes arrives, he inserts a metal or porcelain rod (or neotube) into his head to retrieve the bullet which certainly contributes to his early death. This inspired blunder by a rusty old surgeon was actually fortunate for the President otherwise had he recovered he would have been deaf, dumb and blind for life. They place him on a vacant lodger's double bed diagonally, after failing to remove the headboard and undress him. They then smother his naked body with mustard patches with little concern for his dignity . Stanton arrives shortly and insists that the grief stricken Mary be relocated to another room with her son Robert to comfort her; whilst they keep their macabre vigil over him waiting for his death at 7.22 am when with ironic candour and poetic licence Stanton mouths ' Now the ages have him'.

It is also very sad that Mr. Petersen, who had so gratefully given refuge to the dying President, must have been so effected or otherwise involved with the event, that may have later precipitated his suicide on the grounds of the Smithsonian Institute. Was this his final expression of patriotism or was he simply in the wrong place at the wrong time? Or did he decide it was fitting to take his poison draught sitting on a bench on their grounds? At the same time Stanton's recording secretary, is taking all information down from Rathbone and all these witnesses as to what had happened together with a viable description of the assassin. Stanton then does not raise an immediate search for the murderer but instead has already arranged for the telegraph communications to be cut to allow them (the decoys) to escape the city.

The Talented Laura Keene Rushed To The Dying President's Side. Meanwhile the brave Major Rathbone has momentarily fainted but soon recovers from supposed loss of blood

Chapter 12

Pandemonium and More Illusions.

And what did the audience see and hear and how did they react? Many did not distinctly hear the subdued shot ring out but were immediately distracted on stage, by seeing a tall grey suited man with black hair and a moustache run across the stage. They must have all thought in that instant it was a new version of the play, even if some had noticed Stewart's position when climbing from the darkened orchestra pit onto the bright stage. Remember they were still not aware that Lincoln had been shot, so would not connect him immediately with the deed of assassination. The mind plays tricks when it is surprised such that it then has to depend on the more vaguer sense of memory after the event, distorted by time, to explain what actually happened. Certainly no one saw the man jump from the President's box but afterwards they must have assumed they missed it, because it was only a tiny instant of time. They certainly would remember the bare-headed gentleman with a big black moustache running across the stage.
Taltavul the restaurant owner described his version of the truth however, from the VIP box exactly opposite the President, except no one had booked any other box that night. He had specially attended that night to see his 'favourite', General Grant. He was able to know exactly how the President was shot because he saw the flash of the pistol go off in the box, and filled in all the other details as per Rathbone's account. The problem with this is that he himself admitted in court that Gifford had challenged him on this. He stated that Gifford the theatre manager had said to him the very next day,

"How the hell did you see the flash when the pistol was fired from outside the box".

If he was lying to get Gifford into trouble then he was also giving the game away in the very same breath. An assistant stage hand called Jake Ritterspaugh was probably the 'second' to rush onto the stage, in the belated pursuit of 'Booth', but he stated that Ed Spangler had blocked his path, first by hitting him in the face, and then by shouting at him,

"Don't say which way he went."

seemingly referring to an assassin. However in a later statement by Harry Hawk, the actor on stage, he said it was he who made this remark. But either way it should have been '........which way they went' since Stewart stated he was close on the heels of 'Booth' all the way out to the back door and into the alley. Ed Spangler in his own private statement did not mention this supposed variation of the event, but did note that no one went out the back door, and that he did not recognise the man who ran across the stage, immediately after the shot rang out. And he knew Booth very well.

However, Mr. Sleichmann the assistant Prompts man saw this man hovering in the darkened corner by the Prompter's box, and he assumed it was Booth in his statement. So, it seemed the assassin and Stewart had suddenly become completely separated by then. This might mean that the assassin was still in the corner and Stewart had gone out the back door. However if Mr. Sleichmann was mistaken in his identity of 'Booth' then it was Stewart he saw in the corner and Booth had supposedly gone out the back door. Either way Stewart had lost the trail of Booth, according to Sleichmann, and could not have chased after him outside, when Booth by then was on his horse, according to Stewart. This is all quite apart from the supposed fact that whilst Stewart was chasing Booth across the stage and through the wings to the back door; he alerted everyone by shouting out 'Stop that man…Stop that man…Stop that man' he was that close to him, both in position and in his grammar of the present tense. Despite his alleged desperate shouts Stewart was not helped by anyone, because the 'lame Booth' was so very fast and carried a 'dirk knife,' and had even cut at Withers (who can fiddle many an old tune) in his path to make his exit through the wings, to the back door.

1822- 1885
General Ulysses S. Grant
Served two terms as President 1869-1877

Chapter 13

The Great Escape

The role of young and enterprising Joseph Burroughs, or John 'Peanuts', the stable boy come peanut seller and theatre assistant was quite important. He had to wait outside with Booths horse for a good ¾ hour and sat on a box which was duly observed by a young lady witness. He stated that when 'Booth' came out he struck him on the head with the butt of his knife and jumped on the horse. He therefore must have offered some resistance to warrant Booth's forceful action, but why? Even Mr. Pumphries the owner of the horse had a role to play because he said he never recovered his one eyed bright bay mare. It is unlikely that Booth ever did return for his horse since he was not planning on any kind of horse ride that night, he had put it to bed. If Booth was totally innocent of the murder and had stayed on till the final act he would have had several choices. 1) realised his danger and got on a fast train 2) disappeared on foot, taken a cab, possibly with someone else or 3) stood his ground. There is a fourth possibility however and that is despite all the witnesses, Booth was not inside the theatre at all, that night. The only witness that we can trust on this one however would be Spangler, and he said he had gone for a drink with him at 6.30 pm and took his horse at 9.30 pm. However, Booth could have left the theatre then, without attending the play at all.
This is where the real mystery begins. Item 3) can be discounted because a) he was not apprehended and b) if he was in with the illuminati he still had to disappear, which is the same as category 1) or 2). It was reported that his girlfriend Lucy Hale had been seen with him at the theatre and she was the daughter of Senator Hale. He may have left with her earlier and found refuge in Washington for a while, till the heat was off.
In Laffeyette Baker's book ' The United States Secret Service' he states that the lines were cut 15 minutes after the assassination. Yet he also took pains to say that he thought 'Booth' had played the double bluff game, unbelievably. That is, he fooled the sentry at Anacostia by giving his real name, gambling on the sentry thinking it to be one of Booth's friends, thus providing a false lead. Whatever, it all points to Booth being allowed to escape. But did he know he was being allowed free passage? If we allow item 2) then surely Booth realistically would not have risked giving his real name. 'Herold' was supposed to have crossed the same bridge giving a false name but it shouldn't have mattered either way since the lines were cut, but Herold was not to know it. And in any case, this is all hypothetical play.
Herold was not on the run at all, from trying to kill Seward, since it was just another creative illusion of the illuminati. He may have already shipped his passage to Spain as he had said to his friends three weeks earlier. There is good suggestive evidence of this from Baker himself as you will see below. But there is a big twist in this variation as you will also see later. This more than reinforces the idea, already proven, that neither did the real Booth cross this bridge, as will be also be shown below. In fact you will see

later, that it was two different people who crossed this bridge. Now, Payne who was apprehended, had the misfortune to be boarding at Mary Surratt's house and at her request was digging a ditch for her at the moment the NDP arrived, as informed by Weichmann. And we have Baker's account here, in his usual gothic flair, to suggest how he escaped before they captured him. Thus:

"Payne was spilling blood in Mr. Seward's house, from threshold to sick chamber. Payne having as he thought, made an end of Mr. Seward, which would have been the case but for Mr. Robinson, the nurse, mounted his horse, and attempted to find Booth. But the town was in alarm, and he galloped at once for the open country, taking, as he imagined, the proper road for the East Branch. He rode at a killing pace to Port Lincoln, his horse threw him headlong. Afoot and bewildered, he resolved to return to the city, whose lights he could plainly see; but before doing so he concealed himself some time, and made some almost absurd efforts to disguise himself. Cutting a cross section from the woolen undershirt which covered his muscular arm , he made a rude cap of it, and threw away his bloody coat. This has since been found in the woods, and blood also has been found on his bosom and sleeves. He also spattered himself plentifully with mud and clay, and taking an abandoned pick from the deserted entrenchments near by, he struck out at once for Washington. By the providence which always attends murder, he reached Mrs. Surratt's door just as the officers of the Government were arresting her. They seized Payne at once, who had an awkward lie to urge in his defence- that he had come there to dig a trench. That night he dug a trench deep and broad enough for them both to lie forever. They washed his hands, and found them soft and womanish; his pockets contained tooth and nail-brushes, and a delicate pocket-knife. All this apparel consorted ill with his assumed character".

This kit was standard army issue to officers and enlisted men in those days and Payne was an ex-rebel soldier. For example in WW1 a northern officer's toilet kit consisted of: basin ; hair brush; nail brush; tooth brush; bucket; comb; housewife; nail file; soap; soap-box; shaving outfit; tooth powder; talcum powder; face towels; bath; mirror.. And that was just a small fraction of their total kit- its no wonder the North needed to conquer the 'World'. And note the delayed reaction of the pro-active agent 'Red Shoes'. And then Baker continues:

"Coarse and hard, and calm, Mrs. Surratt shut up her house after the murder, and waited with her daughters till the officers came. She was imperturbable, and rebuked her girls for weeping, and would have gone to jail like a statue, but that in her extremity Payne knocked at her door. He had come he said to dig a ditch for Mrs. Surratt, whom he very well knew. But Mrs. Surratt protested that she had never seen the man at tall, and had no ditch to clean. Her effrontery stamps her as worthy of companionship of Booth. Payne has been identified by a lodger of Mrs. Surratt's has having twice visited the house, under the name of Wood."

Of course, the artful lodger was Louis Weichmann. Here we see another example of Baker's handiwork in perversion. He could literally invent stories and twist everything around. Thus Payne had disguised Seward's 'spilt blood' by rubbing himself down in mud and picking up a pick axe, when in fact he was muddy from digging a ditch for Mrs. Surratt. It is beyond evil! But where or how did Booth disappear? He had money and connections and could well have fled to Canada but John Surratt never disclosed seeing him again, but then why should he because it wouldn't help Booth. There was much talk in Baker's book from people writing in to Baker that Booth went underground in Washington or was disguising as a women (well he was a refined, good looking actor). The alternative, which is definitely not credible, is that he was in with the illuminati according to the '18' missing pages' of his diary, that were ripped out by Baker, because the diary was a forgery.

It is also not so strange that Baker should try to incriminate Stanton later in a coded message, probably to exonerate himself and to state the pages were destroyed by, or in the hands of Stanton. But this decoded message is highly questionable. Booth was not sure, by all accounts, that Lincoln would be at the theatre till the last day (in fact at midday) and would have had to make fast plans to change his schedule from kidnap to assassination of Lincoln, Johnson, Seward and Grant. He certainly would not start writing '18' pages of his assassination plans in any diary and then writing it out again in a letter to John Mathews for the press, telling them of his last minute change to assassination of nearly 'half the cabinet' plus General Grant. On top of this he left some private letters behind because we know he was never captured or killed at all. Indeed this was his finest hour, if hollow victory, and the illuminati intended it so and were probably always scared that Booth would resurrect himself. He didn't, of course, because the risk was too great now that Lincoln was dead. He was the one who intended to kidnap him even though he might possibly have proved that he was not the assassin. He still chanced being murdered by the illuminati before the trial, as indeed happened to the Confederate soldier.

In addition they couldn't capture or kill him in the act of killing Lincoln, because they had to frame someone first to carry out the act , and then let him escape on his horse. Instead, they had to capture someone and kill him much later. And Stanton and Baker between them still hadn't fully decided whether it was Booth or Surratt, at the time.

So Booth had just enough time to make his own disappearance, and then since they couldn't catch him, Baker used the more convenient method of catching some one else and framing them instead. In this case they got away with murdering a soldier but somehow, not his less famous friend, until they hung him as Herold. Booth also had the advantage of not having a lamed leg, if he should go to trial, except the myth had not yet been generated that Booth had bust his leg in the fictional jump. The man so called 'Herold' had surrendered to Lieutenant Doherty at Garrett's barn, who duly brought him back alive. If somehow his lame friend had not resisted arrest, it would have been much more difficult for them to take him to trial and having to impersonate him as the much more famous Booth to the world, thus risking infamy and stupidity. Not, that the latter ever bothered the illuminati who remain forever secretive in their Machiavellian deceptions.

In fact, with a troop of cavalry surrounding the two soldiers in the barn, it is unlikely the two Confederate soldiers would have resisted arrest, since they had done nothing seriously wrong. The lame soldier was simply murdered under supervision of the NDP as per direct orders from Baker via Conger and it was Boston Corbett who pulled the trigger. This soldier had a diary with six photographs of girls, a medallion around his neck and a tattoo on his hand. The local people were very upset about it but even the local paper made a hero out of Corbett. That is why so much fuss and stories were made up about 'Booth' bravely fighting against all odds, thus making an heroic stand, with the dying words Useless, Useless. However, this Unknown Soldier was indeed a very, very brave hero, because he must have thought he was still fighting for his country, even though he knew the war was over. It is not a dying man to be hanging on with sentiment or bravado. It is rare that a dying man can say too much in agony, because he his fully engaged in fighting for his survival, or silently giving in to death. However he just might have said those two words, indicating that he was paralysed and could only raise his arms in offering. But the words, "Tell my mother I died for my country" certainly came from Baker since he knew Booth was devoted to his mother, having Booth's letter to his mother, in his possession. And we have further evidence from Cavalryman Millington that these two men were indeed Confederate soldiers. Thus:

"The ferryman at the Rappahannock told us that Captain Jett of Mosby's command had crossed with two men in a closed carriage a few days before. Our company arrived at Bowling Green about 11 o'clock that night. We surrounded the hotel and captured Jett, who, after forcible persuasion, agreed to guide us to where the two men were. He said they were Confederate soldiers hiding out on account of some trouble they had got into. He led us back on the road by which we had come, to within about three miles of Port Royal. He pointed out a house some distance from the road. We opened the gate carefully and, after surrounding the house, knocked at the door. Garrett came to the door. Asked where the two men were, he said "I know nothing about any men being here." Our officer said to a trooper, "Untie your picket rope. We'll hang the old man and see if it will refresh his memory." "A young man ran from the direction of an outbuilding and asked, "What do you men want? "Our officer said, "We want the two men who are stopping here and at once." He said, "They're in the barn."

And no doubt the Confederate officers were fully aware of the trouble the soldiers had gotten into, since they had journeyed with them, and the soldiers had probably also fought for Moseby's command; possibly by now disbanded or gradually breaking up. Or perhaps they had decided to leave because the war was over and they had done there extra bit. What is certain is Jett was aware of their predicament and that they were vulnerable. It is interesting that there are no real clues as to how Booth did disappear from the theatre. It is probable however that since he did not return to retrieve his belongings at the National Hotel, that he just might have been in the theatre when Lincoln was shot. He must have reacted immediately knowing his life was in great danger, and arranged to leave the city, but certainly not on horse-back. He must have quickly deduced that he was going to be the number one suspect, even if he had already left the theatre, so it must have catapulted him suddenly into another world of escape and evasion and survival. They might even kill him before giving him the luxury of answering any questions and someone had shouted 'Burn the place down' raising the panic stakes. After all he was already very experienced in playing a few of these agent games himself. And the ever colourful Baker tried to re-enact that scene of fear and paranoia, except the vocal persons concerned were probably agitators. Thus:

"The screams of Mrs. Lincoln first disclosed to the audience the fact that the President was shot, when all rose, many pressing toward the stage, and exclaiming, "Hang him! Hang him!" The excitement was of the wildest nature. Others rushed for the President's box, while others cried out, Stand back! Give him fresh air!"

Well, they certainly did not give him fresh air as he lay in a coma in Petersen House. Their must have been about a score or more around him in that tiny airless and shuttered room, like vultures around the kill. It is another interesting observation that some of the staff at the theatre, other than Spangler, were fully aware of Booth's oft routine of riding his horse in the early evening and returning his horse to the theatre stable. Sometimes it was looked after by Spangler, as Gifford had said Spangler was often a drudge for Booth, possibly meaning he would often saddle his horse for him or de-saddle it when he returned. This might suggest that his horse would often be ready and waiting for Booth at the drop of a hat. However could it be a very good explanation, for the supposed fact, that Burroughs after being delegated by Spangler, was easily able to state that instead of de-saddling the horse in the stable, as instructed by Spangler, he merely changed his account for the trial, to say he waited in the alley holding the horse, unwittingly, as a getaway horse ready for Booth's escape. Now, Booth in reality of course had left his horse for Spangler to put away for the night, not intending to return since he would walk or hire a carriage back to his hotel. He could not ride his horse to the hotel leaving it tethered all night, it would be stolen, quite apart from the horse parking restrictions in a big eastern city. And he wouldn't be escaping on his horse, he would be escaping on a fast train.

Now consider the story of Booth's supposed return for his getaway horse. It would then have to be known to Burroughs how long he must wait holding the horse. It would be from 9.30 till just gone 10.15 pm. Now if this was the case, Spangler must have told Burroughs he must wait this long for Booth's return. This meant that Burroughs would be tied up from selling peanuts and carrying out other stage duties for nearly an hour. Surely an idle pastime for this busy young man to say the least. Then when he did wait all this time for 'Booth', he later swore under oath that Booth came out and struck him on the head with the butt of his knife, and further the lamed Booth kicked him out of the way, as he climbed without any help onto his horse. Why would Booth do this to such a loyal young man who was waiting so long and expecting his return? Burroughs could not have known the President was shot already and so to offer resistance; since it only took 'Booth' 30 seconds, according to Rathbone, after shooting the President to land on the stage and possibly another 20 seconds to exit the theatre. It would require at least this reaction time within the theatre to know the President had been shot. Quite apart from this avenue Booth had given the horse to Spangler, and not to Burroughs to put away, and certainly would not be expecting Spangler to hold it so long for a getaway, instead. He knew Spangler was the chief scene mover for the play that had one more act to go -Act 3, that Ed still had to facilitate. So, in effect Booth's getaway is un-proven in this manner, of Burroughs holding a getaway horse for nearly an hour. In Baker's book he refers to both Booth and Herold crossing the navy bridge at Eastern Branch. This in effect, is the crossing over the old bridge across the Anacostia river near the present Anacostia Naval Station - that is, the navy bridge, that leads to Surrattsville (now Clinton) and on to Bryantown. Thus, according to Baker:

"I come now to the ride out of the city by the chief assassin and his dupe. Harold met Booth immediately the crime in the next street, and they rode at a gallop past the Patent Office and over Capitol Hill. As they crossed the Eastern Branch at Uniontown, Booth gave his proper name to the officer at the bridge. This, would seem to have been foolish, was, in reality, very shrewd. The officers believed that one of Booth's accomplices had given his name in order to put them out of the real Booth's track. So they made efforts elsewhere, and Booth got a start."

You can make of this what you will but it defies common sense to such a degree that all of it is a complete fabrication. In other words Booth did not cross the navy bridge at all. He may have taken a northern route out of the city or whatever. However other research indicates that Booth did travel south and then west at some later stage; because the detective Andrew Potter who was issued a War department pass to Port Royal to trace Booth, on 18 April 1865, according to the reliable L. Gutteridge & R. Neff ('Dark Union'); but this is challenged by Steers-Chaconas who say this pass was just a request dated for April 11th through a Lt. Colonel J Hardie, and possibly for a different Andrew Potter. Another two great Mystorians are James L. Swanson and Daniel Weinberg; and Swanson's latest effort is enough to put even Baker to shame in its vividness of expression and imagination. Anyway Potter is supposed to have traced Booth through Southern Maryland, to West Virginia and further west, so let us follow this argument for a while. The sentry at the navy bridge was Sergeant Cobb and he stated that a man called Booth crossed the bridge; but the second man called Smith he could only say was very near the size of Herold, but he was not certain about him when shown Herold's likeness, but that he had crossed later. This might suggest the sentry was being truthful, and had not yet received any telegraph to stop anyone crossing the bridge at the time. And any number of Smiths and Jones could have crossed the bridge at that point in time, say shortly before 11 pm. Also no one knew the identity of the assassin at this stage, because even Stanton and Baker had not made up their minds whether it was Booth or Surratt. Even the New York Times and Herald papers who got the news from its source at 11.16 pm, had only stated that it was a young man. However if we recall what John Surratt had said in his lecture, this bridge had only recently been barred with gates and guarded as if in preparation for an event; the war was just finished so this was odd. Perhaps indeed as Baker said, it was a false start but also a false trail set up by him. And this false trail is the one that Baker had planned all along. But instead of Booth and Herold crossing the navy bridge it was Tyson and Hensted, the two decoy Detectives.

Chapter 14

The Journey

There are ample clues in Baker's fully descriptive and clandestine account of 'Booth's' escape and his journey into Southern Maryland and crossing of the Potomac. It's as if written in diary form; but instead of Booth and Herold these two men were the same two men that gave their names to Dr. Mudd, that is Tyson and Hensted. Because Baker describes precise details and times of how these men arrive at John Lloyd's tavern and then continue, in the very next paragraph, to Dr. Mudd's house. Thus continuing from the navy bridge above we have the history of their escape and journey:

"At midnight, precisely, the two horse-men stopped at Surrattsville, Booth remaining on his nag, while Harold descended and knocked lustily at the inn door. Lloyd the landlord , came down at once , when Harold pushed passed him into the bar, and obtained a bottle of whiskey, some of which he gave to Booth immediately. While Booth was drinking, Harold went up stairs and brought down one of the carbines. Lloyd started to get the other, but Harold said :

"We don't want it; Booth has broken his leg, and can't carry it."

Note how 'Herold's' character has changed from a 'dupe' or trainee druggist, to a lustful assertive type. And the second carbine remained in the hall, where later the arresting officers found it. To continue:

"As the two horsemen started to go off , Booth cried out to Lloyd:

"Don't you want to hear some news?"

"I don't care much about it cried Lloyd," by his own account.

"We have murdered , said Booth, the President and Secretary of State."

And , with this horrible confession, Booth and Harold dashed away in the midnight, across Prince George's County. On Saturday, before sunrise, Booth and Harold, who had ridden all night without stopping elsewhere, reached the house of Dr. Mudd, three miles from Bryantown. They contracted with him, for twenty-five dollars in greenbacks, to set the broken leg . Harold who knew Dr. Mudd , introduced Booth under another name, and stated that he had fallen from his horse during the night. The doctor remarked of Booth that he draped the lower part of his face while the leg was being set; he was silent, and in pain. Having no splints in the house, they split up an old fashioned wooden band-box and prepared them. The doctor was assisted by an Englishman, who at the same time began to hew out a pair of crutches. The inferior bone of the left leg was broken vertically across, and, because vertically it did not yield when the crippled man walked upon it. The riding boot of Booth had to be cut from his foot; within were the words 'J. Wilkes.' The doctor says he did not notice these. The two men waited around the house all day, but towards evening they slipped their horses from the stable and rode away in the direction of Allen's Fresh. Below Ervantown run certain deep and slimey swamps. Along the belt

of these Booth and Harold picked up a negro named Swan , who volunteered to show them the road for two dollars. They gave him five more to show them the route to Allen's Fresh; but really wished, as their actions intimated, to gain the house of one Sam Coxe , a notorious rebel, and well advised of the plot. They reached the house at midnight. It is a fine dwelling, one of the best in Maryland; and after halloing for some time, Coxe came to the door himself. As soon as he opened it, and beheld who the strangers were, he instantly blew out the candle he held in his hand, and, without a word, pulled them into the room, the negro remaining in the yard. The Confederates remained in Coxe's house till 4 a.m. during which time the negro saw them eat and drink heartily ; but when they reappeared they spoke in a loud tone, so that Swan could here them, against the hospitality of Coxe. All this was meant to influence the darky; but their motives were as apparent as there words. He conducted them three miles further on , when they told him that now they knew the way, and giving him five dollars more, making twelve in all, told him to go back. (Note: because here, Baker needs another false witness).
But when the negro , in the dusk of the morning, looked after them as he receded, he saw that both horses' heads were turned once more towards Coxe's, and it was this man, doubtless who harboured the fugitives from Sunday to Thursday, aided, possibly, by such neighbours as the Wilson's and the Adams's".

And so here we have from the mouth of the illuminati itself, the boastful confession that they had murdered both the President and the Secretary of State; as indeed they had planned to do so, except 'Red Shoes' was stricken with a bad case of cold feet. Even though Baker knew this in retrospect, he still couldn't help boasting about it, in this pre-staged cameo, that it was their original intention to do so. We can assume that the Wilson's and Adams family had also been marked as suspicious and possibly for arrest as harbourers, as indeed Coxe was arrested for the same reason.
We can see also how Baker is taking care of another time gap. He suggests the fugitives have stayed over at Coxes' house for five days , that would be from 16th April (Easter Sunday) till Thursday 20th April. This is necessary to help explain how it still took another four days to cross the Potomac and get to the Rappahannock River. In reality however they actually stayed with the Union garrison of sixty five men at Chapel Point, near Port Tobacco, getting there that same evening of the16th April (Easter Sunday). In addition they paid for Dr. Mudd's service, making it legitimate and therefore confirming that it was not done for charity or for an old friend. Exactly as they had paid greenbacks to Swan for his help. Also, even Baker admits here that Booth gave a false name to Dr. Mudd. And finally we have the clue of how Tyson fooled Dr. Mudd by pretending his leg would not support him when he put his weight on it. Some footballers do it a lot.
Now follows the same methods, Baker's detectives used to implicate Dr. Mudd and Sam Coxe, and other locals unconnected are simply arrested without any evidence at all. Except that Lloyd was probably a fully paid up member of the plot, since he had already arranged for fresh horses to be ready for the dummy riders. He needed to be arrested because he lived as a publican in the pro- southern region of Maryland. But of course he was also an ex policeman, and once a policeman always a policeman:

" The few unionists of Prince George's and Charles Counties, long persecuted and intimidated, came forward and gave important testimony. Among these was one Roby, a very fat and very zealous old gentleman , whose professions were as ample as his perspiration. He told the officers of the secret meetings for conspiracy's sake at Lloyd's hotel, and although a very John Gilpin on horseback, rode here and there to his great loss of wind and repose, fastening fire coals on the guilty or suspected. Lloyd was turned over to Mr. Cottingham, who had established a jail at Robytown. That night his house was searched, and Booth's carbine found hidden in the wall. Three days forward Lloyd confessed.

The little party under the untiring hand of Lovett, examined all the farm-houses below Washington , resorting to many shrewd expedients, and taking note of the great swamps to the East of Port Tobacco ; they reached Newport at last, and fastened tacit guilt upon many residents. Beyond Bryantown they overhauled the residence of Dr. Mudd, and found Booth's boots (note: the plural here). This was before Lloyd confessed , and was the first positive trace the officers had that they were really close upon the assassins. I do not recall anything more wild and startling than this vague and dangerous exploration of

Courtesy of Google Earth

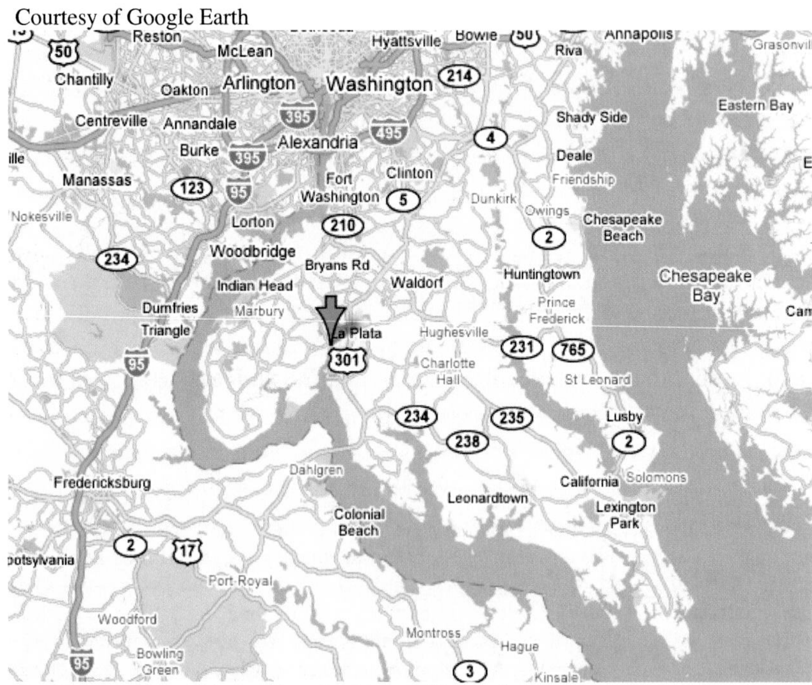

The Dummy Escape Route Over the Navy Bridge to Surrattsville (Clinton).Thence to Bryantown and Port Tobacco (arrowed), by the Two Decoys, Tyson and Hensted. Beantown is close to Waldorf in fact, where Dr.Mudd lived. Later they crossed the Potomac at Mattox Creek (Popes Creek), near the bridge now, birthplace of George Washington, in a flat Canoe.

a dimly known, hostile and ignorant country. To these few detectives we owe much of the subsequent successful precaution of the pursuit. They were the Hebrew spies. By this time the country was filling up with soldiers, but previously a second memorable detective party went out under the personal command of Major O'Bierne. It consisted besides that officer, of Lee, D'Angelis, Callan, Hoey, Bostwick, Hanover, Bevins, and McHenry, and embarked at Washington on a stem -tug for Chappel's Point. Here a military station had long been established for the prevention of blockade and mail running across the Potomac. It was commanded by Lieutenant Laverty, and garrisoned by sixty five men. On

Tuesday night Major O'Bierne's party reached this place, and soon afterwards a telegraph station was established hereby an invaluable man to the expedition, Captain Beckwith, General Grant's chief cipher operator, who tapped the Point Lookout wire, and placed the War Department within a moment's reach of events."

Laverty and Hoey were the officer and detective that went into Mr. Claggert's house under the usual rouse of pretending to be Booth and Herold, and getting him arrested like Tyson and Hensted did to Dr. Mudd and Sam Coxe. And officer Lee arrested Adzerodt ('Chris' Crangle?) in Port Tobacco. 'Chapel's Point' is the one point where the movement of 'Booth' across the Potomac would have been telegraphed to Washington, by Captain Beckworth and Mr. Cheyney, in addition to information of rebel manoeuvres. In fact it is called Chapel Point near Port Tobacco on the Estuary of the beautiful Port Tobacco River only 10 miles south of Bryantown. The crossing point where Booth (Tyson) and Herold (Hensted) crossed at Methxy Creek (Mattox Creek) is now called Popes Creek, famous today as Washington's birth place and crab fishing. Indeed, Tyson and Hensted would have gone through Allen's Fresh and the Zakiah swamp delta, through which the Zakiah then flows into the Potomac via the Wicomico River Estuary, as described by Baker.

George Washington's father Augustine died in 1743 having a tobacco plantation of some 15 acres and 64 bonded workers at Pope's Creek. Indeed it is not difficult to imagine how Washington crossed the Potomac, because he lived there and must have crossed it dozens of times. And this 'Booth' saga follows suit. Well, Baker always had is eye on history and famous people like Ceaser and Washington. However his moral assessment of Port Tobacco was not so optimistic:

:

" Major O'Bierne's party started at once, over the worst road in the world, for Port Tobacco.

If any place in the world is utterly given over to depravity, it is Port Tobacco. From this town, by a sinuous creek there is flat bottomed navigation to the Potomac , and across that river to Mattox Creek. Before the war, Port Tobacco was the seat of a tobacco aristocracy and a haunt of negro traders. It passed very naturally into a rebel post for blockade runners and a rebel post-office general. Gambling, corner-fighting, and shooting matches were its lyceum education. Violence and ignorance had every suffrage in the town. Its people were smugglers , to all intents, and there was neither a Bible nor geography to the whole region adjacent. Assassination was never very unpopular at Port Tobacco, and when its victim was a Northern President, it became quite heroic. A month before a provost -marshal nearby was slain in his bed-chamber. For such a town and district, the detective police were the only effective missionaries. The hotel there was called the Brawner House; it has a bar in the nethermost cellar, and its patrons, carousing in that imperfect light, look like the denizens of some burglar's crib, talking robbery between their cups; its dining- room is dark and tumble- down, and the cuisine bears traces of Kaffir origin; a barbecue is nothing to a dinner there. The court-house of Port Tobacco is the most superfluous house in the place, except the church. It stands in the center of the town, in a square, and the dwellings lie about it closely, as if to throttle justice. Five hundred people exist in Port Tobacco; life there reminds me , in connection with the slimy river and the adjacent swamps, of the greatest reptile period of the world, when iguanodons , the pterodactyls, and plesiosauri ate each other.

Into this abstract of Gomorrah the few detectives went like angels who visited Lot. They pretended to be inquiring for friends, or to have business designs, and the first people they heard of were Harold and

Atzeroth. The latter had visited Port Tobacco three weeks before the murder, and intimated at that time his design of fleeing the country. But everyone denied having seen him subsequent to the crime.
Atzeroth had been in town just prior to the crime. He had been living with a widowed woman, named Mrs. Wheeler , and she was immediately called upon by Major O'Bierne. He did not tell her what Azeroth had done, but vaguely hinted that he had committed some terrible crime, and that since he had done her wrong, she could vindicate both herself and justice by telling his whereabouts. The woman admitted that Adzeroth had been her bane, but she loved him and refused to betray him.
His trunk was found in her garret, and in it the key to his paint shop in Port Tobacco. The latter was fruitlessly searched but the probable whereabouts of Atzeroth in Montgomery County obtained, and Major O'Bierne telegraphing there immediately, the desperate fellow was found and locked up. A man named Crangle, who had succeeded Atzeroth, who had succeeded Atzeroth in Mrs, Wheeler's pliable affections, was arrested at once and put in jail. A number of disloyal people were indicated or "spotted" as in no wise angry at the President's taking off, and for all such a provost prison was established."

In fact Adzerodt was arrested by Officer Lee working with Major O'Bierne here, not in Montgomery County just north of Washington. This indicates another Baker lie which also suggests that Adzerodt was not in Washington that fateful night. In fact one has to suspect that this Crangle was in fact Adzerodt, living at his home in Port Tobacco with Mrs. Wheeler. Because Baker's officers pretended they had arrested Mrs. Wheeler's fresh lover, overnight, unless she was indeed a fast worker. And again we see that Herold was planning to leave the country if we take it that Baker has gotten the context of the 'latter' instead of the 'former' wrong.
Yet again we can see how the regular practice of arresting innocent people was put into play. People were simply arrested for not appearing to be angry. That had to be the Victorian equivalent of the 'thought police.' If you looked sad you were done for. It's no wonder some Americans are still angry and will pull a weapon. On the lighter side of Baker's humour we have the case of the diseased woman which does raise Baker's charming profile in the romantic idiom; as well as in his blighted, sadistic humour department. Rather like Jesus, a strange man, meeting the 'Woman at the Well' in St. John's gospel but without the inspiration of an allegorical doctrine.

" A few miles from Port Tobacco dwelt a solitary woman , who, when questioned, said that for many nights she had heard, after she retired to bed, a man enter her cellar, and be there all night, departing before dawn. Major O'Bierne and the detectives ordered her to place a lamp in her window the next night she heard him enter; and at dark they established a cordon of armed officers around the place. At midnight punctually she exhibited the light, when the officers broke into the house and thoroughly searched it, without result. Yet the woman positively asserted that she had heard the man enter.
It was found afterwards that she was of diseased mind."

Or, a clever mind that had kept them occupied.

Chapter 15

The Crossing of the Potomac and Rappahannock Rivers.

The intrepid duo crossed over the Potomac into King George County, Va. Only 5 miles north of Dahigran, at Bluff Point. Then it was just 15 miles to Port Conway, travelling through Edgehill and Shiloh, cross the Rappahannock River into Port Royal in Caroline County, but they did not need to go this far because the two soldiers had been reported by then. We see through the 'eyes' of Baker how 'Booth' and 'Herold' crossed the Potomac at Mattox Creek. Here the water was shallow for some distance requiring some wading and it is a long way across, about two miles or so. A man called Robert Jones provided them with the boat, so they in fact didn't have to nick it. Here is Baker's account:

The Two Decoy Detectives in Mr. Jones' Boat effect Stealth on the Potomac

"At the point where Booth crossed the Potomac the shores are very shallow , and one must wade out some distance to where a boat will float. A white man came up here with a canoe on Friday , and tied it by a stone anchor. Between seven and eight o'clock it disappeared , and in the afternoon some men at work on Methxy Creek, in Virginia , saw Booth and Harold land, tie the boats rope to a stone and fling it ashore, and strike at once across a ploughed field for King George Court House (note: again more false witnesses). Many folks entertained them, without doubt, but we positively hear from them next at Port Royal Ferry, and then at Garrett's farm."

However it was another Robert R. Jones that was the desk clerk at the Kirkwood Hotel who gave evidence against George Adzerodt, so it seems that he was the same false witness who provided the boat. Ah, well there is no end to the supply of 'witnesses', such is the power of the illuminati. The fishing boat is described as a flat bottomed boat, or even a canoe, is portrayed in the drawing. Here we see 'Booth' and 'Herold' in a dramatic cameo with 'Booth' gesturing 'Herold' to stay his oars and be silent as he looks backward and pricks his ears for sounds of movement or anyone following. Unfortunately the artist has been a little too literal, in accurately depicting Tyson and Hensted more like the two detectives. Indeed although 'Booth' has recovered his moustache, they are both wearing round bowler type hats, atypical of the style of Victorian city men or Pinkerton style detectives at the time. Booth's hat was a taller round flat topped hat as described by McGowan and often seen in the photographs of the great actor. Even the trousers here show cross hatching to depict the pin stripes of city men. It is true however that Herold was wearing a dickie bow in 'custody', like Tyson is, in this cameo. This is as far as Tyson and Hensted needed to go because the journey is then taken up by Boyd and his friend at the Rappahannock River at Port Conway. In effect Baker needed witnesses to make this journey transparently clear and some were paid for their services, but in other cases like Coxe, Crangle? (Adzerodt) and Claggert they were arrested for helping them. For example the Afro-American called Swan who witnessed their visit to Coxe's home, he was recalled to Washington as a prosecution witness for the trial. And another Afro-American who witnessed them crossing the Potomac is also recalled to Baker's office. Thus according to Major O'Bierne:

" The same steamer which took down the operator and two detectives, bought back one of the same detectives and a negro. This negro, taken to Colonel Baker's office, stated so positively that he had seen Booth and another man cross the Potomac in a fishing boat, while he was looking down upon them from a bank, that the Colonel was at first sceptical; but, when examined, the negro answered so readily and intelligently, recognizing the man from the photographs, that Baker knew at last that he had the true scent. Straight away he sent to General Hancock for twenty five men, and while the order was going drew down his coast survey maps, with that quick detective intuition amounting to almost inspiration. He cast upon the probable route and destination of the refugees, as well as the point where he would soonest strike them. Booth, he knew, would not keep along the coast, with frequent deep rivers to cross , nor, indeed, in any direction east of Richmond , where he was liable at any time to cross our lines of occupation; nor, being lame, could he ride on horseback, so as to place him very far westward of his point of debarkation in Virginia. But he would travel in a direct course from Bluff Point, where he crossed to Eastern Maryland, and this would take him through Port Royal, on the Rapperhannock River, in time to be intercepted by the outgoing cavalrymen."

Here we see Baker at his best, the great strategic thinker, from which he was to get his promotion and a sizable chunk of the reward money. Of course the witness could not have identified these men as Booth and Herold. That is why at first Baker appeared, or feigned, to be sceptical. The truth is by then he had received information from his agents at Chapel Point about two Confederate soldiers, Boyd and his comrade, trying to cross the Rappahannock river and that is when he got Stanton's permission to dispatch the cavalry. Thus:

" When therefore twenty five men, under one Lieutenant Doherty, arrived at his office doors, Baker placed the whole under control of his former Lieutenant- Colonel, E.J. Conger, and of his cousin, Lieutenant L.B. Baker-the first of Ohio, the last of New York- and bade them go off with all dispatch to Belle Plain, on the Lower Potomac, there to disembark and scour the country faithfully around Port Royal, but not to return unless they captured their men. Quitting Washington at two o'clock P.M. on Monday, the detective and cavalrymen disembarked at Belle Plain, on the border of Stafford County, at ten o'clock, in the darkness. Belle Plain is simply the nearest landing to Fredericksburg, seventy miles from Washington City, and located upon the Potomac Creek".

We see here that Conger was from a Ohio regiment, and is promoted to Lt. Colonel from Lieutenant in a quantum leap. And Baker's cousin is somehow connected to the 16th New York cavalry, as a Lieutenant. In fact they were both Detectives working for the NDP. And so there is a big question mark over them having been detached army officers. And we also have Lieutenant Doherty's own account to compare with:

'About the hour 014 P.M. April 24,1865, when Booth and Herold were taken by their newly made Confederate friends to the Garrett farm, where Booth was killed and Herold captured, I was seated, with another officer of the 16th New York Cavalry, on a bench in the park op-posite the White House. There I received the following orders from a messenger : HEADQUARTERS, DEPARTMENT or WASHINGTON, April 24, 1865. Commanding Officer 16th New York Cavalry.

Sir: You will at once detail a reliable and discreet commission officer with twenty-five men, well mounted, with three days' rations and forage, to report at once to Colonel L. C. Baker, Agent of the War Department, at 211 Pennsylvania Ave. Command of General C. C. Augur.—J. C. SEWELL, A. A. A. Gen'l. In accordance with the foregoing order First Lieutenant E. P. Doherty is hereby detailed for the duty, and will report at once to Colonel Baker, 211 Pennsylvania Ave. —N. B. SWITZER, Colonel 16th New York Cavalry, Bvt. Brig. Gen'l, U. S. A.

I proceeded to the barracks, had 'boots and saddles' sounded, and in less than half an hour had reported to Colonel Baker. I took the first twenty-five men in the saddle, Sergeant Boston Corbett being the only member of my own company. Colonel Baker handed me photographs of the assassins of President Lincoln. He told me no troops had yet been in Fredericksburg, but that I must reach that vicinity with all dispatch. He introduced me to E. J. Conger and L. B. Baker, of the detective force, and said they would accompany me. I proceeded down to the Sixth street wharf, where I found the steamer John S. Ide, and directed Captain Wilson to move down to Aquia Creek and to Belle Plain.'

Actually the photograph given to Doherty was that of Edwin Booth. And here we see again the evidence that Sergeant Corbett was already a member of 'L' company and its only acting non-commissioned officer, on this mission. This maybe because it was a new company or it was specially drafted for new duties. The big question is, on exactly what date was it formed? There was also a (following) 'M' company, so 'L' company should have already been in existence. If that's the case why was 'L' split, or was it specially reformed?

Chapter 16

Ruggles Encounters Boyd at the River

The following account was given to Prentiss Ingraham an ex-soldier, ex-Colonel, adventurer and prolific writer of dime novels and war stories, and of gifted imagination. And published in 1890. He wrote a play called 'Knight of the Plains' portraying the wild west adventures of Bill Cody, army scout and railroad worker. 'Buffalo Bill' got his name from the massive slaughter of the plain's bison to earn his keep of 500 dollars a month. He had been a scout for the infamous 5th cavalry. It is said the slaughter amounted to over 4,000 in much less than a year. This was to feed 'the men' . The far more prolific Sioux nation had managed for centuries with a fraction of this loss and it was their total livelihood. Of course we are all wiser now, or are we? Thus we see the effectiveness of the repeating rifle, and Cody had a knick-name for his-the Lucretia Borgia. One clever man invents a killing machine, dozens of mechanics turn them out, then the killing begins. But then even Leonardo De Vinci had invented many different kinds of war machines in 15th century Italy. So killing is somehow justified at the primitive level, but not mass slaughter, war crimes or national fratricide. It just depends which side your on and how much might you might have, unless your culture is highly advanced, which is exceedingly rare.
The following is the story given by Major M. B. Ruggles directly to the 'lips' of Prentiss supposedly, Copyright: Michael Goad, 2005 to which I am exceptionally grateful:

'At the close of the civil war, Colonel Mosby, to whose command I belonged, surrendered to General Hancock, at Millwood, Virginia. In company with two comrades, A. R. Bainbridge, now in business in New York, and William Jett, now dead, I started for my home in King George County, Virginia. We had heard from United States officers of the assassination of Mr. Lincoln, and that the assassin had been captured in Washington, and little dreamed, when we rode up to the bank of the Rappahannock River, that we were there to come face to face with John Wilkes Booth. Port Conway is on the King George side of the river, there about three hundred yards wide, and opposite Port Royal. The ferry was owned by a man named Rollins, but the scow was run—that is, poled across—by Peyton Washington, a negro. The scow was on the other side of the river when we rode up, and I observed there a wagon, drawn by two very wretched-looking horses. In the wagon were two men. On seeing us approach, one of them came towards us, and, finding that we were Confederate soldiers, said that his name was Boyd, and that his brother had been wounded severely in the leg while escaping from prison, where they had been for some time. He furthermore said that their negro driver, Lucas, refused to take them any farther, and that they were anxious to get on their way, and asked our aid. I at once said we would help them; and while discussing the speedy coming of the scow, the other got out of the wagon, and walking with evident pain, with the aid of a rude crutch, came towards us. He apparently mistrusted his companion, for as he came forward he said,

"I suppose you have been told who I am?"

Thinking he meant that Herold had told us they were Confederate soldiers, escaped from prison, I answered in the affirmative. Instantly he dropped his weight back upon his crutch, and drawing a revolver said sternly, with the utmost coolness:

"Yes, I am John Wilkes Booth, the slayer of Abraham Lincoln, and I am worth just $175,000 to the man who captures me."

We were greatly surprised, and yet the coolness of the man won our admiration; for we saw that he was wounded, desperate, and at bay. His face was haggard, pinched with suffering, his dark eyes sunken, but strangely bright, and though he had shaved off his mustache, upon his lip and face was a beard of some ten days' growth. In response to his defiant words I said that we had been told that Lincoln's

The beautiful Rappahannock River where the ebb and flow of the sea gave it to the Rappahannocks the "river of quick, rising water" or "where the tide ebbs and flows." As the ebb and flow of the breathtaking Blue Danube divides the Magyars from Czechoslovakia.

slayer had been captured; but that, though we did not sanction his act as an assassin, we were not men to take 'blood money'; and that having promised his friend, who proved to he Herold, to take them across the river to a place of safety, we would do so. Though it is contrary to the general belief of the people of the North, I believe that had the war then been going on, Booth, instead of finding an asylum in the South, would have been taken and surrendered to the United States by the Confederate Government. Booth replaced his weapon at my words, and, thanking us, said he was utterly unable to . I dismounted, and we lifted him upon my horse—a fact that seemed to give the saddle and bridle a great pecuniary value, as I learned through correspondence with Mr. Barnum; though they were never exhibited as relics, and are now at my brother's home in Virginia, there kept as souvenirs of my 'days with Mosby. Booth and Herold both seemed to be the worse for their exposure and hardships of the past few days. Booth wore a black soft hat, dark clothes, one cavalry boot,— the one on his wounded leg having been cut off,—and his weapons were a carbine, two revolvers, and a knife, the blade of the latter bearing the stain of blood, for with it he had wounded Major Rathbone. I noticed that his wounded leg was greatly swollen, inflamed, and dark, as from bruised blood, while it seemed to have been wretchedly dressed, the splints being simply pasteboard rudely tied about it. That he suffered intense pain all the time there was no doubt, though he tried to conceal his agony, both physical and mental. When the scow arrived Peyton Washington ferried us across the river. After a ride of three miles we came to the Garrett farm, where we asked for shelter for the fugitives, which was granted. We also remained all night near Garrett's, sleeping in the woods, and the next day Herold went with us to Bowling Green, where we left Jett.

The next day, Herold having decided upon the best course to pursue in his flight, Bainbridge and myself accompanied him back to Garrett's. We found Booth lying on the grass, in front of the house, and sitting by his side I heard from his lips his version of the tragic conspiracy, his fatal shot, his motives, escape, and flight up to his coming to the Garrett's'. In answer to my questions he spoke quietly, repressing now and then a groan of pain, and showing emotion and stern defiance at times. He said, in substance, that the plot had been to capture Mr. Lincoln and carry him a prisoner into the Confederacy, for he believed that by such an act the war could be brought to an end, as the South could dictate terms with such a hostage. Failing in this, he decided at the last moment, as it were, to strike deadly blows at Mr. Lincoln, Mr. Seward, and General Grant. In the plot to kill, Payne_alone was implicated with him, not even Her-old knowing what was to be done. Atzerodt knew nothing of the intended assassination, nor did, according to Booth's statement to me, any other, excepting Payne. The name of Mrs. Surratt was not mentioned by him. He said that Payne was to strike a death blow at Secretary Seward, and he, favored by the fact that President Lincoln and General Grant were to attend the theater together, was to kill both of them. General Grant's having been called away alone saved his life, for, said Booth, 'I would have made no failure with either, as I had laid my plans for success only.' That Andrew Johnson might appear to be implicated in the plot of assassination, Booth said that he had left that morning a note at the hotel where the Vice-President lived, to compromise him. He had no idea, he said, from the information received about Washington, that the war had really ended; for had he not believed that it would have been kept up by the South, he would not have struck the blow as he did. After getting safely out of Washington his intention was to cross the line, as quickly as possible, into the Confederacy. Joining Herold at a rendezvous, they had ridden hard through the night to gain a place of safety; but having a broken leg, and learning after several days, through the papers, that the war was really at an end, he determined to make his way to the silver mines of Mexico, feeling that the South would be no place of refuge for him. It has been said that Booth had plenty of money with him; but he showed me three five-dollar bills, all that he had, excepting a bill of exchange; while Herold had not as much. I asked him why he did not attempt to get to Europe, and his answer was that there was no asylum for such as he where monarchs ruled, as they feared their own lives might be in danger from the example he had set.

It is generally believed that Herold shot his own and Booth's horse; but Booth told me that after weighting them down they led them into the Potomac the night they embarked in the boat to cross, and drawing their heads over the gunwale cut their throats and saw them sink from sight. This would account for the fact that their bodies were never found. Booth seemed to feel that he had been spurred on to the deed through a duty he owed the country to bring the war to an end, and he said that he would never be taken alive. If he had not broken his leg he could readily have distanced all pursuit. He was without doubt disappointed at the reception he met in Virginia, and said that he was prepared to meet any fate. The calm courage of the man in the midst of his great peril, and while racked by suffering, impressed me in spite of myself, for there was no braggadocio about him ; simply a determination to submit to the inevitable, parleying when it should become necessary to do so. The few extracts he read me from his diary showed this. From the examination I made of his broken leg, aided by some experience I had had with wounds, I feel confident that amputation would have been necessary to save his life, and perhaps that would not have prevented a speedy death. Soon after my long conversation with Booth, Bainbridge and myself bade him and Herold good-by and went on our way, remaining that night in the pines, and next day going to Robb's, where we learned that a company of United States cavalry were scouring the country and had captured the fugitives in Garrett's barn. Knowing the barn well, and judging from all the circumstances connected with the burning of it, I feel convinced that Sergeant Boston Corbett has a reputation undeserved as the slayer of Mr. Lincoln's assassin. From the spot where Sergeant Corbett was he could not have seen Booth where he stood, and certainly could not have been able to shoot him in the hack of the head. Having asked Captain Doherty to fall back fifty paces with his men and give him a chance to come out, and very properly and naturally being refused his request by that gallant officer, deserted by Herold, the barn on fire, and seeing that he must perish in the flames or be taken to Washington and hanged, Booth, hopeless, alone, and at bay, placed his pistol to the back of his head, and took his own life. No one saw Corbett fire, and one chamber of Booth's revolver held in his hand was empty, and I am by no means alone in the belief that he killed himself. Learning that Jett was a prisoner, and that we were to be arrested, tried, and hanged, as aiders and abetters, Bainbridge and myself stood not on the order of going, but went at once. Making our way into Essex County and crossing to Westmoreland, we went to our home up in King George County. Some ten days after, I was arrested at night by a squad of United States cavalry. Bainbridge was also captured. We were taken to Washington and placed in the Old Capitol Prison. We were not alone in our misery, however, for Dr. Stewart, at whose house Booth had stopped, William Lucas, the negro who had driven him to the ferry, and a number of others, were there, among them being Jett, who had escaped from Captain Doherty, and had been recaptured at his home in Westmoreland County. From Booth's own words to me as he lay on the grass in front of Garrett's house, I feel assured that in the excitement of the times there were some innocent ones who a were punished for the crimes of Booth and Payne. After the trial, by a strange mistake I was sent to Johnson's Island, where as a Confederate prisoner I had passed half a year; but after a few days spent there I was returned to Washington, and after taking the oath of allegiance I was released.

M.B. Ruggles.

The proofs of this article have been read and corrected (Nov., 1889) by Colonel Ingraham, Major Ruggles, Lieutenant Bainbridge, and Captain Doherty.—EDITOR.'

In Ruggles' account above we see again a good piece of creative and descriptive literature, as transposed by the ghost writer Prentiss Ingraham. The first thing is that Boyd tells Ruggles they are Confederate soldiers escaped from prison and 'Booth' (the Unknown Soldier) has been wounded in the leg. Then 'Booth' who doesn't trust his friend says that he is in fact Booth. So we know somebody is telling 'porkies.' If they were escaped soldiers it's a fair chance they would be wearing their uniforms, so that whatever 'Booth' seemingly told Ruggles is untrue. Or, more to the point, Ruggles has invented their whole dialogues and hidden their true identities. Thus we can deduce that neither did they escape from prison.

Also, we have an alternative explanation for 'Booth's' visit to see Andrew Johnson. That is to drop him in the mud so that he would be implicated in the plot. Now, Ruggles could hardly have been aware of these finer details of the events in Washington, at the time, even though he was in contact with the Union officers. In addition this is coming straight from the 'lips' of Ruggles or Ingraham, years later in 1890, implying that it was Booth himself that had tried to implicate President Johnson. And they got Dr. Mudd mixed up with a 'Dr. Stewart', probably Colonel Stewart in error. Indeed there is no end to the genius of Booth, because of all this spontaneous generation of mythology. And no doubt the reader will draw his own conclusions and necessary truths from this and also see the many more un-truths, having gotten this far, that will help infill the missing gaps of this tragic saga. We have to question Ruggles that they had escaped from prison because we know from Baker's account in the diary, that the Unknown Soldier fell from his horse in the tangle of the forest, and dragged his own painful limbs along after him, on his own. And his friend Boyd met and helped him later near the Rappahannock river. This suggests they were not escaped prisoners but were otherwise in trouble, as explained elsewhere. Suffice to say that otherwise many of the details in this account concord with Baker. And there is an effort here to say that poor old George was innocent. Well at least it might help in clearing his name, since by then he had been long hung and buried. Finally Ruggles was seemingly promoted to Major later, if not self promoted. How did he get promoted from Lieutenant, after he was supposedly sent to prison then swore the oath of allegiance, and by then the war was completely over (see later)? For further guidance we have Lieutenant Doherty to help us out:

"After the detachment had landed I directed the captain of the boat to move off to a place of safe anchorage and await my return. Should I not return before 6 p.m. on the 26th he was to go back to Washington and report to Captain Allen, assistant quartermaster. I proceeded directly south until I struck the main road to Fredericksburg. Here I halted at 4 a.m. A negro informed me that a regiment of cavalry had passed to Fredericksburg the previous evening, going along on the north side of the Rappahannock River. I then determined to push down and go up on the south side, where no troops had been. The detectives asked for a detail of four men and a sergeant to scour the country, while I with the rest of the men continued on towards the Rappahannock. The detectives returned about 3 p.m. without any clue to the whereabouts of the assassins. I went to the ferry at Port Conway and saw Mrs. Rollins, the ferry-man's wife, and another woman sitting on the steps of the ferry-house. Drawing Booth's picture from my pocket I showed it to them, and inferred from their looks that Booth was not far distant. One of them said that Booth and Herold had been brought there in a wagon the evening before by a negro named Lucas, who would carry them no farther. While they were bargaining with her husband to take them to Orange Court House, three Confederate soldiers, Ruggles, Bainbridge, and Jett, rode up and they entered into conversation. By and by they were all taken over the ferry. Booth was put on Ruggles's horse and they proceeded towards Bowling Green. I at once sent the bugler to Sergeant Corbett, telling him to mount the detachment, which I had left a mile behind, feeding, and move down as quickly as possible. Mrs. Rollins went for her husband, who was fishing, and I sent him for the scow, which was on the other side of the river. During his absence the command arrived at the ferry and we were soon over the river. I arrested Rollins the ferryman, and took him as guide to Bowling Green."

Ingraham continues:

'Payne was a deserter from a Confederate Florida regiment. Lieutenant Bainbridge is positive that he heard Booth say:

"After we had been three days in the pines, I deemed it advisable to act on Jones's advice and kill our horses. I could hear in the distance the neighing of the horses of the Federal cavalry as they went scouting through the country, and I was afraid that ours might answer them and betray our whereabouts, so I asked Herold to shoot them, which he did."

So here we have yet another version of what happened to their horses. This in fact nearly concords with Baker, but not with the earlier version of Ruggles who said that 'Booth' had personally told him they had slit the horses throats while crossing the Potomac, so that their carcasses would not be discovered. And this is all under the same account and witnessed. So somebody has forgotten to do their homework.
And Jones was the one who provided Tyson and Hensted with the flat bottomed boat to cross the Potomac. Now we have below a version of how the reward money was divided, which differs greatly from Baker's account. But you will also see later that the commission had to make a re-assessment and Baker was greatly disappointed:

'The following is taken from the report of Generals Joseph Holt, Judge Advocate, and E. D. Townsend, Adjutant-General, U. S. A., to the Secretary of War, Mr. Stanton, on the subject of the arrest of those engaged in the assassination of President Lincoln, which was transmitted to Congress:

"The parties who made the arrest of Booth and Herold were a detachment of the 16th New York Cavalry (consisting of Lieutenant E. P. Doherty, commanding, and two sergeants, seven corporals, and seventeen privates), accompanied by E. J. Conger and L. B. Baker, two employees in the detective service of Colonel L. C. Baker, Provost-Marshal, etc., the officer who originated and directed the expedition, though not personally accompanying it. . . . The military element of the expedition for the arrest of these criminals Booth and Herold is therefore believed to have been that which was essential to its success, and without which its results could not have been attained. As the commander of the detachment employed upon this important duty, Lieutenant Doherty was solely responsible for its discipline and efficiency. He is found to have been active and energetic, and it is believed to be established by the weight of testimony that it was he who personally made the actual seizure of Herold. It was he, too (in conjunction with Mr. Baker), who obtained the first reliable information which rendered the capture of the criminals almost certain; and though, in the direction of the investigation, the initiative would seem more frequently to have been taken by Conger, yet Lieutenant Doherty is shown to have acted and been recognized as the commander of the expedition in the only written instructions which appear to have been issued during the march, to wit, those given by him to the master of the steamer which conveyed the party to and from Belle Plain. Upon the whole, therefore, it is concluded that as such commander he may properly be awarded the one-tenth portion of the whole amount which is payable by law to the commanding officer of a vessel immediately engaged in the capture of a prize, and his share will there-fore be $7500. The services of Messrs. Conger and Baker upon this expedition were, no doubt, of great value; and, inasmuch as these parties immediately rep-

resented the views and intentions of Colonel Baker, their part in carrying out the original plan was particularly important. It is understood that their expenses incurred upon this duty have been reimbursed, and that they have also been paid, or are entitled to be paid, for their general services, as detectives at this period, at the rate of $15 per month. They should, however, both be liberally, and, as it is thought, equally compensated; and it is concluded that of the amount offered as reward there may properly be paid to each the sum of $4090."
Sergeants Corbett and Wendell each received $2545.68; each of the seven corporals received $2291.09; and each of the seventeen privates $2039.53. Of the $75,000 thus distributed as a reward for the arrest of Booth and Herold, Colonel L. C. Baker received the share that "would be payable to the commander of a squadron, by a separate ship of which a prize had been taken," that is, one-twentieth, or $3750.'

We see here possibly the truer version of how the reward money was divided in the end, and not what Baker had quoted below. Baker must have been very annoyed in the end because he had been complaining about getting only 17, 500 dollars, but it seems he only finished up with 3,750 dollars. And its nice to know the soldiers were rewarded a lot more, also. And note Conger and Byron Baker are referred to as Messrs.(civilians) without rank. And we have 'Booth' giving us his probable destination to be the silver mines of Mexico. Well indeed, he was projected to go well south and out of civilised existence. But more interestingly we gain more insight into where Herold wanted to go but thought better of it, that is to Europe. So this ties in with Baker's account of him 'telling the boys in Port Tobacco' that he intended to go to Spain, where there is 'no extradition treaty,'*or his 'neck would stretch.' Now, at a much later date this account is seemingly contradicting this, or at least a change of mind. But see Chapter 22 for more intrigue on the subject of Herold's disappearance.

* These terms are most likely coined by Baker, especially 'no extradition treaty.'

Buffalo Bill

Man of Action and Enterprise.
The plains' bison were easy meat.

Chapter 17

The Siege at Garrett's Barn

The two soldiers who were intercepted by the three Confederate officers, including the lucid and eloquent Lt. Ruggles, (the son of the giant and grey bearded General Daniel Ruggles who had had a certain Major Alison, of the famed Alison's Rangers, arrested for shooting a US marshal when obstructing a raiding campaign); and Captain William Jett and Lieutenant Bainbridge. There was 100,000 dollars reward and no doubt they had informed the NDP or Washington that a lame renegade soldier and friend were travelling across the Rappahannock River, on receiving information from a Union military source. Baker circled this area on his map into a 10 mile dragnet and immediately despatched a detachment under Lieutenant Doherty on the steamer the John S. Ide under sea Captain Wilson to Belle Plain, Fredericksburg taking only 8 hours to get there at 10 pm on April 24th 1865. Here is Baker's account after they had arrived at the Rapperhannock River on Tuesday 25h April:

"On Tuesday morning they presented themselves at the Port Royal Ferry, and enquired of the ferryman, while he was taking them over in squads of seven at a time, if he had seen any two such men. Continuing their enquiries at Port Royal, they found one Rollins, a fisherman, who referred them to a negro, named Lucas, as having driven two men a short distance towards Bowling Green, in a wagon. It was found that these men answered the description, Booth having a crutch, as previously ascertained.
The day before Booth and Harold had applied at Port Conway for the general ferry-boat, but the ferryman was then fishing , and would not desist for the inconsiderable fare of only two persons; but to their supposed good fortune a lot of Confederate cavalrymen just then came along, who threatened the ferryman with a shot in the head if he did not instantly bring across his craft and transport the entire party. The cavalrymen were of Moseby's disbanded command, returning from Fairfax Court House to their home in Caroline County. Their captain was on his way to visit a sweetheart at Bowling Green , and he had so far taken Booth under his patronage, that when the latter was haggling with Lucas for a team, he offered both Booth and Harold the use of his horse to ride and walk alternately."

This account ties in well with the false story forged by Baker in the soldier's diary, ' .....once more tomorrow the river I will try to cross'. We see from this that indeed the Confederate captain was keeping a very close charge over his quarry. In fact there supposed good fortune was literally the death of them. Jett's visit to Bowling Green, the capitol of Caroline County, to see an old flame, was in fact a cover to inform Chapel Point or Washington by telegraph, that the fugitives had now crossed into Virginia at Port Royal, and the other two Confederates officers carried on with them to Garrett's house; as it happened. Boyd and his comrade were riding in a wagon driven by an Afro-American called Lucas. It also shows how keen these renegade officers were to help the soldier's get on with their journey, by threatening the ferryman.

Baker Circles a Ten Mile Dragnet around Port Conway on the Rappahannock River whilst Byron Baker and Conger Look on.

These officers and soldiers had probably fought under the same command- Moseby's. We also have Cavalryman Millington's account as a cross reference to help us out:

'Lieutenant Dougherty showed us a photograph of Booth and told us he had crossed the Potomac near Port Tobacco." "We arrived at Acquia Creek and went ashore about 10 o'clock that night. We started scouting through the country, searching all houses and buildings, routing out the inmates and making a thorough search. Next morning early we met some men who had been fishing. They said that a closed hack had passed a few days before, with two men in it. A Confederate captain was in charge, who warned them not to come near. They thought one of the men in the carriage resembled the photograph that we showed them of Booth. We were then on the road to the Rappahannock, toward Fort Conway, where we arrived about 2 O'clock. We had not eaten since leaving Washington, so we were told to fall out and rustle some rations." "When I returned, with four comrades, we saw some of our company crossing the river in a scow about 20 feet long and 8 feet wide. This ferryboat could hold 10 men with horses, at a trip. In our turn we crossed the river. Mr. Rowlen, owner of the ferry, said he had ferried a carriage a few days previously, and that Captain Jett, formerly of Mosby's command, was in charge. He believed we would be apt to find him near Bowling Green, about 15 miles from Port Royal, and he volunteered to guide us. Our command was across the river by 4pm and we started. We had traveled about three miles and were approaching the Garrett farm, when we met a man on horseback, who turned and fled. Some of our men pursued, but he escaped in the young pines and as it was nearly dusk he escaped." "We arrived at Bowling Green at 11 o'clock that night. We left our horses, with every fourth man counted out to hold the horses. We surrounded the hotel, where we captured Captain Jett. At first he refused to tell us where he had left the two men, but after some forcible persuasion he agreed to show us. He said he didn't know who they were, except that the were Confederate soldiers who had got into trouble in Maryland and wanted to hide out until the trouble had blown over.'

The 'fishermen' could have been the NDP, indeed possibly Tyson and Hensted.
So Jett had told the cavalry that the fugitives were Confederate soldiers, wanting to hide out after some trouble in Maryland. They eventually caught up with Captain Jett at Goldman's Hotel in Bowling Green and he led them to Garrett's farm. Jett was immediately arrested by Doherty and requisitioned to be led to Boyd's location near the farm that same night. Jett was then allowed to go free later. In fact he escaped from Lt. Doherty because of travelling with, or hiding in the wagon containing the dead Confederate soldier, accompanied by Luther Baker, against Doherty's explicit orders. Note by this time Conger, in overall charge, had returned for Washington with the diary and 'Unknown Soldier's' personal effects, including his primitive compass. Doherty was obviously unaware of a secret deal guaranteed to Jett for supplying the information directly to Chapel Point or Washington, of the approximate location of these two Confederate soldiers, one lamed. This deal was confirmed at the hotel where Jett had been arrested by Doherty.

War Department, Washington, April 20, 1865.

$100,000 REWARD!

THE MURDERER

Of our late beloved President, ABRAHAM LINCOLN,

IS STILL AT LARGE.

$50,000 REWARD!

will be paid by this Department for his apprehension, in addition to any reward offered by Municipal Authorities or State Executives.

$25,000 REWA[illegible]!

will be paid for the apprehension of JOHN H. SURRATT, one [illegible] ...ices.

$25,000 REV[illegible]ARD!

will be paid for the apprehension of DANIEL C. HARROLD, another of Booth's accomplices.

LIBERAL REWARDS will be paid for any information that shall conduce to the arrest of either of the above-named criminals, or their accomplices.

All persons harboring or secreting the said persons, or either of them, or aiding or assisting their concealment or escape, will be treated as accomplices in the murder of the President and the attempted assassination of the Secretary of State, and shall be subject to trial before a Military Commission and the punishment of DEATH.

Let the stain of innocent blood be removed from the land by the arrest and punishment of the murderers.

All good citizens are exhorted to aid public justice on this occasion. Every man should consider his own conscience charged with this solemn duty, and rest neither night nor day until it be accomplished.

EDWIN M. STANTON, *Secretary of War.*

DESCRIPTIONS.—BOOTH is 5 feet 7 or 8 inches high, slender build, high forehead, black hair, black eyes, and wears a heavy black moustache. [illegible]

GEO. F. NESBITT & CO., Printers and Stationers, cor. Pearl and Pine Streets, N. Y.

20th April yet no mention of a lame Booth. Surratt is in Canada and who is Daniel C. Harrold? Obviously poor communications between Washington and New York.

However, before agreeing to give the exact location of the two rebel soldiers Jett asked Conger to tell Doherty to leave the hotel room so that Jett confided only with Lieutenant Conger (later 'Lieutenant-Colonel').

Later Jett became ostracised by the locals as the informer but he said he had no choice in the matter, being under arrest he was obliged to inform or go on trial and possibly be hung, notwithstanding he possibly had been the long distance informer, probably along with Ruggles and Bainbridge. This is true because Stanton had issued a proclamation on the 20th April, that anyone found helping, harbouring or hiding the fugitives would face the death penalty. Thus from Baker again when they arrived at Bowling Green:

"This is the court house of Caroline County, a small and scattered place, having within it an ancient tavern, no longer used for other than lodging purposes; but here they hauled from his bed the captain aforesaid, and bade him dress himself. As soon as he comprehended the matter, he became pallid, and eagerly narrated the facts in his possession. Booth to his knowledge , was lying at the house of one Garrett, which they had passed, and Harold had departed the existing day with the intention of rejoining him. Taking the captain along for a guide, the worn-out horsemen retraced their steps, though some were so haggard and wasted, with travel they had to be kicked into intelligence before they could climb to their saddles. The objects of the chase just at hand, the detectives full of sanguine purpose, hurried the cortege so well along, that by two o'clock early morning all halted at Garrett's gate. In the pale moonlight, three hundred yards from the main road, to the left, a plain, old farm-house looked grayly through the environing locusts. It was worn, and whitewashed, and two storied, and its half human windows glowered down upon the silent cavalrymen like watching owls, which stood as sentries over some horrible secret asleep within. Dimly seen behind, an old barn, high and weather beaten, faced the roadside gate, for the house itself lay to the left of its old lane; and nestling beneath the barn, a few long corn-cribs lay, with a cattle-shed at hand. In the dead stillness, Baker dismounted and forced the outer gate, Conger kept close behind him, and the horsemen followed cautiously. They made no noise in the soft clay, nor broke the all fore-boding silence anywhere, till the second gate swung open gratingly, yet even then no hoarse nor shrill response came back, save distant croaking, as of frogs or owls, or the whiz of some passing night hawk. So they surrounded the pleasant old homestead, each horseman, carbine in poise, adjusted under the grove of locusts, so as to inclose the dwelling with a circle of fire. After a pause Baker rode to the kitchen door on the side, and dismounting , rapped and hollooed lustily. An old man, in drawers and night-shirt, hastily un-drew the bolts, and stood on the threshold, peering shiveringly into the darkness. Baker seized him by the throat at once, and held a pistol to his ear.

"Who is this that calls me?" cried the old man.

"Where are the men who stay with you?" challenged Baker.

"If you prevaricate you are a dead man!"

The old man who proved to be the head of the family , was so overawed and paralysed that he stammered and shook and said not a word.

"Go light a candle," cried Baker, sternly,

"And be quick about it."

The trembling old man obeyed, and in a moment the imperfect rays flared upon his whitening hairs, and bluishly pallid face. Then the question was repeated, backed up by the glimmering pistol.

"Where are these men?" The old man held to the wall, and his knees smote each other.

"They are gone," he said. "We haven't got them in the house; I assure you that they are gone."

In the interim Conger had also entered, and while the household and its invaders were thus in weird tableau, a young man appeared, as if he had risen from the ground. The eyes of everybody turned upon him in a second; but, while he blanched, he did not loose loquacity.

"Father", he said. "we had better tell the truth about the matter."

"Those men whom you seek, gentlemen are in the barn, I know. They went there to sleep."

Leaving one soldier to guard the old man-and the soldier was very glad of the job, as it relieved him of personal hazard in the approaching combat-all the rest with cocked pistols at the young man's head, followed onto the barn. It lay a hundred yards from the house, the front barn-door facing the west gable, and was an old spacious structure, with floors only a trifle above the ground level.
The troops dismounted, were stationed at regular intervals around it, and ten yards distant at every point, four special guards placed to command the door, and all with weapons in subtle preparation, while Baker and Conger went direct to the door. It had a padlock upon it, and the key of this Baker secured at once. In the interval of silence that ensued , the rustling of planks and straw was heard inside, as if persons rising from sleep. At the same time Baker hailed:-

"To the persons in this barn I have a proposal to make. We are about to send to you the son of the man in whose custody you are found. Either surrender him your arms, and then give yourselves up, or we'll set fire to the place. We mean to take you both or have a bonfire and shooting match."

No answer came to this of any kind. The lad John M Garrett, who was in deadly fear, was hear pushed through the door by a sudden opening of it, and immediately Lieutenant Baker locked the door on the outside. The boy was heard to state his appeal in under tones.

Booth replied:- "----- you. Get out of here. You have betrayed me."

At the same time he placed his hand in his pocket, as if for a pistol. A remonstrance followed; but the boy slipped on and over the re-opened portal, reporting that his errand had failed, and that he dare not enter again. All this time the candle brought from the house to the barn was burning close beside the two detectives, rendering it easy for anyone within to have shot them dead. This observed the light was cautiously removed, and everyone took care to keep out of its reflection. By this time the crisis of the position was at hand; the cavalry exhibited very variable inclinations, some to run away, others to shoot Booth without a summons; but all excited and fitfully silent. At the house nearby, the female folks were seen collected in the doorway, and the necessities of the case provoked prompt conclusions The boy was placed at a remote point, and the summons repeated by Baker:-

"You must surrender inside there! Give up your arms and appear; there's no chance for escape. We give you five minutes to make up your mind."

A bold, clarion reply came from within, so strong as to be heard at the house door:-

"Who are you, and what do you want with us?"

Baker again urged:- "We want you to deliver up your arms and become our prisoners"

"But who are you?" hallooed the same strong voice.

"That makes no difference; we know who you are, and we want you. We have here fifty men, armed with carbines and pistols. You cannot escape."

There was a long pause, and then Booth said:-

" Captain this is a hard case, I swear. Perhaps I am being taken by my own friends."

It is clear from this that the soldier is referring to a Captain whom he thinks might be a fellow Confederate, perhaps even Captain Jett, because their were no other Captains about. It also indicates from the verbal tone and status that this soldier is not an officer and even calls himself a lamed man (below). And he repeatedly defers to the officer, as to a Captain.

"No reply from the detectives.

"Well give us a little time to consider."

"Very well. Take time"

Here ensued a long and eventful pause. What thronging memories it brought back to Booth we can only guess. In this little interval he made the resolve to die. But he was cool and steady to the end. Baker, after a lapse, hailed for the last time:-

"Well we have waited long enough; surrender your arms and come out, or we'll fire the barn."

Booth answered thus:-

" I am but a cripple-a one legged man. Withdraw your forces from one hundred yards from the door, and I will come out. Give me a chance for my life, captain. I will never be taken alive!"

"We did not come here to fight but to capture you. I say again appear, or the barn shall be fired."

Then with a long breath, which could be heard outside, Booth cried, in sudden calmness, still invisible, as were to him his enemies:-

"Well, then, my brave boys, prepare a stretcher for me!"

There was a pause repeated, broken by low discussions within between Booth and his associate, the former saying, as if in answer to some remonstrance or appeal:

"Get away from me. You are a -------- coward, and mean to leave me in my distress; but go---go! I don't want you to stay--- I won't have you stay!"

Then he shouted aloud :-

"There's a man inside who wants to surrender."

"Let him come, if he will bring his arms."

Here Harold, rattling at the door, said:

"Let me out; open the door; I want to surrender."

"Hand out your arms, then."

"I have not got any."

"You are the man who carried the carbine yesterday; bring it out!"

"On the word and honour of a gentleman, he has no arms with him. They are mine, and I have got them."

Here we have Baker trying to imply that this soldier is a gentleman, because of course it is 'Booth' he is trying to portray. In the context of a commissioned officer however (such as Captain Boyd) we still have no evidence, especially as he should have said ......'on the word and honour of an officer and a gentleman.'

"At this time Harold was quite up to the door, within whispering distance of Baker. The latter told him to put out his hands to be handcuffed, at the same time drawing out the door a little distance. Harold thrust forth his hands, when Baker seizing him, jerked him into the night, and straight away delivered him over to a deputation of cavalrymen. The fellow began to talk of his innocence, and plead so noisily, that Conger threatened to gag him, unless he ceased."

Indeed this truly innocent young soldier protested his innocence every day right up to the gallows when he was still crying it out, and even after being hung, according to Baker.

"Then Booth made his last appeal, in the same clear, unbroken voice:-

"Captain, give me a chance. Draw off your men and I will fight them singly. I could have killed you six times to-night, but I believe you to be a brave man, and would not murder you. Give a lame man a show."

It was too late for parley. All this time Booth's voice had sounded from the middle of the barn.
Ere he ceased speaking, Colonel Conger slipped around to the rear, drew some loose straws through a crack, and lit a match upon them. They were dry and blazed up in an instant, carrying a sheet of smoke

and flame through the parted planks, and heaving in a twinkling a world of heat and light upon the magazine within. The blaze lit up the black recesses of the great barn, till every wasp's nest and cobweb in the roof were luminous; flinging streaks of red and violet across the tumbled farm gear in the corner, ploughs, harrows, hoes, rakes, sugar- mills, and making every separate grain in the high bin adjacent gleam like a mote of precious gold. They tinged the beams, the upright columns, the barricades, where clover and timothy, piled high, held toward the hot incendiary their separate straws for the funeral pile. They bathed the murderer's retreat in a beautiful illumination, and while in bold outline his figure stood revealed, they rose like an impenetrable wall to guard from sight the hated enemy who lit them.'

These excellent, poetic and descriptive passages here again, indicates the influence of John Milton upon the ghost writer- Phinius Headly, or indeed on any Victorian writer.

'Behind the blaze , with his eye to a crack, Conger saw Wilkes Booth standing upon a crutch. He likens him at this instant to his brother Edwin, whom, he says, he so much resembled that he believed, for the moment, the whole pursuit to have been a mistake. At the gleam of the fire, Wilkes dropped his crutch and carbine, and on both hands crept to the spot to espy the incendiary and shoot him dead. His eyes were lustrous, like fever, and swelled and rolled in terrible beauty, while his teeth were fixed, and he wore the expression of one in the calmness before frenzy. In vain he peered, with vengeance in his look; the blaze that made him visible concealed his enemy. A second he turned glaring at the fire, as if to leap upon it and extinguish it, but it had made such headway that this was a futile impulse, and he dismissed it. As calmly as upon the battle-field a veteran stands, amidst the hail of ball, and shell, and plunging iron, Booth turned at a man's stride, and pushed for the door, carbine in poise, and the last resolve of death, which we name despair, sat on his high, bloodless forehead.'

In fact Edwin did not look at all like John Booth. So here we have this eloquent and romantic fiction writer describing how Conger peered 'with his eye to the crack' through the barn door (or wall). It is interesting because it may have been the same crack through which Sergeant Corbett shot Booth. However next you will see the 'disobedient' sergeant actually peering through 'an eyehole' to draw upon him the fatal bead. But the wording is even more ominous here, because it was through another eyehole in which the President was shot. What an horrendous coincidence. Both Conger and Corbett have an eye for spy holes.

'As so he dashed, intent to expire not unaccompanied, a disobedient sergeant, at an eyehole, drew upon him the fatal bead. The barn was all glorious with conflagration, and in the beautiful ruin this outlawed man strode like all that we know of wicked valor, stern in the face of death. A shock, a shout, a gathering up of his splendid figure, as if to overtip the statue God gave him, and John Wilkes Booth fell headlong to the floor, lying there in a heap, a little life remaining. But no.

"He has shot himself," cried Baker,

unaware of the source of the report, and rushing in , he grasped his arm, to guard against any feint or strategy. A moment convinced him that further struggle with the prone flesh was useless. Booth did not move, nor breathe, nor gasp. Conger and the two sergeants now entered, and, taking up the body, they bore it in haste from the advancing flame, and laid it without upon the grass, all fresh with heavenly dew.

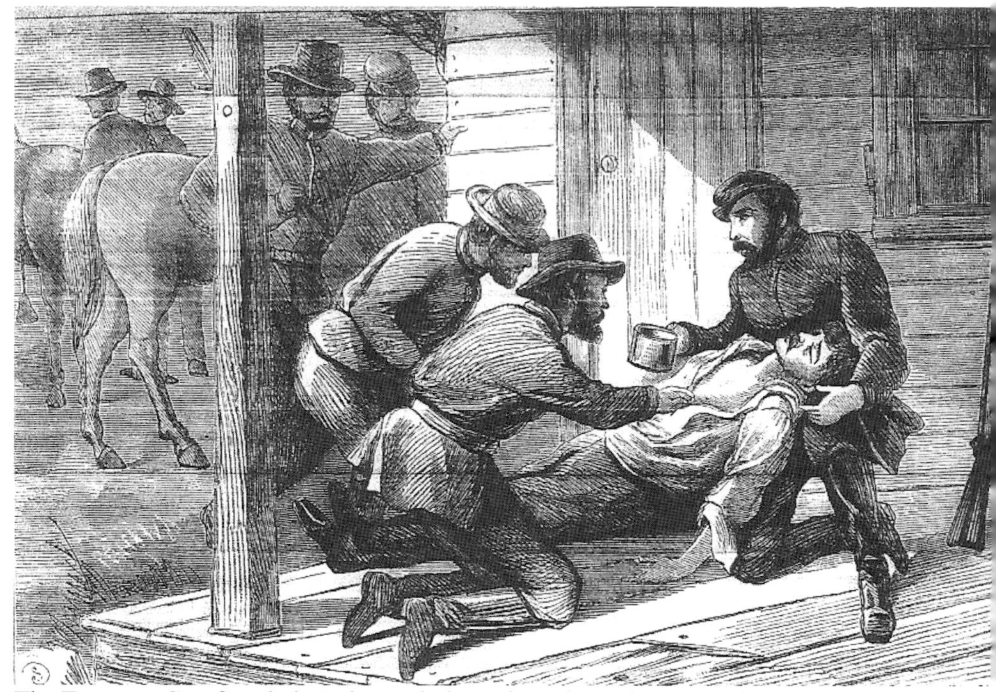

The Troopers Comfort their Dying Rebel Brother The Unknown Soldier in Boston's Lap

"Water," cried Conger; "bring water."

When this was dashed into his face, he revived, a moment, and stirred his lips. Baker put his ear close down and heard him say:-

"Tell mother-and-die-for my country."

They lifted him again, the fire encroaching in hotness upon them, and placed him upon the porch before the dwelling. A mattress was brought down, on which they placed him, and propped his head, and gave him water and brandy. The women of the household, joined meantime by another son, who had been found in one of the corn-cribs, watching, so he said, to see that Booth and Harold did not steal the horses, were nervous, but prompt due to the dying man all kindnesses, although waved sternly back by the detectives. They dipped a rag in brandy and water, and this being put between Booth's teeth, he sucked it greedily. When he was able to articulate again, he muttered to Baker the same words, with an addenda:-

"Tell mother I died for my country, I thought I did it for the best."

Baker repeated this, saying at the same time,

"Booth, do I repeat it correctly?" Booth nodded his head."

Of course Baker has insured that the dying soldier should confirm he is 'Booth' by getting him to nod his head, in answering the question.

'By this time the greyness of the dawn was approaching ; moving figures, inquisitively coming near, were to be seen distinctly , and the cocks began to crow gutturally, though the barn this time was a hulk of blaze and ashes, sending toward the zenith a spiral line of dense smoke. The women became importunate at this time that the troops might be ordered to extinguish the fire, which was sprawling toward their precious corn cribs. Not even death could banish the call of interest.(Yes, their very livelihood: Author). Soldiers were sent to put out the fire, and Booth, relieved of the bustle around him, drew near to death a pace. Twice he was heard to say,

"Kill me-- kill me!"

His lips often moved, but could complete no appreciable sound. He made once a motion, which the quick eye of Conger understood to mean that his throat pained him. Conger put his finger their, when the dying man attempted to cough, but only caused the blood at his perforated neck to flow more lively. He had very little, although shot quite through, beneath and behind the ears, his collar being severed on both sides. A soldier had been meanwhile dispatched for a doctor, but the route and return was quite six miles, and the sinner was sinking fast. Still the women made efforts to get to see him, but were always rebuffed, and all the brandy they could find was demanded by the assassin, who motioned for strong drink every two minutes. He made frequent desires to be turned over- not by speech, but by gesture- and was alternately placed upon his back, belly, and side. His tremendous vitality evidenced itself almost miraculously. Now and then his heart would cease to throb, and his pulse would be as cold as a dead man's. Directly life would begin anew, the face would finish up effulgently, the eyes open and brighten, and soon relapsing, stillness reasserted, would again be dispossessed by the same magnificent triumph of man over mortality. Finally, the fussy little doctor arrived, in time to be useless. He probed the wound to see if the ball were not in it, and shook his head sagely, and talked learnedly.'

This is interesting because Lincoln's wound was probed in exactly the same manner by the Surgeon General. Both, seemingly to search for the bullet as if an exercise in forensic science. Thus it seems that some doctors and surgeons rarely differ in their search for objective knowledge, having given up trying to heal people.

'Just at his coming, Booth had asked to have his hands raised and shown him. They were so paralysed that he did not know their location. When they were displayed, he muttered, with a sad lethargy,

"Useless-- Useless!"

These were the last words he ever uttered.'

Yes, but even these words were a dictionary compared to the absolute zero amount of description relating to what 'Booth' was wearing that might tally with the dress he was wearing when he fled from Washington. Not even the famous moustache. However other accounts, in the local press, say they were in Confederate uniforms. And the dead soldier had a tattoo on his hand, and a Christian medallion around his neck. These were confirmed by the autopsy however. And Baker has the satanic gift of making a hero out of the Unknown Soldier that he has been responsible, in his perversion, for being the instrument of his murder.

'As he began to die , the sun rose and began to throw beams into all the tree tops. It was at a man's height when the struggle of death twitched and lingered in the fading bravo's face. His jaw drew spasmodically and obliquely downward; his eyeballs rolled towards his feet, and began to swell; lividness like a horrible shadow, fastened upon him, and with a sort of gurgle, and sudden check, he stretched his feet, and threw his head back, and gave up the ghost.
They sewed him up in a saddle-blanket. This was his shroud; too like a soldier's. (Indeed). Harold, meantime, had been tied to a tree, but was now released for the march. Colonel Conger pushed on immediately for Washington; the cortege was to follow. Booth's only arms were a carbine, knife and two revolvers.'

Is that all? How did he manage his carbine and his crutch? Well you may remember 'Herold' had told Lloyd they only needed one carbine because 'Booth' was lame, so it was Herold's, but in any case he could have used Herold's carbine as a crutch, at a push, butt downwards. In fact the Unknown Soldier probably had no crutch. And note how Herold's character has changed back to being a dupe. And it was supposedly the same 'dirk' knife used to slash Rathbone in the theatre, but how did they manage to pick up the extra revolvers, and what about the ammo.? Well Mary was supposed to have delivered extra revolvers and field glasses to Lloyd, like the good strategic General she was. But Baker forgot to mention the less than dynamic duo picking these items up. As a cross reference we also have Cavalryman Millington's account:

'Part of our company was detailed to surround the barn and part to surround the house. I was with the party sent to the barn. Our lieutenant. who heard some whispering in the barn, called,

" Come out at once."

One of the men inside the barn asked,

"Who are you?" Our officer said,

"It doesn't make any difference who we are, but we know who you are. You had better come out at once."

The man in the barn who had done the talking was the man we were after - Booth. He refused to come out. He said,

"If you will withdraw your men 30 rods, I will come out and we'll shoot it out."

We could hear Booth accusing the man who was with him, David E. Harold, of being a coward. Harold was willing to surrender and Booth said,

"You're a coward to desert me." Finally, Booth called out and said,

"Harold will surrender, but I will not." Our captain said,

"Tell Harold to pass out his arms and come out." Booth said,

"Harold has no arms. They belong to me."

Our officer told Harold to come to the door. He came and as he opened the door Lieutenant Dougherty grabbed him and pulled him out. With a picket rope he tied him to a locust tree, called me and told me to guard him. I said to Harold,

"Who was in the barn with you? Was it Booth?" He said,

"Yes, Booth is in the barn." and he added,

"Booth told me, when he asked me to help him, that he was going to kidnap Lincoln: he didn't tell me he was going to kill him." I said,

"When you learned that Booth had killed Lincoln, why did you help him to escape?" Harold said,

"Booth threatened to kill me if I didn't help him get away. Booth came out of the rear of the theatre immediately after shooting Lincoln and we went to Dr. Mudd's home. After Dr. Mudd had set Booth's leg we went to Port Tobacco and hid that day. That night we got a fisherman to take us over the river into Virginia. It was so rough that the fisherman said it was unsafe, but Booth told him we had to cross at once and he would kill him if he didn't take us."

Once more the officer summoned Booth to surrender. Booth responded,

"I'll fight you single handed, but I'll never surrender."

Detective Conger went to the opposite side of the barn and lit some loose straw under the sill. I heard a shot and a moment later saw the door was open. Booth had been shot through the neck. They brought him out, carried him to the Garrett house and put him on the porch. A soldier was sent to Port Royal for a doctor, who arrived about daylight. Meanwhile, the barn had burned down and some of the men were hunting in the ruins for relics. They found two revolvers and one of our boys got Booth's carbine. The revolvers were spoiled by the fire. Booth lived about three hours. He was wrapped in a government blanket, his body was placed in a old wagon and a Negro drove the rig to Acquia Creek, which we reached at dusk.'

There is a mine of information in this account which ties up more closely with Baker than it does with his own Lieutenant. For example the two revolvers, burned in the fire are fictional to match Baker's account. Thus he confirms Baker, in the following manner: Booth and Herold met up outside the theatre, immediately after shooting

Lincoln. Then they went straight to Dr. Mudd, but he omits saying they stopped by at Lloyd's place. Well, there was a lot to remember and Baker probably thought it unnecessary to fill in all the details anyway. Then they went straight to Port Tobacco. This is nearly true because the Detective decoys, Tyson and Hensted found lodgings at the garrison near there, at the army base at Chapel Point on the following day, I.e. on Easter Sunday the 16th of April. However they had spent part of the night of the 15th at Sam Coxe's house, leaving at 4 a.m. And just as they did for Dr, Mudd they took his kindness and hospitality, then straight after they left, the arresting officers came along. So as you can see, this was their standard operational procedure. No mystery at all. Indeed it sounds they were the night shift detectives, with the day shift following them up at 1) Lloyd's tavern 2) Dr. Mudd's home and 3) Sam Coxe's home. Three out of three, not too bad for two nights work of diabolical treachery. Then on the 20th George Adzerodt whom 'they played off' as Crangle. Then on the 26th taking Garrett's sons, by the 16th NY Cavalry, leaving fratricide, mayhem and destitution in their path.

And as detailed above Baker also had to find lodgings for 'Booth' and 'Herold' at Samuel Coxe's house, which Tyson and Hensted did, by paying off the false witness Swan, twelve greenbacks, outside Coxe's house. But when Swan looked back he did not in fact see them go back into Sam Coxe's house, to stay five days. This is because Sam Coxe was arrested 3 days later by the tracker force under Major O'Bierne, Lieutenant Laverty and Officer Lee, either on the 18th or 19th of April. This was just before arriving in Port Tobacco on the 20th to arrest 'Crangle' at Mrs. Wheeler's home, but Crangle was in fact probably Adzerodt. Instead of going back into Coxe's home, they high tailed it straight to Chapel Point only 10 or 12 miles from Bryantown.

So in fact from Dr. Mudd's home, they went for another night's work at Sam Coxe's , after they had been given full board and twelve hours rest, and care and generosity. And fixing a perfectly healthy leg for 25 greenbacks. But the real cost to Dr. Mudd in return, was four years hard labour, an early death and a lifetime of abuse. His name and his children's, children's names to be dis-honoured, forever. This is the abject and perverse work of an evil government, under the guise of Democracy. It could happen to any one, at any point in time. This is why people should be forever vigilant whenever dealing with the anything connected with the government, or indeed just be vigilant always. Perhaps the song 'Strangers in the Night' is more than a romantic song, innocently sung by Nancy and Frank Sinatra. Now we have Doherty's account just for a final cross reference:

'At dark we passed the Garrett farm, not then dreaming that the assassins were concealed there. Arriving at Bowling Green, I surrounded Goldman's Hotel. After some hesitation the door was opened by Mrs. Goldman. I inquired of her who were the male inmates of the house. She replied that there was only her wounded son, and I directed her to show me his room, telling her that if my men were fired on I should burn the building and take the inmates prisoners to Washington. She took me up one flight of stairs to her son's room, and as I entered Captain Jett sprang from his bed, half-dressed. Her son lay on another bed, wounded. Jett admitted his identity, and drawing Mr. Stanton's proclamation from my pocket I read it to him, and then said,

"I have known your movements for the past two or three days, and if you do not tell me the truth I will hang you; but if you give me the information I want, I will protect you."
He was greatly excited, and told me that he had left Booth at Garrett's house, three miles from Port Conway, the evening before, and that Herold had come to Bowling Green with him, and returned that morning. I had Jett's horse taken from the stable, and, placing a guard over him, we retraced our steps towards Garrett's. It was now about midnight, and my men, having been out since the 24th without sleep and with very little food, were exhausted; those who had been left on the edge of the town had fallen asleep. I had some difficulty in arousing them, but when they learned that we were on Booth's track new life seemed to be infused into them. I placed Corbett in the rear with orders to allow no man to fall out of line. Upon reaching Garrett's orchard fence I halted, and in company with Rollins and the detectives took a survey of the premises. I had the fence taken down. I told off six men, gave out the countersign of 'Boston,' and sent the six men as a patrol in rear of the out-buildings, with instructions to allow no one to pass through the field or to approach them without the countersign. The gates in front of Garrett's house were quietly opened, and in a minute the whole premises were surrounded. I dismounted, and knocked loudly at the front door. Old Mr. Garrett came out. I seized him, and asked him where the men were who were there yesterday. He replied that they had gone to the woods when the cavalry passed the previous afternoon. While I was speaking with him some of the men had entered the house to search it. Soon one of the soldiers sang out.

"O Lieutenant! I have a man here I found in the corn-crib".

It was young Garrett, and I demanded the whereabouts of the fugitives. He replied,

"In the barn."

Leaving a few men around the house, we proceeded in the direction of the barn, which we surrounded. I kicked on the door of the barn several times without receiving a reply. Meantime another son of Garrett's had been captured. The barn was secured with a pad-lock, and young Garrett carried the key. I unlocked the door, and again summoned the inmates of the building to surrender. After some delay Booth said,

"For whom do you take me?"

I replied, "It doesn't make any difference. Come out."

He said, "I am a cripple and alone".

I said, "I know who is with you, and you had better surrender."

He replied, "I may be taken by my friends, but not by my foes".

I said, " If you don't come out, I'll burn the building".

I directed a corporal to pile up some hay in a crack in the wall of the barn, and set the building on fire. As the corporal was picking up the hay and brush Booth said,

"If you come back here I will put a bullet through you".

I then motioned to the corporal to desist, and decided to wait for daylight and then to enter the barn by both doors and overpower the assassins. Booth then said, in a drawling voice,

"O Captain! there is a man in here who wants to surrender awful bad",

I replied, "You had better follow his example and come out."

His answer was, "No, I have not made up my mind; but draw your men up fifty paces off and give me a chance for my life."

I told him I had not come to fight; that I had fifty men, and could take him. Then he said,

"Well, my brave boys, prepare me a stretcher, and place another stain on our glorious banner."

At this moment Herold reached the door. I asked him to hand out his arms; he replied that he had none. I told him I knew exactly what weapons he had. Booth replied,

"I own all the arms, and may have to use them on you, gentlemen."

I then said to Herold,

"Let me see your hands".

He put them through the partly opened door and I seized him by the wrists. I handed him over to a non-commissioned officer. Just at this moment I heard a shot, and thought Booth had shot himself. Throwing open the door, I saw that the straw and hay behind Booth were on fire. He was half-turning towards it. He had a crutch, and he held a carbine in his hand. I rushed into the burning barn, followed by my men, and as he was falling caught him under the arms and pulled him out of the barn. The burning building becoming too hot, I had him carried to the veranda of Garrett's house.

Booth received his death-shot in this manner. While I was taking Herold out of the barn one of the detectives went to the rear, and pulling out some protruding straw set fire to it. I had placed Sergeant Boston Corbett at a large crack in the side of the barn, and he, seeing by the igniting hay that Booth was leveling his carbine at either Herold or myself, fired, to disable him in the arm; but Booth making a sudden move, the aim erred, and the bullet struck Booth in the back of the head, about an inch below the spot where his shot had entered the head of Mr. Lincoln. Booth asked me by signs to raise his hands. I lifted them up and he gasped,

"Useless, use-less!"

We gave him brandy and water, but he could not swallow it. I sent to Port Royal for a physician, who could do nothing when he came, and at seven o'clock Booth breathed his last. He had on his person a diary, a large bowie knife, two pistols, a compass, and a draft on Canada for £60. I took a saddle blanket off my horse, and, borrowing a darning needle from Miss Garrett, sewed his body in it. The men found an old wagon, and impressed it, with the negro driver. The body was placed upon it, and two hours after Booth's death I was on the way back to Belle Plain, where I had left the steamboat. I had

BOOTH KILLED.

Full Account of the Pursuit and its Result.

He is Traced into St. Mary's County, Maryland.

Harrold and Booth Discovered in a Barn.

Booth Declares He will not be Taken Alive.

The Barn Set on Fire to Force Them Out.

SERGT. BOSTON CORBETT FIRES AT BOOTH

He is Shot Through the Neck and Dies in Three Hours.

His Body and Harrold Brought to Washington.

[OFFICIAL.]

WAR DEPARTMENT,
WASHINGTON, April 27, 1865—9:20 A. M.

Maj.-Gen. John A. Dix, New-York:

J. WILKES BOOTH and HARROLD were chased from the swamp in St. Mary's County, Maryland, to Garrett's farm, near Port Royal, on the Rappahannock, by Col. BAKER's force.

The barn in which they took refuge was fired.

BOOTH, in making his escape, was shot through the head and killed, lingering about three hours, and HARROLD was captured. BOOTH's body and HARROLD are now here.

EDWIN M. STANTON,
Secretary of War.

DETAILS OF THE CAPTURE OF BOOTH.

Special Dispatch to the New-York Times.

WASHINGTON, Thursday, April 27.

About 8 o'clock last evening we received the intelligence of the capture of J. WILKES BOOTH, the assassin of ABRAHAM LINCOLN, and one of his accomplices in the murder, DAVID C. HARROLD. The following are such of the particulars as we were enabled to gather, which, with the exception of the *precise locality where the occurrence took place*, we give as being reliable and correct. It having been pretty clearly ascertained that BOOTH and his accomplice had crossed the Potomac River at or near Aquia Creek, our cavalry scouts in that vicinity have been in consequence unusually active in their endeavors to get on their trail. Early yesterday morning a squad of about twelve men, belonging to the Sixteenth New-York Cavalry, under command of a Lieutenant, whose name we did not learn, succeeded in discovering the fugitives *in a barn on the road leading from Port Royal to* Bowling Green in Caroline County, Va. As soon as they were discovered, the place was surrounded and the assassins ordered to surrender. This they both refused to do, BOOTH declaring that he would not be taken alive, and offering to fight the whole squad if he would be permitted to place *himself twenty yards* distant from them. His proposition was not, however, acceded to, and as they persisted in their refusal to surrender, the Lieutenant determined to burn them out, and accordingly set fire to the barn, shortly after which HARROLD came out and gave himself up. BOOTH *remained* in the burning building *for some* time, and until driven out by the fire, when he rushed out and was immediately shot through the neck by the sergeant of the squad.

Since the above we have had an interview with two of the cavalrymen engaged in the capture of the assassins. From them we learn that the whole party consisted of twenty-eight, including two detectives. The first information respecting BOOTH's crossing the river, and his probable whereabouts, was obtained from disbanded rebel soldiers who were met with in all directions in that part of the country. From one and another of these the clue to BOOTH's movements was gathered and held until just at daybreak they came upon the barn, where he and HARROLD were secreted. A parley was held, and BOOTH manifested the most desperate determination not to be taken alive, and to take as many of the lives of the party as possible. Lieut. EDWARD P. DOHERTY, who commanded the scouting party, determined to make short work of him. When HARROLD saw the preparations for firing the barn, he declared his willingness to surrender, and said he would not fight if they would let him out. BOOTH, on the contrary, was impudently defiant, offering at first to fight the whole squad at one hundred yards, and subsequently at fifty yards. He was hobbling on crutches, apparently very lame. He swore he would die like a man, etc. HARROLD having been secured, as soon as the burning hay lighted the interior of the barn sufficiently to render the scowling face of BOOTH, the assassin, visible, Sergeant BOSTON CORBETT fired upon him and he fell. The ball passed through his neck. He was pulled out of the barn, and one of his crutches, and carbine and revolvers secured; the wretch lived about two hours, whispering blasphemies against the government, and messages to his mother, desiring her to be informed that he died for his country. At the time BOOTH was shot he was leaning upon one crutch and preparing to shoot his captors. Only one shot was fired in the entire affair—that which killed the assassin.

Lieut. DOHERTY is one of the bravest fellows in the cavalry service, having distinguished himself in a sharp affair at Culpepper Court-house and on other occasions. The Sixteenth New-York Cavalry is commanded by Col. NELSON SWEITZER, and has been doing duty in Fairfax County. This regiment formed part of the cavalry escort on the day of the President's obsequies in Washington. The body of BOOTH and the assassin's accomplice, HARROLD, were placed on board the *Ida* and sent to Washington, arriving here about 1 o'clock this morning.

ACCURATE ACCOUNT OF THE PURSUIT AND CAPTURE OF BOOTH.

Special Dispatch to the New-York Times.

WASHINGTON, Thursday, April 27.

Without recurring to the circumstances that brought together and put to work a large body of detectives in pursuit of the assassin BOOTH and his accessories in crime, I propose to state briefly and consecutively the incidents in the pursuit from the time the detachment started from this city until their arrival here this morning with the corpse of BOOTH and the body of HARROLD. The following facts I obtained from Col. BAKER and the other persons engaged with him.

From the time the Secretary of War telegraphed Col. L. C. BAKER at New-York, twelve days ago, to come here immediately and take charge of the matter of ferreting out the facts, and arresting the criminals in the assassination, up to last Sunday, but little progress was made in the right direction. All the lower counties of Maryland were scoured by a large force consisting of 1,600 cavalry and 500 detectives and citizens. On Sunday last Col. BAKER learned of a little boy in Maryland some facts which satisfied him that BOOTH and HARROLD had crossed the river about 11 o'clock A. M., and had gone into Virginia. A telegraph operator with a small body of soldiers was sent down the river to tap the wires at a given place and make certain inquiries. This party returned on Monday morning last, bringing with them a negro man whom they picked up at Swan Point, who, on being closely interrogated, disclosed that he had seen parties cross in a boat, and the description of these parties assured Col. BAKER that BOOTH and HARROLD were the men. No examination or search had yet been made by official authority in Virginia. Demand was made upon Gen. HANCOCK for a detachment of cavalry, and twenty-eight of the Sixteenth New-York were immediately sent to Col. BAKER, under command of Lieut. DOHERTY, one of this detachment being BOSTON CORBETT. The whole party were put in charge of Lieut. L. B. BAKER and Lieut.-Col. E. J. CONGER. They were instructed to go immediately to Port Royal; that BOOTH had crossed the river, and had had about time to reach that point; that he could not ride on horseback, and must therefore have traveled slowly.

At twenty-five minutes past four o'clock on Monday afternoon, this force left the Sixth-street wharf in the steamer *Ida*. They were directed that when they arrived at the landing place—Belle Plain—they should shove or swim their horses to the shore, if they could not make a landing, for they must have the horses on land. That night the party went down the river four miles, but heard nothing satisfactory. They finally, at daylight, brought up below Port Royal some miles. They returned, finding no trace of the criminals till they got to Port Royal Ferry. Lieut. BAKER rode up, found the ferryman, and made inquiries. The ferryman stoutly denied having seen any such persons as those described. Lieut. BAKER throttled him and threatened him, yet he denied any knowledge of the persons sought. By the side of the ferryman a negro was sitting. Lieut. BAKER presented a likeness of BOOTH and HARROLD. The negro upon looking at these exclaimed, "Why, Massa, them's the gentleman we brought cross the river yesterday." The ferryman then admitted that he had brought BOOTH and HARROLD over the river in his boat. The cavalry was started off and went fourteen miles beyond Garrett's place. There they met a negro who said he saw two men sitting on Garrett's porch that afternoon. The description of one accorded with that of BOOTH. Lieut. BAKER and his party returned to GARRETT's house. GARRETT denied that the two men had been there. BAKER threatened to shoot him if he did not tell the truth. GARRETT's son thereupon came out of the house and said the two men were in the barn. The barn was at once surrounded. This was about 2 A. M. BAKER went up and rapped at the door. BOOTH asked "Who are you, friends or foes? Are you Confederates? I have got five men in here, and we can protect ourselves." Col. BAKER replied, "I have fifty men out here; you are surrounded, and you may as well come out and surrender." BOOTH answered, "I shall never give up; I'll not be taken alive." The instructions were that every means possible must be taken to arrest BOOTH alive, and BAKER, CONGER and DOHERTY held a consultation a few feet from the barn. In the meantime BOOTH was cursing HARROLD for his cowardice, charging him with a desire to meanly surrender, etc.

Col. BAKER and his party returned and held a parley with BOOTH, thus consuming about an hour and a quarter. Another consultation of officers was held, and it was determined that, in view of the probability of an attack from a tolerably large force of rebel cavalry, which they had learned were in the neighborhood, the barn should be fired, and BOOTH thus forced to come out.

CONGER gathered a lot of brush, and placed it against and under the barn, and pulled some hay out of the cracks, in the mean time holding a lighted candle in his hand. BOOTH could now see through the openings of the barn all their movements. The lighted candle was applied to the hay and brush, and directly the flames caught the hay inside the barn. BOOTH rushed towards the burning hay and tried to put out the fire. Failing in this, he ran back to the middle of the floor, gathered up his arms and stood still pondering for a moment. Whilst BOOTH was standing in this position Sergt. BOSTON CORBETT ran up to the barn door and fired. Col. BAKER, not perceiving where the shot came from, exclaimed "he has shot himself," and rushed into the barn and found BOOTH yet standing with a carbine in hand. BAKER clasped BOOTH around the arms and breast; the balance of the party had also, in the mean time, got inside. CORBETT then exclaimed "I shot him." BOOTH fell upon the floor apparently paralized. Water was sent for and the wound bathed. It was now just 3:15 o'clock. The ball had apparently passed through the neck and the spine. In a few moments BOOTH revived. He made an effort to lift his hands up before his eyes. In this he was assisted, and upon seeing them he exclaimed somewhat incoherently, "Useless!—useless!—blood! blood!! and swooned away. He revived from time to time, and expressed himself entirely satisfied with what he had done. He expired at 7.10 yesterday morning.

The body was placed in a cart and conveyed to the steamer *Ida*, and brought upon that vessel to the navy-yard, where the boat arrived at 5:20 o'clock this morning.

While the barn was burning, HARROLD rushed out and was grappled by Lieut. BAKER, thrown to the ground and secured.

CORBETT says he fired with the intention of wounding BOOTH in the shoulder, and did not intend to kill him.

BOOTH had in his possession a diary, in which he had noted events of each day since the assassination of Mr. LINCOLN. This diary is in possession of the War Department. He had also a Spencer carbine, a seven-shooter, a revolver, a pocket pistol and a knife. The latter is supposed to be the one with which he stabbed Mayor RATHBONE. His clothing was of dark blue, not Confederate gray, as has been stated.

CORBETT, who shot BOOTH, was born in England, and is about 33 years old. He came to this country some years since, and resided for several years in Troy, N. Y. He resided for a time in Boston, where he became a member of a Methodist Church, and took in baptism the name of "Boston." He is a man of small stature, slight form, mild countenance and quiet deportment.

Surgeon-Gen. BARNES says the ball did not enter the brain. The body, when he examined it this afternoon, was not in a rapid state of decomposition, but was considerably bruised by jolting about in the cart. It is placed in charge of Col. BAKER, in the attire in which he died, with instructions not to allow any one to approach it, nor to take from it any

Stanton's Account to the New York Times of the killing of the Unknown Soldier and the Arrest of his companion Boyd.

Washington at 2 a.m., April 27. I placed the body of Booth and the prisoner Herold on board the monitor Montauk, after which I marched my worn-out command up through the navy yard to their quarters. The next morning an autopsy was held, and measures were taken to identify the body of Booth. The portion of the neck and head through which the bullet had passed was cut out, and is to-day preserved in the National Museum of Anatomy at Washington. The body was buried in a cell in the Penitentiary, where it remained nearly four years, with the bodies of the other assassins. It was then given to his friends, and now lies in a cemetery in Baltimore.

Edward P. Doherty.'

It is amazing how poetic justice indicates here the flight of Boston's unerring bullet:

'and the bullet struck Booth in the back of the head, about an inch below the spot where his shot had entered the head of Mr. Lincoln.'

This account differs in quite a few details compared to Baker's and of course it favours Doherty in the more direct commanding role as would be expected, since he is the senior army officer. One would have to believe Doherty over Conger and Baker because of the greater army discipline. And apart from this, there is less hype and exaggeration. The only 'un-truths' would tend to be any omissions. It also seems he is trying to protect Corbett by giving a good reason for his deed. And it does ring more true.

The only question are:
1) The photographs he was given should have told him he'd got the wrong men. But he only had the photograph of Edwin Booth. And Stanton's original posters had no photographs, but Baker's posters did have John Wilkes and Herold on them.
2) They were Confederate soldiers according to the local press (The Herald) and so Doherty must have realised that something was amiss. However being an army officer and carrying out his orders he could not afford to dwell on it. In any case the ulterior deed was done before he could do anything about. That is why Baker sent Conger and Baker along. They also knew where to find Jett. Also, Conger returned immediately to Washington alone with the dead soldier's possessions. Note he also picked up the soldier's primitive field compass, which certainly was never mentioned by Baker beforehand, who instead, said Mary had bought 'Booth' field-glasses. But they do have two things in common....... They have circular glass and both can be called field-glasses or field-compasses. Well, Baker never had been a soldier!
And Doherty confirms Conger's act in setting light to the barn and in doing so it aided the immediate act of Corbett, being nearby, inserting his carbine into the crack and shooting the Unknown Soldier. And they acted right away as soon as Doherty was occupied in taking the soldier Boyd by the hands. It is was also a noble act that Lieutenant Doherty caught 'Booth' in his arms and saved him from the fire, after he was mortally wounded.
3) Finally, Lieutenant Doherty mentions nothing about Conger seeing Jett privately

before divulging the whereabouts of the fugitives. But this would be just a convenient omission, and not overtly serious, although it would mean raising a serious issue and a challenge to the NDP.
Here we also see how the large Bowie knife enters into the equation, as opposed to the originally supposed dirk knife held by the assassin, as quoted in the New York Times.
Indeed a Bowie knife would be the right kind of weapon for a soldier, or indeed a frontiers man. This famous knife was immortalised by James (Jim) Bowie (1796-1830) who was born in Kentucky and fought many a knife fight, and supposedly killed in three fights with it. He fought the British in Louisiana and after many close quarter combats he married in Texas but lived also in Mexico and swore allegiance there. He bought land and a textile mill but fell into debt. He took to adventure again, in Silver mining, fighting the Mexican Indians and only just survived. He moved across the south west, finishing up in Texas and became a nominal Colonel in volunteer Regiments. He tried to resign his commission whenever the fighting with the Mexicans stopped, getting bored easily. He finally advocated the defence of the Alamo with 109 men , joined by William Trevis, with 36 men then Davy Crockett with 12 men. This force defended the fort against 1500 men of the Mexican General Santa Anna, but he took ill during his command and died in his cot using his trusty knife as his last defence, with honour. At least fourteen films have been made of Bowie's life and epic adventures, plus literature and TV films. My favourite being 'The Alamo' with Richard Widmark as Bowie including John Wayne as Davy Crockett and Lawrence Harvey as Colonel Trevis. Indeed Widmark was a great actor, and always acted strongly, with great conviction in any film, on a par with Richard Boone perhaps. The knife probably stemmed from the Spanish navaja clasp knife. It is similar to but larger than the Finnish hunters and trapper's puukko knife, the atypical frontal curve being ideal for skinning. It had many modifications and became famous because of the legendary Bowie from circa 1830. It could be anything from 6" to 12" long and up to 2" wide. It was made and often modified by James Black, blacksmith in Old Washington , Arkansas as a frontiers and fighting knife, and especially for Bowie. It was also made in Sheffield, England in later years.

Jim Bowie

1796- 1836

Bowie Knife

Circa 1830

Chapter 18

The Autopsy on the Montauk

The party returned to Washington on the iron clad 'Montauk' and docked at the old Navy Fort near the Arsenal prison on the Potomac. Baker's vivid imagination and Phinias's writing skills continue:

"They found about him bills of exchange, Canada money, and a diary. A venerable old negro living in the vicinity had the misfortune to possess a horse. This horse was a relic of former generations, and showed by his protruding ribs the general leanness of the land. He moved in an eccentric amble, and when put upon his speed was generally backward. To this old negro's horse was harnessed a very shaky and absurd wagon, which rattled like approaching dissolution, and each part of it ran without any connection or correspondence with any other part. It had no tail-board, and its shafts were sharp as famine; and into this mimicry of a vehicle the murderer was to be sent to the Potomac River, while the man he had murdered was moving in state across the mourning continent. The old negro geared up his wagon by means of a set of fossil harnesses, and when it was backed to Garrett's porch, they laid within it the discoloured corpse. The corpse was tied with rope around the legs, and made fast to the wagon side. Harold's legs were tied to stirrups, and he was placed in the centre of four murderous looking cavalrymen. The two sons of Garrett were taken along despite the sobs and petitions of the old folks and women, but the rebel captain who had given Booth a lift got off amid the night's agitations, and was not rearrested."

In fact according to Lieutenant Doherty the rebel Captain Jett went off with Lieutenant Baker ahead of Doherty's command and that's how he escaped, and pre-planned of course. And naturally Baker scores again for his promotion, by his detectives arresting innocent civilians, causing destitution to the families. Note Baker's (or his ghost writer's) humour seems to intensify itself in relation to the local Afro- Americans. But this local man had the transport that they had not planned for, be it ever so basic. Baker himself measures his own importance against the essential man (to overcome his inferiority), who are really infinitely richer than he both in spirit and in honest endeavour. It is also a fact that in those days Virginia and much of the South had a preponderance of Afro-Americans over white people. And Murderer is Baker's favourite word.

"So moved the cavalcade of retribution, with death in its midst, along the road to Port Royal. When the wagon started, Booth's wound, now scarcely dribbling, began to run anew. It fell through the crack of the wagon, and fell dripping upon the axle, and spotting the road with terrible wafers. It stained the planks and soaked the blankets; and the old negro, at a stoppage, dabbled his hands in it by mistake; he drew back instantly, with a shudder and stiffled expletive, 'Gor-r-r, dat'll never come off in de world; it's murderer's blood. He wrung his hands, and looked imploringly at the officers, and shuddered again,; Gor-r-r, I wouldn't have dat on me for tousand tousand dollars'."

The 'murderer's' blood being a figment of Baker's twisted imagination, that somehow manages to transfer his own Christian guilt onto the Unknown Soldier, as a release mechanism.

"The progress of the team was slow, with frequent danger of shipwreck altogether, but toward noon the cortege filed through Port Royal, where the citizens came out to ask the matter, and why a man's body, covered with sombre blankets, was going by with so great escort. They were told that it was a wounded Confederate, and so held their tongues. The little ferry, again in requisition, took them over by squads, they pushed from Port Conway to Belle Plain, which they reached in the middle of the afternoon. All the way the blood dribbled from the corpse in a slow incessant, sanguine exudition. The old negro was niggardly dismissed with two paper dollars. The dead man untied and cast upon the vessel's deck, steam gotten up in a little while, and the broad Potomac shores saw this skeleton ship flit by, as the bloody sun threw gashes and blots of un-healthy light along the silver surface. All the way associate with the carcass went Harold, shuddering in so grim companionship, and in awakened fears of his own approaching ordeal, beyond which loomed already, the gossamer fabric of a scaffold. He tried to talk for his own exoneration, saying he had ridden as was his wont, beyond the East Branch, and returning found Booth wounded, who begged him to be his companion. Of his crime he knew nothing, so help him God, &c. But nobody listened to him. All interest of crime , courage, and retribution centred in the dead flesh at his feet. At Washington, high and low turned out to look on Booth. Only a few were permitted to look at his corpse for purpose of recognition. It was fairly preserved, though on one side of his face distorted, and looking blue like death, and wildly bandit-like, as if beaten by avenging winds.
Finally the Secretary of War, without instructions of any kind, committed to Colonel Lafayette C. Baker, of the Secret Service, the stark corpse of J. Wilkes Booth. The Secret Service never fulfilled its vocation more secretly,

"What have you done with the body?" said I to Baker.

"That is known," he answered,

"to only one man living beside myself. It is gone; I will not tell you where; the only man who knows it is sworn to silence; never till the great trumpeter comes shall the grave of Booth be discovered."

And this is true. Last night, the 27th of April, a small row-boat received the carcass of the murderer; two men were in it; they carried the body off into the darkness, like his great crime, may it remain forever; impassable, invisible, nondescript, condemned to that worse than damnation-annihilation.
The river bottom may ooze about it, laden with great shot and drowning manacles. The earth may have opened to give it that silence and forgiveness which man will never give to its memory. The fishes may swim around it, or the daisies grow white above it; but we shall never know. Mysterious, incomprehensible, unattainable, like the dim times through which we live, we think upon it as if we only dreamed in a perturbed fever; the assassin of a nation's head rests somewhere in the elements, and that is all; but if the indignant seas or the profound turf shall ever vomit this corpse from their recesses, and it receives Christian burial from someone who does not recognize it, let the last words those decaying lips ever uttered be carved above them with a dagger, to tell the history of a young, and once promising life.'

From this account we see that the brave soldier's body was indeed well preserved giving the lie to Dr. May's account that he could not say positively that it was Booth, except from the scar in his neck from which he had 'operated' on years before to remove a 'tumour', because the body had decayed beyond recognition. However later Baker says the body had decayed further on the boat at the end of the post-mortem:

In order to establish the body of the assassin beyond all question, the Secretary of War directed me to summon a number of witnesses residing in the city of Washington, who had previously known the murderer. Some two years previous to the assassination of the President, Booth had had a tumor or carbuncle cut from his neck by a surgeon. On inquiry I ascertained that Dr. May, a well known and very skilful surgeon, of twenty five years practice in Washington, had performed the operation.
Accordingly I called on Dr. May, who, before seeing the body, minutely described the exact location of the tumour, the nature and date of the operation, &c. After being sworn, he pointed to the scar on the neck, which was then plainly visible. Five other witnesses were examined, all of whom had known the witnesses for years. The various newspaper accounts' referring to the mutilation of Booth's body, are equally absurd. General Barnes, Surgeon General U.S.A., was on board the gun-boat where the post mortem examination was held, with his assistants. General Barnes cut from Booth's neck about two inches of the spinal column through which the ball had passed; this piece of bone, which is now on exhibition in the Government Medical Museum, in Washington, is the only relic of the assassin's body above ground, and this is the only mutilation of the remains that ever occurred. Immediately after the conclusion of the medical examination, the Secretary of War gave orders as to the disposition of the body, which had become very offensive, owing to the condition it had remained in after death; the leg broken in jumping from the box to the stage, was much discoloured and broken, the blood having saturated his under-clothing.

Indeed, Dr. May did see the body but in his statement he could not positively recognise the man as Booth due to the amount of decay. This is nonsense of course because the soldier was in uniform and had a real tattoo, for starters. And Dr. May had never operated on Booth. It was a statement given in the negative to satisfy the authorities.
And why did Barnes cut two inches from the soldier's neck? What kind of autopsy is this? Another search for an assassin's bullet, like he did on his live President? Or to cut out the carbuncle again?
All of this account has been collated from Baker himself and his officers, and written by his ghost writer, who a year or two later had become a foreign correspondent of a leading New York daily paper. And we see here how Stanton has left all the responsibility to Baker. And the only other man he is referring to, who knows where the body was buried, is Byron Baker. And the captive soldier could not have been anywhere near to East Branch, near Washington. In any case Baker's own version states that 'Booth' and 'Herold' started together outside the theatre galloping past the Mint and so forth. So although Baker is implying the soldier must be lying, he is also implying that the soldier is trying to say, he met up with 'Booth' at East Branch, (of the Potomac) near Alexandria just outside Washington. Again we see how Baker forks the tongues of innocent men. And further:

Surgeon General Barnes Probes the Unknown Soldier's Brain as he did the President's.

'It is not improper to state, that only two persons on earth know where the body of Booth lies. Lieutenant Baker, on whose lap his dying head was laid, and myself, having the dark secret to keep. The night before the removal of the remains I was ordered, by the Secretary of War, to have them securely guarded, that no one might touch them; as

"every hair of his head would be a valued relic to the sympathizers with the South in Washington."

I had not had my clothes off for nearly two weeks, and was granted leave of absence from the vessel, on whose deck was lying the corpse of the assassin, covered with two blankets sewed together like a sack, completely concealing it. Upon my return, I was greatly surprised and indignant, to find persons of high position, and some of secession proclivities, around the dead body, the coarse shroud parted at the seam, and a lady at that moment cutting off a lock, of the black, curled, and beautiful hair.'

According to other sources, this soldier was of red or fair complexion.

'I seized the fair hands, and, after a refusal to give me the relic, forcibly took it, and then cleared the deck, to the amazement and displeasure of some of the party. The diary kept by Booth after the murder of the President, to which I referred in connection with the giving of the personal effects of Booth to the Secretary of War, recorded the adventures of the fugitive; one of these was the killing of his horse in the tangled forest to avoid detection, and then sleeping between the animal's legs to get the warmth while it remained in the dead body, during the long hours of the horrible night. With dawn, he dragged his own painful limbs along his untrodden path of flight from the apparently slow, but certain grasp of avenging justice.'

Here again Baker faithfully describes the account of the Unknown Soldier's horse fall, confirming the true contents of the diary, before he had ripped them out and forged Booth's hand. He then handed it to Stanton in the company of the recently 'promoted' Colonel Conger. As explained before this explains the true contents of the soldier's diary. Perhaps there was a lot more writing in it. But the diary was out of date and the soldier may have just used it to make occasional notes or messages. Being a soldier, probably with Moseby's command, maybe he had ripped out some pages himself; but unlikely since all his own records are gone, in a successive series, that is, the pages of Jan 1st till June16th, 1864 = 168 days, since it was a leap year. And since each page of the diary contained six days. We have 168/6 = 28 pages. The myth of 18 missing pages may have originated from Baker himself, but nobody may have bothered to check this essential fact 'officially', ever since. The reason Baker would have chose 18 is that it would (superficially) bring the diary up to 18th April (108 days), theoretically. However, 17 pages would have brought it up to the 12th April, two days too soon to describe the deed. Also, it's less pages to account for. In fact the forged writing is dated Friday, 14th April, on the real page of June 17th, 1864.
As far as Baker is concerned the soldier wanted to avoid detection, so he shot his horse. Of course that is an insane reason, both the horse and rider had been injured. However because it's another Baker lie (about detection), it therefore gives the truth about the soldier recording this event. And therefore proves that Baker ripped out all of the soldier's writings. In fact the exaggerations on this theme have grown beyond all norms of rationality, so that even the myths have become insane. Thus one account says that Booth and Herold slit their horses throats while swimming across the Potomac. This of course would have been music to the minds of the illuminati. In fact however, most of the illuminati today would have little interest and even less understanding of the subject, because its 'history'. That is unless they could hire some crooked lawyers to make a 'pile' out of it. So, certain members of the public were allowed to see the body on the deck of the Montauk and one lady tried to obtain evidence, but was rudely interrupted by Baker himself. That is strange as you would have thought there were guards around the body to prevent this sort of thing.
Again its an example of Baker showing us he is being pro-active but at the same time pretending that the public had access to the body. The post-mortem had been carried out by Surgeon General Barnes, exactly the same as he did on the President. He certainly got caught up on his expertise in brain surgery. You can also see from the drawing there was no shortage of army witnesses. They had brought in a civilian Dr. May who was a well known practitioner, of twenty five years, in Washington, and had supposedly removed 'Booth's' neck tumour years before in Philadelphia. They are a long way apart and Booth only ever stayed at the National Hotel periodically, in Washington. They had

also kept many of the 'conspirators' on the Saugus, where you will see them in their cells. That is unusual when you consider they should have been put in prison. Perhaps it was the only convenient military prison because the old prison fort had now become an Arsenal. In fact however the Arsenal (the Old Penitentiary) was still being used as a prison for some suspects. Also it would be a good security move, so that no contact with other civilian prisoners would be possible. And the 'Unknown Soldier' was buried there and the four innocent people hung at the Arsenal, under the camouflage of justice. The post mortem was to prove it was 'Booth' and the defining surgical proof was the tumour verified by Dr. May, yet he was unable to recognise Booth in any other way, because the body had supposedly decayed so badly after one days journey, in April time. Even Trooper Millington had said the weather had been very cold and wet, that Easter. So yet again we see that the evidence is as weak as it could possibly be, apart from the total and sublime absence of common sense.

Boyd and the Unknown Soldier were taken back on the Montauk

THE UNION IRON CLAD MONITOR "MONTAUK" DESTROYING THE REBEL STEAMSHIP "NASHVILLE"
IN THE OGEECHEE RIVER NEAR SAVANNAH, GA., FEB. 27, 1863

Chapter 19

The Macabre Burial in the Arsenal

The burial of this brave soldier by Baker and Baker really capped the pinnacle, or indeed the abject and icy, satanic depths of this gothic horror story. I don't think Edgar Allen Poe could have made it more macabre. In fact he may have got his idea for 'Premature Burial' from it. It seemed there were in fact a few people along the Potomac that night, seemingly unbeknown to Baker, watching the demonic duo as they rowed with fiendish purpose, in hell bound horror through the stygian calm waters, like the wandering of Pluto and Charon beyond the icy gas planets of Jupiter, Saturn, Uranus and Neptune on the River Styx, to find a suitable place where the estuary widened and away from the public gaze. It was to effect a hidden spot, so that they could pretend to dump the body in the estuary. In fact, under the cover of darkness and the pre-dawn river mist, they then back-tracked to the Navy Fort Arsenal and moored along the fortress river bank wall with its limited access hole, to the basement tunnel. A kind of 'Traitors Gate' entrance and very fitting for these two barbaric traitors, supposedly of good Christian stock. I will let Baker (and Phineas) describe it for you better in their usual graphic and gothic style:

"At noon that night with my trust lieutenant, a man of thoroughly Christian principles, I placed the body in a small boat, and we rode away from the silent leviathan of Mars, which had borne the loathsome body to the nation's capital; with no watchful eye upon us, but that of Him who scattered above us the shining stars. It was a strange, wild hour on the calm Potomac; and yet, so great was my exhaustion and fatigue, that I fell to dozing with the oar in my hand, and the sack containing the assassin's corpse at my feet. Further I cannot go- it is best to let the curtain of un-broken secrecy and mystery remain between the burial and all human curiosity."

But later, Baker could not resist giving us the final chapter in his book, due he said from public pressure. I rather suspect he would have told us anyway. This is Baker's sub conscious release mechanism in good nervous working order; a form of purging his un-fathomed depths of buried guilt; why not share it with the world by showing them you were just carrying out your difficult public service duties, like a good patriot should.
To continue now, without Phineas:

"In compliance with a promise made in the Prospectus of this work, as well as to gratify public curiosity, and, if possible, forever put at rest the many absurd and foolish rumours in circulation concerning the final disposition of the remains of the assassin, J. Wilkes Booth, I submit the following facts:-

The Macabre Burial of the Unknown Soldier

With the assistance of Lieut. L.B. Baker, I took the body from the -boat direct to the old penitentiary, adjoining the Arsenal grounds. The building had not been used as a prison for some years previously. The Ordinance Department had filled the ground floor cells with fixed ammunition- one of the largest of these cells was selected as the burial-place of Booth- the ammunition was removed, a large flat stone lifted from its place and a rude grave dug; the body was dropped in, the grave filled up, the stone replaced, and there rests to this hour all that remained of John Wilkes Booth."

In the 'Unlocked Book' there is a record of John being visited by a doctor at Asia's home and having a neck tumour removed. In 'fact' a 'gas lamp' was accidentally knocked over in the operation by the doctor but John quickly smothered the flames with his hands. But this book had been doctored itself when it was finally published in 1938, long after Asia had died. And gas lamps were fixed by pipes to the walls in Victorian days. The incandescent lamp came in towards the end of the century. However the paraffin lamp and the older Argand oil lamp were available instead of candelabras. So this story has been written looking backwards and should have used the word , oil lamp, if it had been direct from Asia's writings. In any case Booth was a perfect specimen of manhood with never a blemish on his skin, let alone a carbuncle. And he would never let a surgeon eat at his table, let alone entertain one.

So now we see how a story is fabricated by Baker to confirm Dr. May's 'confirmation' that a tumour had been removed from his neck. Then to prove or disguise this, the Surgeon General has removed a two inch section of neck where the bullet entered which happened to coincide with the tumour. Then it is displayed in a museum as public evidence. Well talk about Gothic horror, Poe had nothing on Baker. Thus since the date of the supposed removal of the tumour would have been around the start of the Victorian period:

Courtesy of the Art Library and Building Conservation Directory London. 2005:

At the start of the Victorian period most houses were lit by candles and oil lamps. Interior fittings included chandeliers (suspended from the ceiling) and sconces (fixed to the wall). However these were mainly used on special occasions, and most ordinary events after sunset took place using portable light sources such as candlesticks, candelabra (bracketed candlesticks) and oil lamps, and by the light of the fire. By the end of the period gas lighting was common in urban homes and electricity was being introduced in many.

The Argand Oil Lamp circa 1850

Chapter 20

The Final Trail

So, this account so far has shown how the myth of Booth's escape, and sojourn into the wilderness of Southern Maryland and crossing the Potomac and Rapperhannock rivers, was generated by Baker, including the killing of the Confederate soldier, the arrest of Boyd, Dr. Mudd, Mr. Adzerodt, Mr. Crangle (?), Sam Coxe, Mr. Claggert, Lucas the drover of the wagon, the two sons of Mr. Garrett and many other innocent victims. The reality is that Booth was not lame and had friends and money so he would have been quite versatile, and probably went north or even stayed disguised and not lame, in Washington, until he could arrange passage by train to New York or Canada or to the Bahamas or anywhere. The Potter and Wright detectives supposedly traced him to the farm at Harper's Ferry but he was not there. However they picked up his trail again at Lydia, Alabama and again in Enid, Oklahoma (the source town of the stories about David E George and John St. Helen) but then they lost it altogether.

This version of Booth's trail is certainly not the line of thinking in this book however, and this false trail is only as far as Potter could ascertain. Andrew Potter reported that one of the three men ('Booth', Johnson and Hysted*), they were following, had a lame leg so it certainly wasn't Booth. Notwithstanding the high standards of 'Baker's Secret Service', Potter and Co. may have been misled by the locals who would give them stories about the lamed 'Booth' trio, including a gentleman actor and his valet, at boarding houses, taverns, hotels and even hiding in a cave, and of 'Booth' burying deeds and so forth, to further stretch their (or our) imaginations on a wild goose chase. In fact Potter probably knew he was following a false trail, as this was Baker's false trail right from the start - when the dynamic duo teamed up outside the Ford theatre and galloped past the Mint, over Capitol Hill and the navy bridge into Southern Maryland.

We have further evidence from Baker of this dummy trail and to where it was leading, in a letter to Stanton, dated over a year later. Thus:

Washington City, July 7th, 1866.

............On Sunday morning , the 16th I called on the Secretary of War, to learn the particulars of the assassination, and what measures had been taken to secure the capture of the assassins. I could learn but little beyond the simple fact that J. Wilkes Booth was the supposed assassin, and that Harold was his accomplice . I asked if any photographs of the supposed assassins, or descriptions of their persons had

*Johnson is said to be Booth's servant or valet.

* Hysted is elsewhere quoted as Henson but both are similar to the name of Hensted, Tyson's buddy.

The updated posters from Baker with photographs but Herold's name is now David C. Harold which is nearly right.

been secured or published. To my surprise I learned that nothing of the kind had been done; during the afternoon of Sunday rumors were freely circulated throughout the city connecting the name of John Surratt and others with the assassination. I immediately secured pictures of those mentioned above , on Monday the 17th had them copied , with a full and accurate description of each assassin printed in a circular, in which I offered a reward of Ten Thousand Dollars. These with there photographs and descriptions, I despatched to a number of detective agents in all parts of the country. I also mailed large numbers to different localities . These photographs and descriptions were the first ever published or circulated. At this time it was almost impossible to obtain any information of a reliable character; the unparallel atrocity of this terrible event , and the fact that the assassins had for the time being escaped , had seemingly paralyzed the entire community. The local detective force of New York, Philadelphia, Baltimore and other cities, had arrived and with the entire military force of this department, had reported to General Auger , whose headquarters were in Washington. On Monday, 18th April , or Tuesday following, I dispatched six men of my force into lower Maryland. After being absent four or five days, they returned , unsuccessful, toward the end of the week succeeding the assassination.

No reliable information having been obtained, as far as I knew, concerning the whereabouts of the assassins , having become thoroughly convinced that Booth and Harold had passed into lower Maryland via Anacosta or Navy Yard Bridge, within an hour after the assassination, and being aware that nearly every rod of ground in Lower Maryland must have been repeatedly passed over by the great number of persons engaged in the search, I finally decided in my own mind, that Booth and Harold must have crossed the river into Virginia. After crossing they could not go towards Richmond or down the Potomac , as the federal troops were in possession of that entire section of country; the only possible way left open for escape was to take south-western course, in order to reach the mountains of Tennessee or Kentucky, where such aid could be secured as would ensure there ultimate escape from the country. On examining the map , I ascertained where the principal crossings of the Rappahannock were located. On Sunday morning April 23, I asked Major Eckert to furnish me with a competent telegraph operator, and necessary apparatus, with the intention of opening an office at Port Tobacco. This request was complied with, as indicated by the note appended:

Office United States Military Telegraph,
War Department, Washington D.C. April 23, 1865.

Colonel Baker:
This will introduce you to Mr. Beckwith, a cipher operator, of great scouting experience, who may be of great service to you, in addition to his telegraphing. I also send with him Mr. Cheney, a repair man, to make speedy connections wherever it may be found necessary.

Yours truly,
Thos. F. Eckert".

Main points:
So, even here on the 17th of April it is John Surratt that is the main suspect. So how could Dr. Mudd have possibly known that Booth was the culprit of an assassination, when even the illuminatti had not yet made up their minds whom it might be? It's pure evil and stupidity given into the hands of power. What has gone wrong with schooling when the dunce's later take over in life? And here is further evidence that Tyson and Hensted had crossed the navy bridge less than one hour after the assassination. That is just before the New York Times had been informed of the assassination at 11.16 p.m. And the original idea was to implicate Surratt and Booth. Herold was included later when it was realised that Surratt was no where near Washington at the time, although

his mother lived there, he lived in Baltimore. So Herold was probably a last minute substitution. Hence Stanton got his name completely wrong, the first time, Daniel C Harrold. This is understandable as he had to liaise with Baker in New York. When Baker came back he used the name Harold on the poster, as he later did in his book.
The detectives under Major O'Bierne did in fact make a large number of arrests including Adzerodt, who was arrested at his home in Port Tobacco by Officer Lee on the 20th April, proving he could not have been in arrested at his cousin's home in Germantown, Montgomery County. The prosecution however said Adzerodt was arrested by Officer John Lee at the Kirkwood Hotel on the 15th April after a pistol was found under his pillow , including an enormous Bowie knife. Yet another version of this fabulous 'Tower of Babel'. It also proves how the prosecution manufactured and falsified its case against Dr. Mudd. This letter of Baker's proves that the assassin's name could not have been released on the 15th. Indeed it was John Surratt's name that was first released on the 20th April by Stanton. Booth's name and photograph, was only being prepared for printing on Baker's poster on the 17th April, and without a lame leg. Indeed no reliable information on Booth at all, except naming John Surratt. Yet, Dr. Mudd had 'fixed Booth's' leg on the 15th April and the two men had gone from his house the same day.

The question is when did 'Booth' really become lame?

This in turn raises the question: Did Dr. Mudd fix a real injury or a make believe injury? If Baker was not aware of finding a lame 'Booth' until informed by his agents in the field then how was it arranged that 'Booth' was lame on arriving at Dr. Mudd's house? Or was it 'feasible' that Boyd and friend that visited Dr. Mudd? The answer is that Baker wanted to claim total credit for using his reasoning powers in directing the campaign and capture of Booth in order to gain promotion (which he did, to Brigadier-General). However he did not plan the lame 'Booth' story from the start. It came about by Tyson acting as a lame man as a ruse to gain hospitality from Dr. Mudd at four in the morning. So although Booth, Surratt and Herold were advertised in the photographs on the posters , no mention was made of a lame 'Booth'. It therefore has to be implied that Captain Jett had this inside information, somehow. And indeed as explained above in Chapter 13, Ruggles said they had been in contact with the Union force near Chapel Point, according to Prentiss Ingraham's account. It is unlikely Jett would know by any other source than from Chapel Point. Otherwise he might have become a spontaneous agent, or on supplying information under arrest became an unwilling agent, in order to assist in his capture. In fact Jett and Co. may have found out about the lamed leg ruse at Chapel Point when Tyson and Hensted had been staying there, since the 16th of April. Indeed they may have run into the two decoys when the latter were carrying out their stealth 'recce' across the Potomac, as this would explain the co-incidence of timing better, and then the Confederate officers, need not have gone anywhere near Chapel

Point's Union garrison itself.
It is not likely that Boyd went to Dr. Mudd's farm with his soldier comrade on horse-back, because it took nearly 10 days for them to get to the Rappahannock River, less than 25 miles away. Also while its true Baker said the Unknown Soldier had fallen from his horse, how come both finished up at the river without horses and travelling in a wagon driven by an Afro-American, called Lucas? Besides the NDP could not have visited Dr. Mudd's home at nearly the same time a lame soldier arrived, just by chance. In other words Boyd and his comrade happened to be crossing the Rappahannock river at the same time as the Confederate officer trio. In fact they had tried to cross 12 hours earlier but the ferryman was waiting for more passengers. Captain Jett separated from the others when he went into Bowling Green himself (supposedly to meet a girlfriend). The other two officer's stayed with Boyd and comrade, leading them as it happened, to Garrett's farm. It is also intriguing to suspect that all of these Confederate soldiers had probably just fought there last skirmish together in the area, with Moseby's Partition Rangers.
When Doherty's 16th Cavalry arrived in Bowling Green at the Goldman's Tavern boarding house , that is when Jett was arrested by Doherty, but clandestinely, Jett told Conger where Boyd was located at Garrett's Barn. Later Jett was allowed to escape by Luther Byron Baker, possibly with his reward money. But did he share it with Ruggles and Bainbridge in the end? However according to Ruggles, he and Bainbridge were later arrested at their homes in King George's County and Jett in Westmoreland County. All three were supposedly sent to prison, and Jett died at some stage before 1880. And so in this way they may have forfeited their Judas money and were branded as criminals for their greed, with shame to their name in the community, a fitting end for them. Indeed Ruggles and Bainbridge were supposedly arrested ten days later and sent to the Old Capitol Prison for six months. And even Lucas was taken there. And Jett was arrested at his home in Westmoreland County (and testified at the conspirator's trial), near the very shores of the Potomac where he had probably met the decoys, Tyson and Hensted. Well, governments certainly are the experts on treachery, because it's their daily stock and trade, going back to the divine kings of old, and filters right down through the officer class, generation after generation. In the case of Baker, he and Conger got the lion's share of the War Department's reward yet Baker, thought he should have got a lot more. But in fact he finally got much less. That is despite the fact that he had earlier offered $10,000 extra, to the reward money himself. Thus:

"A commission was finally appointed by the Secretary of War , composed of General Holt, Judge Advocate-General, and General Townshend. In this report, the Commision gave the entire credit of the capture of the assassins to me, although they gave me but a small portion of the reward. After another long delay the Committee on Claims reported as follows:-The committee further report, that the expedition which resulted in the capture of Booth and Harold was planned and directed by Colonel (now General) Lafayette C. Baker , Lieutenant Everton J. Conger, Lieutenant B. Baker, then in the detective service, Lieutenant Edward P. Doherty, and twenty six privates of the Sixteenth New York

Cavalry. And the committee further report, that Major James R. O' Bierne, then provost-marshal of the District of Columbia. General H.H. Welles, then under General Auger's command, George Cottingham and Alexander Lovett, detectives and Samuel H. Beckwith, a telegraph operator, rendered important service leading to the arrest of Booth and Harold. The committee do not regard the capture of Booth and Harold as purely Military service, and do not feel bound to award compensation to mere rank, without regard to the extent and merit of the services performed, but look to the rank and position of the officers engaged in such services as evidence of the opportunity afforded them and the duty imposed on them to exercise greater care, skill, and diligence, than persons in a subordinate position. The Committee report in their opinion the sum of seventy five thousand dollar's should be distributed as follows:-

To Lafayette C. Baker, chief detective	17,500
To Everton J. Conger	17,500
To Luther B. Baker	5,000
To James O'Bierne	2,000
To: George Cottingham	1,500
To H.H. Wells	1,500
To Alexander Lovett	1,000
To Samuel H. Beckwith	500
To Lieutenant Edward P. Doherty, Sixteenth New York Cavalry	2,500
The men	26,000
Total	$75,000

The remainder of the original $100,000 may have been used to pay off ex-PC Lloyd, Government clerk- Weichman, David E. Herold (see below) and also many other bribes were being paid out as we have seen. But in essence Baker and the army profited the lot. This for assassination of the greatest President, murder and imprisonment of innocent soldiers and citizens of Washington, Maryland, Virginia, Florida and Pennsylvania. In effect a secret element of the army and NDP, coup. But not everyone was happy, including Baker:

"The report of this committee was still very unsatisfactory for a majority of those claiming rewards, and an effort was immediately made, to have the decision reversed. A systematic effort by lobbyists at the capitol to have this report set aside. The most wilful and malicious misrepresentations were made concerning myself. I had taken but little interest in this matter, never having demanded that myself and those acting under my orders should have the entire credit for the capture of Booth and Harold. On the day this report was submitted to Congress, the lobbyists, interested parties, and certain disloyal members of congress, immediately started a story that I had turned Copperhead, and was in the employ of Andy Johnson. I had no opportunity to controvert these statements; the question went to the house; the report of the Committee on Claims was disapproved and altered, giving me a much a much smaller sum than that awarded me by the committee. The honourable Mr. Hotchkiss, however who had thoroughly investigated the matter, and become influenced by they that had been working against me, and of the misrepresentations that had been made concerning my affiliation with the Copperhead party, defeated the report in a speech of nearly an hour, in which he manfully sustained my claim to the reward, and defended, with great ability, the personal attacks made upon me."

In fact as we have seen above in Prentiss Ingraham's account that Baker may have ended up with only 3,750 dollars. The Copperheads were a loosely formed liberal faction of the Northern Democrats who opposed the war and thought that Lincoln's cause for abolition was destroying the natural fabric and stability of the Union. They were called Copperheads because of the copper headed badges they wore. It is indeed ironic that Baker should be suspected of being sympathetic towards them. However it is not so far fetched because now that Lincoln was dead a Democrat was taking over, and indeed Stanton had been a Democrat. Baker himself would have no problem changing sides, after all he was a gothic realist. But he didn't change colour fast enough before Johnson nabbed his tail. Fortunately for him Mr. Hotchkiss had the gift of the gab, but the tide was turning for a while. Note, Conger appears not to have been promoted to Lieutenant Colonel. It's just typical of Baker promoting his favourite army officer attached to the NDP, with a high rank below him, to become his right hand man and prime false witness.

'Herold' Prior to Hanging

The Face and Neck of 'Herold ' has now been Doctored on the Webb. But you can still make out the V collar's ghostly image, from the 'thin blue line' (see below), and the loose coat sleeves of Boyd and his long wavy hair at the sides. The cracked appearance evident elsewhere on the print is due to grain boundary degradation on old photographs

Chapter 21

Booth's Second Death and his Resurrection

It is now happily put about that Booth was not rich according to the 'Money Trail' by 'Hall and Maione' which merely reinforces the image of a greedy Booth intending to make a pile of money, or even a fortune out of the deed. This of course reinforces the American dream that everyone should always be seeking treasure, gold or money otherwise they are not the real McCoy, or they have a bolt missing and keep the devil for company. Well, motivation it is true is important to get people moving, besides sitting back and feigning patriotism. This money trail quotes statements from a large number of witnesses, that were supposed friends or colleagues of Booth, to the authorities, so cannot be considered as proof in this book. They do however seem to trace Booth's accounts from eastern banks prior to the assassination, only to blatantly try to reinforce the myth, that he was not so rich as an actor, and so that his main motivation was greed. All of this is prophetic rubbish, the real people making money were the cotton profiteers what Lincoln had called 'the d…. cotton profiteers, d… them and he wished they would all get their d…… heads shot off.'

This is an obvious reference to the Northern Speculator's profiteering . A specific one being and acting under the emissary of John W. Kein operating out of 1781/2 Water St., NY, using the steamboat 'Fulton' and plying their business from Savannah, Georgia. Hall and Maione also suggest that Booth was still alive and was actively trying to get access to his frozen bonds and cash, otherwise he would blow the whistle. Apart from all this supply of data on his financial accounts, Booth's mother had a large house in New York with a servant according to Surratt (however this house actually belonged to Edwin who was rich and famous); and different sources including his own letters, quote he was earning up to $10,000 or even $20,000 p.a. by this time, such was his acting fame. He was also making money from stocks and bonds and had shares in an oil company, though now frozen or in part possession of the state. In fact the oil company shares were past on to Junius and other bonds to his mother. This is according to his beloved sister Asia. He also had bought a certain acreage of land in Boston, (and had speculated in buying more land in Southern Maryland), maybe he had a cottage there in the more remote countryside. He often bought or hired horses and carriages and mixed with the elite in society, eg his girlfriend in Washington was Lucy, the daughter of Senator Hale, to whom he was secretly engaged. And he was an old friend of Andrew Johnson when he was the Governor of Tennessee. Johnson was soon to turn the tables on Stanton and Baker, perhaps favouring Booth and he released the victims before ending his term of office.

To continue with his whereabouts; Potter claims to have followed him to 'his' farm at Harpers Ferry in West Virginia, but he was gone. It is more possible that Booth went back to New York and then, it is said, to England. Indeed he may well of met John

Surratt again in NY or in England but John denied this in his lectures, obviously on good purpose. It is unlikely that he 'continued' west to Oklahoma on the 'Potter route', as rumoured, then on through Texas, New Mexico, Arizona, Nevada to California (although Edwin had lived in California with his father in the early days, and with Junius later) and then to India, Ceylon (Sri Lanka) or Japan where he died in the 20th century; because these stories would logically follow on from the lame Booth trail. Except Baker had projected his destination to be the Silver Mines of Mexico. Baker also said Booth had transferred his actor's costumes to Nassau from Canada in 1861, but it is another possible address. However, Baker did not waste any time outlining Booth's long term wicked designs, even then. Thus:

" It was at this time that Booth devised his triumphant route through the South. The dramatic element seems to have never been lacking in his design, and with all his base purposes never failed to consider some subsequent notoriety to be enjoyed. He therefore shipped, before the end of 1861, his theatrical wardrobe from Canada to Nassau. After the commission of his crime he intended to reclaim it, and 'star' through the South, drawing many as much by his crime as his abilities".

Well, it is again patently clear, that all this malevolent design of Booth's, four years before the event, comes straight from Baker's perverted imagination. And this was typical of the illuminati then, or indeed at any point in time. There is no mention of Booth's own house in NY by anyone other than Surratt, but it is possible he could have disguised and hidden away in the big city, meanwhile occasionally staying with friends, before quickly escaping abroad. Edwin said he had lost all contact with him, but then he would to protect him, and himself. It also appears in Asia's book that she never saw her beloved brother again. Indeed she was guarded day and night by a Detective inside her house. One time a young fair headed actor called Claude Burroughs called with a message from Edwin, but he was a plant, and took a letter from her. Later Edwin said he never sent this actor. Thus, Burroughs was indeed another actor who had been 'bought ' by the illuminati. The house Detective who was very subtle, even tried to get her to get the Doctor to certify that she was ill, as a cover for her not going to prison. This was just another ploy. Asia was very strong and did not weep or seek sympathy, and he got lonely himself and asked her if he could let his wife stay. She said,

"No Sir you must carry out your duties correctly and not be distracted by your wife."

And she rarely offered him any sympathy of intellectual comfort or discussion. He was dumbfounded and it must have put his nose out of joint. It was more important for her to stay at home in order to receive mail and for them to catch Booth, should he pay her a clandestine visit. That is why they never put Asia in prison; but her brothers Junius, and Joseph who had just got back from over 3 years in Australia, and her husband John Sleeper Clarke were sent to the Capitol Prison for a while. Because Edwin was rich and famous they just put a guard around him. Every letter that came to her house was opened by the Detective and handed over to Baker. The letters were mostly from Edwin but the letters from John already in her possession were also taken. Hence the letter addressed to Asia was used in forging the diary by Baker. Thus: To Asia, Fri 14th. The Ides……….etc. to complete the deception. And to cap all their evil they send a message via an associate, of the death of her brother. But she took it well and in one way she was relieved of the ever increasing burdening stress of further inquisitions and trial followed by more torture and final death by hanging. At least he had died a hero's death, or so it seemed.

Remember the southern and western trail that Baker had engineered using the two detective decoys, Tyson and Hensted acting as Booth and Herold, were followed up by the blood hounds O'Bierne, Lee, Laverty and Hoey, shortly followed up later by Potter & Co. This trail then ended for the public when Boyd and his Confederate friend, were followed by the hunter force under Conger, Doherty and Baker, with the killing of the Unknown Soldier by Corbett. Their accounts had to be believed especially after Baker had clandestinely arranged for the kill. In effect they had forced a round peg into a square hole, but then the illuminati had a whole range of such powers, especially with the ever faithful press at their disposal. It is possible however that Booth went straight back to New York in disguise (like John Surratt used to get around), and then straight on to Canada to try to settle his affairs using his servant and many friends. Later Kate Scott, once an army nurse, in Pennsylvania penned an affidavit swearing he was still alive. Why did she do this without Booth's permission? Besides she was connected in a false will left by 'Booth' relating to Andrew Potter as her trustee, so this is yet another deception. Potter had said Booth had buried some deeds in a cave in Oklahoma. Obviously he would come up with them and get Kate Scott to claim she was carrying Booth's child. They would have not searched for Booth too seriously in New York and in any case he had to be a lame man, but were hoping they might catch him visiting Asia in Philadelphia. In effect a disguised Booth in New York or Canada with his money could almost live a normal life there under a different name, short haircut and no moustache. Others say he went to England, which would be logical considering his father and grandfather Richard were both English. But the latter had moved to Baltimore when Booth was a boy. And John Surratt went to England first before he went to Italy and became a ceremonial soldier for a while. Both were masters of disguise. There is no indication at all in Asia's book that she ever saw him again. However perhaps John had decided he would never resurrect himself to save his family further grief, or worse. And Edwin had told Asia to put him out of her life, and just keep his memory.

It is amusing for me to personally remember when I was staying in New York near the end of the 60's, there was a wonderful chain of steak restaurants of Edwardian character called 'Your Father's Moustache'. I wonder if they were hiding Booth's ghost? Again this book can give no proof of where he really lived and died, so I recommend you read his sister Asia Booth Clark's account in the edited auto-biography, but neither will you find the answer there, in ….'The Unlocked Book' but he certainly did not die in a tobacco shed in Virginia. However one should also read 'This One Mad Act' by Izola L. Forrester, famous writer and grand daughter of Booth, who makes it clear in her masterpiece that John lived on and kept in contact with his family. Her mother was Ogarita Booth an actress who was born in 1859 as Booth's own daughter, it is said. All of this is quite apart from the famous adventures and money making of 'Booth's' mummy of Finus L. Bates that travelled around the country by train to be exhibited at theatres and circuses such as Barnham's Circus; and all the associated strange and unexplained tragedies connected with it, resulting from chaos. This was after 'Booth' had 'died' in Oklahoma as John St. Helen after doing a few plays in the cow-towns around the mid-west but quickly recovered again on his death bed, and became resurrected, changing his name finally (we think) to David E. George. The name (John) St. Helen (St. Helen-feast day July 31st 418) was a tragic Swedish noblewoman from Skovde convicted of murdering her son -in- law. Then after her husband died when she had given all his wealth to charity, she was killed as a martyr. David E. George is a clever composite of David E. Herold and George Azerodt and are just other juicy sagas and money spinners. These stories mostly originate around Enid, Oklahoma where Potter had finally given up his wild goose chase. Their proofs are all undone in this book because they referred to Booth's boot, or to a lame character actor, whose supposed name was Booth. That is why the FBI, to give it some credit, was never bothered about Booth's boot , 'diary' or his dirty linen either; although the purloined diary is now in the Ford theatre and Booth's letters somewhere, and the false boot is in a Washington museum beneath the Ford Theatre, making more money.

Izola L. Forrester
Brilliant Author

1878 -1944

Finus L. Bates with his Mummy
David E. George Alias John St. Helen

Chapter 22

The Strange Case of David E. Herold and the Confederate Prisoner.

The conspirators were kept on the iron clad vessel , the Saugus, in seemingly freshly painted black cells for the professional photographs. The Unknown Soldier was kept on the Montauk separately for the autopsy and so selected visitors and VIP's could come on board to witness the guarded and honourable body of this valiant soldier, portrayed as Wilkes Booth. Samuel Arnold was arrested at home (or taken to Fortress Monroe)

Samuel Arnold a man of Principle And Honour

without handcuffs. This man had warned Booth not to go ahead with the kidnapping and his letter was found amongst Booth's belongings, held by the National Hotel, then handed into the NDP. In regards to Herold since he also disappeared quickly then he may have 'gone abroad to Spain or Canada or anywhere, because he had got wind (like Surratt) that the kidnap plot was out of the bag, up to three weeks before.' But see the more probable facts below. Thus Baker quotes:

"Harold, three weeks before the murder, visited Port Tobacco, and said that the next time the boys heard of him he would be in Spain; he added that with Spain there was no extradition treaty. He said at Surrattsville he meant to make a barrel of money, or his neck would stretch."

Herold: First Take in Handcuffs in clean Over Coat. Waist coat with two buttons fastened

Herold: Second Take in Trooper's Hat and Dusty Over Coat. But he is too fat for the waist coat.

Unidentified Man has waistcoat, hat and over coat just like Herold's outfit. Looks weather worn and unshaven for a few days. Is this Boyd the friend of the Unknown Soldier? He was isolated on the Saugus because he was talking to everyone about his friend not being Booth, and he was an innocent man. No wonder he protested when they took him out of his cell straight to the hangman, Christian Rath, without the luxury of a trial. Well at least there was no hypocrisy to put up with. The official version is: "Man arrested on suspicion of being one of the Lincoln Assassination Conspirators. Name not disclosed. [Identified as Hartmann Richter]" They said he was an Uncle of George Adzerodt?? Then changed it, to fit the image, as him being his cousin because he's obviously no older than George. Well their stupid lies are indeed endless. Richter was quite well off with a big house. Note the distinctive blue edge to the collar bordering his white shirt highlighting the 'V' is also visible in the hanging pictures.

This in reality means that he was already scared (or a dupe) and wanted to get some money together (or a reward) and flee to Spain as soon as possible. This young man was an apprenticed druggist and was fairly well connected. Thus Baker again:

"This Harold was a gunner, and therefore versed in arms; had traversed the whole lower portion of Maryland, and was therefore a geographer as well as a tool. His friends lived at every farm-house between Washington and Leonardsville, and he was respectfully enough connected, so as to make his association creditable as well as useful."

An official drawing of Herold's Weeping Sisters with Herold in Chains at the Navy Yard, looking fat and contented, where is father worked for the Navy as a Quartermaster.

However, we have a final twist in this tail with regards to Herold. You will remember that his face was blotted out in the photograph when he was hung and his body later dug up and his head decapitated. Well, there is too much evidence to show that he was indeed 'captured' and put in handcuffs and that his sisters visited him in prison, as they lived in Washington. His father also worked in the Navy yard as a quartermaster, or senior clerk. Also he had attended the same Catholic college as Surratt and Weichmann. If you look at all the other prisoners you will see they are in a prison cell some with their handcuffs on. The black cells have large riveted bolts, in the plate iron walls, and we know all of the conspirators except Mrs. Surratt and Dr. Mudd were kept on the ironclad vessels, the 'Montauk' and the 'Saugus'. In 'Herold's' case however although he seemingly has handcuffs on, he is not in a prison cell on these vessels, he his in a 'Spanish' arched interior, building. It is strange because he (really Boyd) came back with the dead body of the Unknown Soldier on the Montauk. This may have been taken in the Navy Yard building. Another small point, is the artists drawing of the weeping sisters. The artist seems to have gone over the top so much in this drawing that all the sisters are weeping their eyes out, with handkerchiefs covering their faces to stem the tears, in a rarefied and profuse cameo of unrelenting grief. And 'Herold' is just lying back seemingly fat and contented, with no handcuffs but a long chain. OK its just a depiction of an artist. But all artists, good or bad, always have a message to give us and this artist's message telegraphs a melodramatic acting scene, perhaps unwittingly and stupidly. Also, two sister's gave evidence at the trial and said he was at home on the 15th February, including another witness. Well this is not the 15th April but why should it state February 15th? In what way does that date have any relevance to his defence, two months before the deed? Also if you look at Herold's clothes, in the real photograph of him, they are a very odd mixture and in particular we have what looks like a grey Confederate waistcoat, seemingly hastily put on because half the buttons are loose. And because of all the loose talk about Confederate soldiers, this waist-coat would help fulfil the image. Yet at the same time he has an off white shirt with a dicky bow fully tied, more in keeping with a trainee druggist one would have thought, perhaps western style though, in his casual evening style. Outside of this he has a heavy coat in which the sleeves look pinched at the shoulders. In fact this coat is similar to the Confederate soldier shown below in his cell, probably 'Boyd'. To cap it all, he is wearing a 'cowboy' hat which looks stupid on him. Indeed it looks like a ranger's or a trooper's hat, certainly not a Confederate's hat, which would have been more fitting. Finally he seems to have been liberally coated with white dust, but its spotty. Its not the kind of pattern of dust you would expect from the elements in this geographical region of swamps and fairly temperate or wet seasonal weather. Its more in line with a dry or arid climate, but the dust is white, again western style. In other words it looks like we have another illusion here. Indeed it is Herold but in what role or capacity is he fulfilling? Up till now the author has made out a good case for all the characters. Now I ask the reader to follow these leads and come up with the answer for Herold. There is another related and sinister clue however, and it's this. There is a photograph of another prisoner with a Southerner's goatee beard. He is thin and indeed looks like the classic image of a Confederate, with a neatly trimmed Victorian beard with narrow side chops impeccably cut (in the second photograph but unshaven in the first one), thick smooth long wavy hair and a dark overcoat. He his without handcuffs but he is in a black cell on the Saugus, probably, since the Confederate soldier was returned on the Montauk and probably transferred to the Saugus. This prisoner was supposedly released later, according to the caption. Indeed their were many innocent prisoners, but not on the Saugus and Montauk, and only the 6 main conspirators were kept on the Saugus, to ensure secrecy. And why do have we have two ready photographs of this man? There was only one photographer especially allowed on board and his name was Andrew Gardner, who used specialised equipment and glass plates for developing, for the

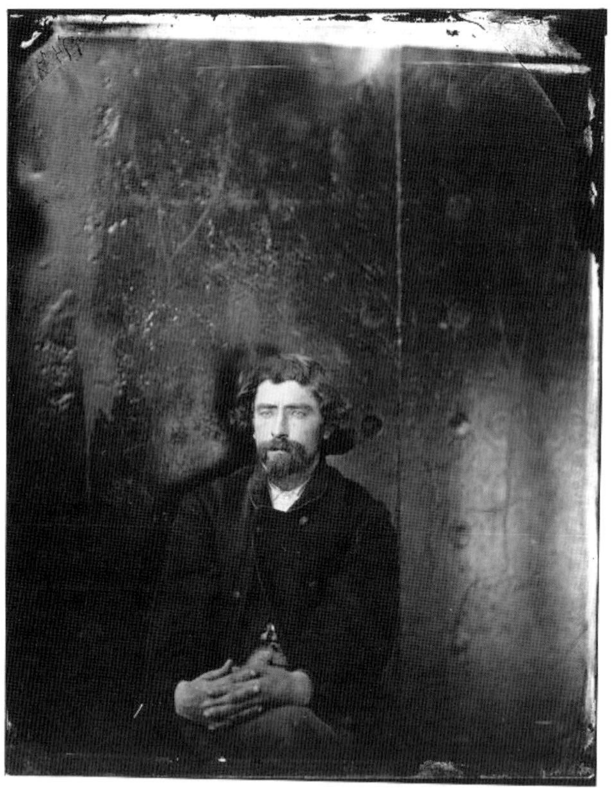

The Unidentified man again on the Saugus, looks like a Confederate
Or is it Michael O'Laughlin? No it's not, as you see from the hair parting.

Michael O' Laughlin 1840-1867.
Died of Yellow Fever in Prison.

government records. Is he then in fact Boyd, the man that Ruggles first addressed at the Rappahannock River that helped his lamed Confederate friend? If so, then this was possibly the man that was hung in Herold's place and his skull was exhibited in a Washington museum, minus his beard. It was 're-found' in 1992 and placed in the Smithsonian Institute, then finally buried in a grave in Geneva Cemetery in Seminole County, Florida near to Lewis Payne's mother, by all accounts. They would have ordered him to shave his beard off of course, before the public hanging. It is said that Payne's head also wound up in a museum but could it be, not Payne's head, but Boyd's head instead? This in order to prevent any later identification from grave hunters. Also if you examine the hanging of the four you will see this man is third from Mary and has a dark blue or black loose coat with light trousers, and a white shirt in the sharp 'V' of his coat, similar to the man above. Herold's coat if buttoned could not make such a small 'V' shape and with a plain grey waist coat underneath, not an exposed white shirt. He his also thin and small, similar to Azerodt in height (to his right). A close up analysis of this photograph will highlight more evidence e.g. from his buttons and blue rimmed coat collar. Herold was a stouter and bigger man, also in a dark coat but of a different style and not so dark.

Tragic Mary, Brave Lewis, 'Boyd' the Unidentified Confederate (Dark black coat, the V of the Collar and White Shirt) and poor old George Adzerodt. The ghouls look on.

The strange case of Herold now becomes clear. If Herold was in court as the close up drawing of him indicated, then it explains why the conspirators were hooded and why he was not. Indeed, the hoods were for the purpose of the penultimate deception. The decapitation of Boyd's head with his body in 'Herold's' grave being the final one. Herold must then have been released with a big payoff to disappear perhaps abroad, out west or even to Spain as he had originally planned according to Baker; (remember 'Red Shoes', who 'recovered in good order', got 5000 dollars an enormous sum in those days). And Baker always called him the 'Dupe'. The dictionary defines this word thus- a victim of deception, or to cheat or make a fool of. This word also graduates to duplicate. Of course if this is the case then he was in on the government plot with Louis Weichmann all along. And must also have provided loads of information about 'telling (on) the boys in Port Tobacco.' And about Adzerodt and where he lived with his lady friend as he was 'well connected,' according to Baker.

This then completes the picture of 'the Dupe' described in Baker's Book. He was substituted at the last minute for Surratt, the original assassin the illuminatti had planned for, since they sent two decoys Tyson and Hensted; to pass over the navy bridge at 11 p.m. It is possible however that they had originally planned for three escapees because Potter was following three men and there were three men on the posters. Thus Andrew Johnson had been on the illuminates list for assassination and ironically the third fugitive on the Potter trail was called Johnson. Of course since 'Adzerodt' had reneged that meant the real assassin had bottled out. In the coded letter there is a reference to this possible agent. Thus 'Old Crook has Johnson in charge'.

It seems that Herold also had some military training, possibly army, since he had map knowledge. The source of Baker's information, was not only John Lloyd or Louis Weichmann, it was Herold himself. Also, with Herold's local knowledge and contacts in Washington, where he worked, he may well have carried out his plans to book a steamer passage, with the reward money and go to Spain. No one, except his close family and friends, ever discovered how he really disappeared. His family never visited the grave of the Confederate soldier Boyd, who was hung in his place, and buried by the authorities in the Congressional Cemetery; with his headstone and name David E Herold. How kind of them to go to this trouble and expense for the family. Well… there are no limits to the illuminates alternative path, that is chaos.

And what of this Boyd and his comrade's families? Well the one who was killed with his diary (the Unknown Soldier) is rumoured to have been Captain James William Boyd who had seven motherless children, since his wife Caroline had died a year before. But this is very unlikely since the man was quoted as having a medallion around his neck, a tattoo on his hand and six photos of women. And whoever has seen a lame officer stranded after any battle, or even a lamed officer… except Horatio Nelson. And all the many artist drawings make him look like a common soldier full of true grit. And real Captains rarely get killed or hung as common criminals, without someone kicking up a fuss. And it was Ruggles who first spoke to a man at the river, who called himself Boyd.

But it was his comrade that had the lame leg in the wagon. Also JW Boyd was released from a prison in Ohio, weeks before so he must have reached his home in Jackson, Tennessee safely without doing a detour hundreds of miles round to Virginia. This officer had also made a special request to be released earlier and suddenly got permission within 24hours from the War Department, after writing for his release several times.
So what was in the diary? As Baker said the soldier fell from his horse in the tangle of forest and had to shoot it, and he then snuggled up to it to keep warm in the night, and then dragged his painful limbs along after him in the cold, grey light of dawn. But who fixed his leg? Hardly his comrade Boyd, who had met him later on. On the other hand and much more likely, he was just lame and nobody had fixed it, that would make it yet another illusion. So look what happened to this good Samaritan. Ruggles had said that the two of them had escaped from prison, but the nearest prison was over one hundred miles away in the Delaware peninsula, on Bloodsworth Island in the Chesapeake Bay. Neither of them were officers otherwise they would have surrendered with honour, using the Victorian gentleman's code. Besides, the war was over. But the really interesting insight into how Captain Jett picked out his fellow Confederates, one with a lame leg is probably connected to Chapel Point, near Port Tobacco. This whole area of Southern Maryland and northern Virginia, had been a campaign area of final resistance from Moseby's Rangers. And the Union had a covert base their under Lieutenant Laverty commanding 65 men, rather a lot for a Lieutenant. According to Ruggles the three Confederate officers had communicated with the Union troops in this area and discovered the more detailed news of Washington's manhunt for the two assassins. The grapevine in the area would have been fairly widespread by then, and the news may have been intensified in this area. After all Major Beckworth had just set up two way communications, by telegraph, to Washington here. Also this is where Tyson and Hensted had stayed for a week, from the 16th till the 23rd April before crossing the Potomac, to finish their dummy run, not too far from the Rappahannock River.
The final honour must surely be awarded to the press for their quick response and diligence in getting the news to the public and for their considered insight into descriptive journalism. Here is a very good example of the New York Times quoting a story that has been pre-fabricated. This dispatch was sent in at 11.16 pm exactly one hour after the President was shot:

"The audience heard the shot, but supposing it fired in the regular course of the play, did not heed it till Mrs. Lincoln's screams drew their attention. The whole affair occupied scarcely half a minute, and the assassin was gone. As yet he has not been found."

It so happened that Rathbone gave a statement on Monday the 17th saying that he estimated the time to be 30 seconds. Yet Rathbone could not have given this information to the press before 11.16 pm on the 14th since he was fully occupied with attending the dying president in the Ford theatre; and the press was not admitted to Petersen House, where Rathbone was suffering from 'loss of blood' and had momentarily fainted. He was then taken straight away to his home by carriage at 11pm, still suffering from 'loss of blood', yet strangely not to hospital with a massive knife wound. The alternative is to lightly assume Rathbone got his timing from the press. Indeed this might be closer to the truth, if you consider it had got its news, from the original source of the pre-fabricated account. Its exactly the same time interval given in a near death scene in the Dick Tracey, Special Agent film starring the fabulous Madonna, as a Marilyn Monroe look alike, and Warren Beatty in 1990. And this time slot was also used in my favourite TV detective, the loveable and irrepressible Columbo in his well worn 'Mac', with Peter Falk referring to a cunning clockwork plot set up by a man of gifted intelligence. So it's a well worn phrase these days. Well, the master's of illusion can think forward as well as backward with their mitres, compasses, electronic surveillance and time machines. But all of this refined and advanced technology has the opposite effect on the intelligence of their minds. However it does not stop them laying the groundwork for extra-sensory perception in modern day scenarios.

There are now programs on TV in England investigating people who say they can predict events and national disasters in their dreams i.e. pre-cognisance of an event. This would help explain why so many people new about 9/11 before it happened. Indeed there were thousands of 'put options' that share prices would fall on United and American Airlines, and they did fall dramatically. These kinds of programs are blessed by the illuminati including the tricks of 'magic' and endless violent plot-less crimes and third rate acting, and of course most people prefer their dreams to reality e.g. the 'American Dream' which keeps them going, if they have lost their faith in God. If only one person could predict the stock market accurately, he or she would become a quadrillionaire in only a few years and could control all of the world's banks. Indeed if he or she was a force for good they would be able to release the world of much of its poverty and educate young people into the ways of objective truth (likened to the logical process of reasoning, rationalism and empirical reason based on experience) and morality. And by setting certain standards of working ethics, and awareness of Buddhist like philosophies of the mind and spirit, to gain true freedom, and to challenge evil not to embrace it. In fact the opposite is happening today where evil (partly through wide spread drugs, illicit sex and greed) is gaining ground rapidly now that true Christianity is dying, or already dead in many parts of the Western world, leaving a spiritual void in the youth, with just a limited direction of moral purpose. Another paragraph in this New York Times press release also concords with the original concept of the plot. Thus:

"It is impossible to get the full facts of the case , but appears that a young man entered the President's box from the theatre, during the last act of the play of 'Our American Cousin,' with pistol in hand. He shot the President in the head and instantly jumped from the box upon the stage, and immediately disappeared through the side access and rear of the theatre, brandishing a dirk knife and dropping a kid glove on the stage."

In fact they got the most important fact exactly right. That is, the pistol shot was Stewart's cue to run across the stage immediately, as indeed Ed Spangler noted accurately. The 30 second time frame of Rathbone's fictious fight with Booth was easily fitted in, in retrospect, after the event. No witness could ever dispute a time interval or window that in fact did not exist, at the time. It only existed in anyone's mind afterwards and therefore open to cross examination. And who would want to argue with the official line? Except Ed who got 6 years hard labour. Note, there were also two points of false evidence in this release:

1. A kid glove indicates it was a gentleman. Indeed it was the description of Booth, on that very day. But it was just another illusion, that was found on the stage.
2. A dirk knife, or a dirk, is a descriptive term in the Scottish vernacular. Yet in many later and therefore less accurate accounts, this is described either as a hunting knife, or even a Bowie knife, and it gets bigger all the time.

In regards to the Scottish frame of mind we have Stewart, Crawford, McGowan, Harris and Leale as the prime witnesses and all connected to the army. In actual fact the dirk knife was just another illusion. And the derringer? Well I'll leave that up to you, wise reader. There are still two missing pieces from the jigsaw puzzle however, and it is the assassin and the weapon. There are two known possibilities for the set up and the assassin:

1. Thomas J. Raybold. Ex-Union Military Officer.
2. Thomas P. Corbett. Union Sergeant.

Raybold is a candidate, at least well in with the illuminati, because although he was supposed to be sick that day, after he had set up Lincoln's chair in the morning, he had liaised with the treasury man in setting up the flags. He then went home, leaving Harry with all the responsibility, then he came back in the evening counting the takings in the office at 10 pm. Also, he had bust the lock to door 8. Yet Merrick also swore that he had bust another lock, the same day, on door 7, supposedly on 7th March. He was a brash, wilful character and had resigned his commission after rapid promotion, after serving only serving 8 months and only one month as a Captain, in August 1862. This means he had done something seriously wrong and may have had revenge on his mind, why not make Lincoln pay. He had been employed at the theatre for just over a year. He said he had forgotten to tell Gifford he had bust the locks and had never bothered to repair them, after five weeks, yet he boasted he was in charge, over Gifford. In any case Gifford would have discovered the broken locks, if broken for five weeks. No doubt it was Raybold who also shaved out the bevel with a pen knife in the spy-hole, and gouged the slot for the imaginary brace. And most probably drilled the hole, since young Harry had denied any knowledge of the spy-hole under oath.

Yon faithful 'Johnny' Corbett was an honest and good soldier but he had the death penalty over his head and he was a born survivor. He lived a charmed life afterwards but

was a very dangerous man. He seemed to have much more on his mind than shooting the Unknown Soldier. And people were scared of him whenever his anger was raised. Even the Sheriff had to get a posse to apprehend him in Kansas. He must of thought himself an invincible and avenging angel. And he was a crack shot with any weapon. I hope it wasn't Boston that did it, because I really admired this man's truth.
As for the weapon, we have the choice of a .36, .38 or a .41 calibre. If it was a .36 then it was possibly the Navy Colt revolver. The actual weight of the shot however is significantly high for this calibre. If it was a .38 then it could have been a .38 Colt revolver. If it was .41 then it was likely the Southern derringer, or similar, but would hardly penetrate the bone. The hole in the door was estimated to be just over a ¼" by Mr. Plant, a reliable and highly experienced cabinet worker, and he could not have been more than 1/8" out, so this would make it 3/8" optimum, giving us a .38 calibre weapon, as determined in Chapter 10. But the projectile would have to be conoidal to give us the desired weight and penetration, that is a bullet and not a ball.

And finally having read this book you can see why real history is not taught to our children but mythology, in order to complete the deception and to initiate them into our bizarre culture. The Greeks had a word for it and Homer lives on having given us our greatest hero's, that we can never match.

And so this story ends but not the illuminati
Keep your eyes open and see their illusions
Take care now ye of the gentle people
For the kindest folks are true
Ye all set a spell now

Trains And Boats And Drones
Were Passing By They Mean
A trip to Paris And Rome
For Someone But
Not For Me
You See
?

Epilogue

Cast not your pearls to swine
Lest they devour your mind

1808-1875
Andrew Johnson
Found his True Strength
In his Compassion

In an ideal, just and truly Democratic world, let us imagine now and high time, to put the record straight. The Senate and Congress to challenge the army, to begin the healing process. Or indeed be called to account in order to provide a check, and then a series of counter checks against a further slide towards the tide of anarchy. Certain procedures built into the Constitution by law and to ask the President's influence, yet again, for a full pardon for Dr. Mudd, in just another tiny step for man. If there are a score or more good people, amongst the serious Senate and Congress, worth the trouble. This continual hiding away from the responsibility of this monumental deed is not going to stem future situations whereby the powers behind the Executive, over-ride democracy, law and morality. The world to go on thinking every time another President is assassinated, without apparent reason, yet really because he said No, - Oh, well it's just another American coup and still we Know-Nothing? The misuse of power, led to chaos and the first assassination, and because it was covered up successfully, it has set the precedent for several more, in the same vein. Assassinations occurred in the following sequence: Lincoln 1865, Garfield 1901, McKinley 1921 and Kennedy 1963, over 142 years, one every 36 years. So the next one is overdue and no one to care. There is low risk from the right at present, as it all depends on the nature of the President in office. Lincoln was a brave man, but Andrew Johnson also had the final good courage, to stop the rot. Let these two great Presidents be our marker, so the United States can show the world that whatever its faults, it has the God given faith that it will overcome, in the struggle for Democracy for all peoples. The civil war was a cold and calculated mistake but as Lincoln said if we can win the freedom for all our citizens, then the prize will have been worth the great sacrifice.

Appendix I

The Prosecution and Defence of Edward Spangler

JACOB RITTERSPAUGH. *For the Prosecution.—May 19.*
I know the prisoner, Edward Spangler. He boarded where I did, at Mrs. Scott's, on the corner of Seventh and G Streets. He had no room in the house; he took his meals there, and slept at the theater. He used to keep his valise at the house, and when the detectives came asked if Spangler had any thing there, I gave it to them. He had no clothes there, nothing but that valise; I do not know what it contained. I am commonly called Jake about the theater. *Recalled for the Prosecution.—May 30.*I was a carpenter in Ford's Theater down to the 14th of April last, and was there on the night when the President was shot. He occupied the upper box on the left-hand side of the stage, the right as you come in from the front. My business was to shift wings on the stage and pull them off, and fetch things out of the cellar when needed. I was standing on the stage behind the scenes on the night of the 14th, when some One called out that the President was shot, and directly I saw a man that had no hat on running toward the back door.He had a knife in his hand, and I ran to stop him, and ran through the last entrance, and asI came up to him he tore the door open. I made for him, and he struck at me with the knife, and I jumped back then. He then ran out and slammed the door shut. I then went to get the door open quick, and I thought it was a kind of fast; I could not get it open. In a moment afterward I opened the door, and the man had just got on his horse and was running down the alley; and then I came in. I came back on the stage where I had left Edward Spangler, and he hit me on the face with the back of his hand, and he said, "Don't say which way he went." I asked him what he meant by slapping me in the mouth, and he said, "For God's sake, shut up;" and that was the last he said. The man of whom I speak is Edward Spangler, the prisoner at the bar. I did not see any one else go out before the man with the knife. A tall, stout man went out after me.
Cross-examined by Mr. EWING.
When I heard the pistol fired I was standing in the center of the stage, listening to the play, and Spangler was at the same place, just about ready to shove the scenes; I stood nearest the door. I am certain we both stood there when the pistol was fired. I did not at first know what had happened. Some one called out "Stop that man;" and then I heard some say that the President was shot, and not till then did I know what had occurred. When I came back, Spangler was at the same place where I had left him. There was a crowd in there by that time, both actors and strangers. When Spangler slapped me there were some of the actors near who had taken part in the play; one they called Jenny—I do not what part she took—was standing perhaps three or four feet from me; I do not know whether she heard he said; he did not say it so very loud. He spoke in his usual tone, but he looked as if he was scared, and a kind of crying. I heard the people halloo, "Burn the theater!" "Hang him and shoot him!" I did not, that I know of, tell a number of persons what Spangler said when he slapped me. I did not tell either of the Fords; I told it to nobody but Gifford, the boss. At Carroll Prison, the same week that I was released, I told him that Spangler said I should not say which way the man went. I told a detective that Spangler hit me in the mouth with his open hand. I do not know his name, he was one of Colonel Baker's men; had black whiskers and moustache, and weighed about one hundred and forty pounds, I should think. He came up to the house where I board in the afternoon of the day on which I was released, and I told him then. I have no recollection of telling any one else, though I might have said something at the table, and the rest might have heard. I saw Booth open the back door of the theater and shut it, but I did not know who he was then; I did not see his face right. I was the first person that got to the door after he left; I opened the door, but did not shut it. The big man that ran out after me might have been five or six yards from me when I heard him, or it might have been somebody else, call out, "Which way?" I cried out, "This way," and then ran out, leaving the door open. By that time the man had got on his horse and gone off down the alley. I saw the big man outside, and have not seen him since. I did not take particular notice of him; but he was a tolerably tall man. It might have been two or three minutes after I went out till I came back to where Spangler was standing, and found him kind of scared, and as if he had been crying. I did not say anything to him before he said that to me. It was Spangler's place, with another man, to shove the scenes on; he was where he ought to be to do the work he had to do. I did not hear any one call Booth's name. It was not til the people were all out, and I came outside, that I heard some say it was Booth, and some say it was not. Spangler and I boarded together; we went home to supper together, on the evening of the assassination, at 6 o'clock, and returned at 7.
WILLIAM EATON. *Recalled for the Prosecution.—May 19.* I arrested the prisoner, Edward Spangler, in a house on the South-east corner, I think, of Seventh and H; I believe it was his boarding-house. It was the next week after the assassination. I did not search him; my orders were to arrest him.
CHARLES H. ROSCH. *For the Prosecution.—May 19.* After the arrest of the prisoner, Edward Spangler, I went, in company with two of the Provost Marshal's detectives, to the house on the north-east corner of Seventh and H Streets, where he took his meals. When we inquired for his trunk, we were told that he kept it at the theater; but the man at the house handed us a carpet-bag, in which we found a piece of rope measuring eight-one feet out of which the twist was very carefully taken. The bag was locked, but we found a key that unlocked it. It contained nothing but the rope, some blank paper, and a dirty shirt-collar. I was not present when Spangler was arrested. I went to his house between 9 and 10 o'clock on the night of Monday, April 17.
Cross-examined by Mr. EWING. It was a man, called Jake, apparently a German, that told me it was Spangler's bag, and that it was all he had at the house. He said he worked at the theater with Spangler. There were two other persons there, boarders I presume. We got the rope from a bed-room on the second floor that faced toward the south; the bag was right near where Jake had his trunk. I am satisfied that the coil of rope I see here now is the same that I took from Spangler's carpet-bag.
C. D. HESS *For the Defense.—May 31. By* Mr. EWING. I am manager of Grover's Theater, and I have been in the habit of seeing John Wilkes Booth very frequently. On the day before the assassination he came into the office during the afternoon, interrupting me and the prompter of the theater in reading a manuscript. He seated himself in a chair, and entered into a conversation on the general illumination of the city that night. He asked me if I intended to illuminate. I said yes, I should, to a certain extent; but that the next night would be my great night of the illumination, that being the celebration of the fall of Sumter. He then asked, "Do you intend to" or "Are you going to invite the President?" My reply, I think, was, "Yes, that reminds me that I must send that invitation." I had it in my mind for several days to invite the Presidential party that night, the 14th. I sent my invitation to Mrs. Lincoln. My notes were usually addressed to her, as the best means of accomplishing the object. Booth's manner, and his entering in the way he did, struck me as rather peculiar. He must have observed that we were busy, and it was not usual for him to come into the office and take a seat, unless he was invited. He did upon this occasion, and made such a point of it that we were both considerably surprised. He pushed the matter so far that I got up and put the manuscript away, and entered into conversation with him. It is customary in theaters to keep the passage-way between the scenes and the Greenroom and the dressing-rooms clear, but much depends upon the space there is for storing scenes and furniture. [The counsel was eliciting from the witness the position of the box usually occupied by the President on visiting Grover's Theater, and nature of the leap that an assassin would have to make in endeavoring to escape from the box, when objection was made to the testimony as irrelevant.]
Mr. EWING. I wish merely to show that, from the construction of Ford's Theater, it would be easier for the assassin to effect his escape from Ford's Theater than it would be from Grover's. The purpose is plainly to show that Ford's Theater was selected by Booth, and why Ford's Theater is spoken of by him as the one where he intended to capture or assassinate the President, and to relieve the employees of Ford's Theater, Mr. Spangler among them, from the imputation which naturally arises from Booth's selecting that theater as the one in which to commit the crime. The Commission sustained the objection.
H. CLAY FORD. *For the Defense.—May 31. By* Mr. EWING. On the 14th of April last I was treasurer of Ford's Theater. I returned to the theater from my breakfast about half-past 11 o'clock that day, when my brother, James R. Ford, told me that the President had engaged a box for that night. John

Wilkes Booth was at the theater about half an hour afterward. I do not know that the fact of the President's going to the theater that night was c ommunicated to Booth, but I think it is very likely he found it out while there. I saw him going down the street while I was standing in the door of the theater; as he came up he commenced talking to the parties standing around. Mr. Raybold then went into the theater and brought him out a letter that was there for him. He sat down on the steps and commenced reading it. This was about 12 o'clock. He staid there perhaps half an hour. I went into the office, and when I came out again he was gone. I told Mr. Raybold about fixing up and decorating the box for the President that night, but he had the neuralgia in his face, and I fixed up the box in his place. I found two flags in the box already there, which I got Mr. Raybold to help me put up. Another flag I got from the Treasury Department. It was the Treasury regimental flag. I put this blue regimental flag in the center, and the two American flags above. There was nothing unusual in the decorations of the box, except the picture of Washington placed on the pillar in the middle of the box. This had never been used before. We usually used small flags to decorate the box; but as General Grant was expected to come with the President, we borrowed this flag from the Treasury regiment to decorate with. The furniture placed in the box consisted of one chair brought from the stage and a sofa, a few chairs out of the reception room, and a rocking-char, which belonged to the same set, I had brought from my bed-room. This chair had been in the reception-room, but the ushers sitting in it had greased it with their hair, and I had it removed to my room, it being a very nice chair. The only reason for putting that chair in the box was that it belonged to the set, and I sent for it make the box as neat as possible. I received no suggestions from any one as to the decoration of the box, excepting from Mr. Raybold and the gentleman who brought the flag from the Treasury Department. All that Spangler had to do with the box was to take the partition out. There are two boxes divided by a partition, which, when the President attended the theater, was always removed to make the box into one. Spangler and the other carpenter, Jake, removed it. The President had been to the theater, I suppose, about six times during the winter and spring; three or four times during Mr. Forrest's engagements, and twice during Mr. Clark's engagement. These are the only times I remember. I did not direct Spangler with respect to the removal of the partition; I believe Mr. Raybold sent for him. While we were in the box Spangler was working on the stage; I think he had a pair of flats down on the stage, fixing them in some way. I came for a hammer and nails; he threw up two or three nails and handed me the hammer up from the stage. Spangler, of course, knew that the President was coming to the theater that evening, as he assisted in taking out the partition. In decorating the box I used my penknife to cut the strings to tie up the flags, and left it there in the box. Three or four times during the season Booth had engaged box No. 7, that is part of the President's box, being the one nearest the audience. He engaged no other box. During the play that evening, the "American Cousin," I was in the ticket-office of the theater. I may have been out on the pavement in front two or three times, but I do not remember. I did not see Spangler there. I never saw Spangler wear a moustache.

Cross-examined by ASSISTANT JUDGE ADVOCATE BINGHAM. None of the other boxes were occupied on the night of the President's assassination, and I do not remember any box being taken on that night. I certainly did not know that the boxes were applied for, for that evening, and that the applicants were refused and told that the boxes were already taken. The applicants did not apply to me. Booth did not apply to me, or to any one, for those boxes, to my knowledge, nor did any one else of him. There were four of us in the office who sold tickets. There were not, to my knowledge, any applications for any box except the President's. There may have been applications without my knowledge. I know nothing of the mortise in the wall behind the door of the President's box. I heard of it afterward, but have never seen it, nor did I see the bar said to have been use to fasten the door, nor did I see the hole bored through the first door of the President's box, though I have since heard there was one. I have not been in the box since. The screws of the keepers of the lock to the President's box, I understand, were burst some time ago. They were not to my knowledge, drawn that day, and left so that the lock would not hold the door on its being slightly pressed. It was not done in my presence, and if it was done at all, it was without my knowledge. I do not remember any conversation with Mr. Ferguson before the day of the assassination about decorating the theater in celebration of some victory.

By Mr. AIKEN. The letter that Booth received on the day of the assassination, and read on the steps of the theater, was a long letter, of either four or eight pages of letter-paper—whether one or two sheets I do not know, but was all covered with writing. He sat on the steps while reading his letter, every now and then looking up and laughing. It was while Booth was there I suppose he learned of the President's visit to the theater that evening. There were several around Booth, talking to him. Mr. Gifford was there; Mr. Evans, and actor, and Mr. Grillet, I remember, were there at the time. The President's visit to the theater that evening could not have been known until 12 o'clock, unless it was made known by some one from the Executive Mansion. It was published in the Evening Star, but not in the morning papers. I am not acquainted with John H. Surratt. [Photograph of John H. Surratt exhibited to the witness.] I never saw that person that I know of.

By Mr. EWING. I have never, to my knowledge, seen the prisoner, Herold. The mortise in the passage-way was not noticed by me; the passage was dark, and when the door was thrown back against the wall, as it was that day, I should be likely to notice it had it been there at that time. Had the small hole been bored in the door, or had the screws been loosened, it is not likely I should have noticed them.

By the COURT. I might have stated in the saloon on Tenth Street that the President was to be at the theater that evening, and also that General Grant was to be there.

JAMES R. FORD. *For the Defense.—May 30. By* Mr. EWING. At the time of the assassination, I was business manager at Ford's Theater. I was first apprised of the President's intended visit to the theater on Friday morning, at half-past 10 o'clock. A young man, a messenger from the White House, came and engaged the box. The President has been previously invited to the theater that night, and I had no knowledge of his intention to visit the theater until the reception of that message. I saw John Wilkes Booth about half-past 12, two hours after I received this information. I saw him as I was coming from the Treasury Building, on the corner of Tenth and E Streets. I was going up E Street, toward Eleventh Street; he was coming from the direction of the theater. ***Q.*** State whether, upon any occasion, you have had any conversation with Booth as to the purchase of lands, and, if so, where?

Assistant Judge Advocate BINGHAM. I object to the question. Mr. EWING. Testimony has already been admitted on that point. Assistant Judge Advocate BINGHAM. I know, but it is unimportant as to this man; there is no question about this man in the case. Mr. EWING. It is very important as to one of the prisoners. Assistant Judge Advocate BINGHAM. This witness can not be evidence for any human being on that subject, no matter what Booth said to him about it. I object to it on the ground that it is entirely incompetent, and has nothing in the world to do with the case. If this witness had been involved in it, I admit it might be asked, with a view to exculpate him from any censure before the public. Mr. EWING. The Court will recollect that in Mr. Weichman's testimony there was evidence introduced by the prosecution of an alleged interview between Dr. Mudd and Booth at the National Hotel, in the middle of January, which was introduced as a circumstance showing his connection with the conspiracy, which Booth is supposed to have then had on foot. The accused, Dr. Mudd, is represented to have stated that the conversation related to the purchase of his lands in Maryland. I wish to show by this witness that Booth spoke to him frequently, through the course of the winter, of his speculations, of his former speculations in oil lands, which are shown to have been Actual speculations of the year before, and of his contemplating the investment of money in cheap lands in Lower Maryland. The effect of the testimony is to show that the statement, which has been introduced against the accused, Dr. Mudd, if it was made, was a *bona fide* statement, and related to an actual pending offer, or talk about the sale of his farm to Booth. Assistant Judge Advocate BINGHAM. The only way, if the Court please, in which they can do any thing in regard to this matter of the declaration of Mudd, if it was made, (and, if it was not made, of course it does not concern anybody,) is simply to show by legitimate evidence that there was such a negotiation going on between himself and Booth. The point I make is, that it is not legitimate evidence, or any evidence at all, to introduce a conversation between Booth and this witness at another time and place. It is no evidence at all, it is not colorable evidence, and the Court have nothing in the world to do with it. It would be impossible to ask the witness any questions that would be more irrelevant and incompetent than the question that is now asked him. Mr. EWING. I will state to the Court further that it has already received testimony, as explanatory of the presence of Booth in Charles County, of his avowed object in going there—testimony to which the Judge Advocate made no objection, and which he Must have then regarded as relevant. This testimony is clearly to that point of explanation of Booth's visit to Lower Maryland, as well as an explanation of

the alleged conversation with Mudd in January. Assistant Judge Advocate BINGHAM. The difference is this: the defense attempted to prove negotiations in Charles County, and we thought we would not object to that; but this is another thing altogether. It is an attempt to prove a talk, irrespective of time or place, or any thing else. The Commission sustained the objection.
By Mr. EWING.
Q. Do you know of any thing of the visit made by Booth into Charles County last fall? ***A.*** He told me— Assistant Judge Advocate BINGHAM objected to the witness giving the declarations of Booth. THE WITNESS. I have never known Booth to go there.
Q. Have you ever heard of Booth say what the purpose of any visit which he may have made last fall to Charles County was? Assistant Judge Advocate BINGHAM renewed his objection. The Commission sustained the objection.
By Mr. AIKEN. The notice in the Evening Star that announced the President's intended visit to the theater, also said that General Grant would be there.
By ASSISTANT JUDGE ADVOCATE BURNETT. I wrote the notice for the Star in the ticket-office of the theater about half-past 11 or 12 o'clock, and sent it to the office immediately; I at the same time carried one myself to the National Republican. The notice appeared in the Star about 2 o'clock. Before writing the notice I asked Mr. Phillips, an actor in our establishment, who was on the stage, to do it; he said he would after he had finished writing the regular advertisements. I also spoke to my younger brother about the propriety of writing it. I had not seen Booth previous to writing the notice, nor do I remember speaking to any one else about it.
By Mr. AIKEN. I had sent the notice to the Star office before seeing Booth. [Exhibiting the photograph of John H. Surratt.] I do not know Surratt. I never remember seeing him. John McCullough, the actor, left this city the fourth week in January. He returned with Mr. Forrest at his last engagement. I do not know exactly when, but about the 1st of April.
JOHN T. FORD. ***For the Defense.—May 31.*** I reside in Baltimore, and am proprietor of Ford's Theater in the city of Washington. The prisoner, Edward Spangler, has been in my employ three or four years at intervals, and over two years continuously. Spangler was employed as a stage-hand, frequently misrepresented as the stage-carpenter of the theater. He was a laborer to assist in shoving the scenery in its place, as the necessity of the play required. These were his duties at night, and during the day to assist in doing the rough carpenter work incidental to plays to be produced.
Q. State whether or not his duties were such as to require his presence upon the stage during the whole of a play. ***A.*** Strictly so; his absence for a moment might imperil the success of a play, and cause dissatisfaction to the audience. It is very important to the effect of a play that the scenery should be well attended to in all its changes; and he is absolutely important there every moment from the time the curtain rises until it falls. There are intervals, it is true, but he can not judge how long or how brief a scene might be. On Friday, the day of the assassination, I was in Richmond. Hearing of the partial destruction of that city by fire, I went there, anxious to ascertain the condition of an uncle, a very aged man, and my mother-in-law. I did not hear of the assassination until Sunday night, and then I heard that Edwin Booth was charged with it. On Monday morning I started for Washington by the 6 o'clock boat. While on the boat I saw the Richmond Whig, which confirmed the report I had heard of the assassination on Sunday night. During the performance of the "American Cousin," Spangler's presence on the stage would be necessary. The first scene of the third act is quick, only of a few moments' duration. The second scene is rather a long one, longer perhaps than any other scene in that act, probably eight, ten, or twelve minutes long. Spangler's presence would be necessary unless positively informed of the duration of the scene.The second act depends very much upon the action and the spirit of the actors engaged in it. Sometimes it is much more rapid than at others. In the second act I hardly think there is an interval of more than five or eight minutes between the times that Spangler would have to move the scenes. His constant presence upon the stage would be Absolutely necessary if he attended to his duties. In the intervals between the scenes, he should be preparing for the next change, to be ready at his scene, and to remain on the side where the stage-carpenter had assigned him his post of duty; besides, emergencies often arise during an act that require extra Services of a stage hand. J. B. Wright was the stage-manager, James J. Gifford the stage carpenter. The stage manager directs, the stage-carpenter executes the work belonging to the entire stage. The duty of keeping the passage-way clear and in a proper condition belongs to Gifford's subordinates, the stage hands who were on the side where this passage is. It is the duty of each and every one to keep the passage-way clear, and is as indispensable as keeping The front door clear. The action of the play might be ruined by any obstruction or hindrance there. My positive orders are to keep it always clear and in the best order. It is the passage-way used by all the parties coming from the dressing-rooms. Where a play was performed like the "American Cousin," the ladies were in full dress, and it was absolutely necessary that there should be no obstruction there, in order that the play should be properly performed. Coming from the dressing-rooms and the green-room of the theater, every one had to use that passage. The other side of the stage was not used more than a third as much, probably. Most of the entrances by the actors and actresses essential to be made are on the O. P. side. By entrances to the stage, I mean to the presence of the audience. The stage-manager was a very exacting man in all those details, and I have always found the passage clear, unless there was some spectacular play, in which he required the whole spread of the stage. Then at times it would be partly encumbered, but not enough so to prevent the people going around the stage, or going to the cellar-way and underneath, and passing to the other side by way of the cellar. The "American Cousin" was a very plain play; no obstruction whatever could be excused on account of that play; it was all what we call flats, except one scene. The flats are the large scenes that cross the stage. The prompt side, the side on which the prompter is located, is the position of the stagecarpenter, and opposite to where Spangler worked, which is on the O. P. side, opposite the prompter's place. Keeping the passage-way clear would not be a duty of Spangler's, unless he was specially charged with it. Spangler, I know, considered Baltimore his home. He buried his wife there about a year ago, or less, while in my employ. He usually spent his summer months there, during the vacation of the theater, chiefly in crab-fishing. I have understood that he was a great crab fisher; we used to plague him about it. [Exhibiting a coil of rope found at Spangler's boarding-house, in his carpet-bag.] That rope might be used as a crab-line, though it is rather short for that purpose. Professional crab-fishers use much longer ropes than this, four hundred or five hundred feet long, though I have seen ropes as short as this, which I understand is eighty feet, used by amateurs in that sport. The rope is supported by a buoy, and to it are attached smaller ropes or lines. Spangler seemed to have a great admiration for J. Wilkes Booth; I have noticed that in my business on the stage with the stage-manager.
Booth was a peculiarly fascinating man, and controlled the lower class of people, such as Spangler belonged to, more, I suppose, than ordinary men would. Spangler was not in the employ of Booth, that I know, and only since the assassination have I heard that he was in the habit of waiting upon him. I have never known Spangler to wear a moustache. I have known J. Wilkes Booth since his childhood, and intimately for six or seven years.
Q. State whether you have ever heard Booth speak of Samuel K. Chester, and, if so, in what connection and where. Assistant Judge Advocate BINGHAM. I object to any proof about what he said in regard to Chester.
Q. [By Mr. EWING.] State whether or not Booth ever applied to you to employ Chester, who has been a witness for the prosecution, in your theater. Assistant Judge Advocate BINGHAM. That I object to. It is certainly not competent to introduce the declarations of Booth made to anybody in the absence of a witness that may be called, relative to a transaction of his, to affect him in any way at all. I object to it as wholly incompetent.
Mr. EWING. It is not to attack Chester, may it please the Court, that I make this inquiry, but rather to corroborate him; to show that Booth, while manipulating Chester to introduce him to go into a conspiracy for the capture of the President, was actually at the same time endeavoring to induce Mr. Ford to employ Chester, in order that he might get him here to the theater and use him as an instrument; and it goes to affect the case of several prisoners at the bar—the case of the prisoner Arnold, who in his confession, as orally detailed here, stated that the plan was to capture the President, and Chester corroborates that; and also to assist the case of the prisoner, Spangler, by showing that Booth was not able to get, or did not get, in the theater any instruments to assist him in the purpose, and was endeavoring to get them brought there—men that he had previously manipulated. I think it is legitimate.
Assistant Judge Advocate BINGHAM. Nothing can be clearer, if the Court please, than that it is utterly incompetent. It is not a simple question of relevancy here; it is absolute incompetency. A party who conspires to do a crime may approach the most upright man in the world with whom he has been, before the criminality was known to the world, on terms of intimacy, and whose position in the world, was such that he might be on terms of intimacy

with reputable gentlemen. It is the misfortune of a man that is approached in that way; it is not his crime, and it is not colorably his crime either. It does not follow now, because Booth chose to approach this man Chester, that Booth is therefore armed with the power, living or dead, to come into a court of justice and prove on his own motion, or on the motion of anybody else, what he may have said touching that man to third persons. The law is too jealous of the reputation and character of men to permit any such proceedings as that. The Commission sustained the objection.

Q. Do you think that the leap from the President's box upon the stage would be at all a difficult one for Booth? ***A.*** I should not think a rehearsal of it needed. He was a very bold, fearless man; he always had the reputation of being of that character. He excelled in all manly sports. We never rehearse leaps in the theater, even when they are necessary to the action of the play; they may be gone over the first time a play is performed, but it is not usual. Booth had a reputation for being a great gymnast. He introduced, in some Shakespearean plays, some of the most extraordinary and outrageous leaps—at least they were deemed so by the critics, and were condemned by the press at the time. I saw him on one occasion make on these extraordinary leaps, and the Baltimore Sun condemned it in an editorial the next day—styling him "the gymnastic actor." It was in the play of "Macbeth," the entrance to the witch scene; he jumped from a high rock down on the stage, as high or perhaps higher than the box; I think nearly as high as from the top of the scene; and he made the leap with apparent ease. Booth was in the habit of frequenting Ford's Theater at Washington. I seldom visited the theater but what I found him about or near it, during the day, while I was there. I usually came down to the theater three days a week, devoting the other three to my business in Baltimore, and being there between the hours of 10 and 3. I would nearly always meet Booth there when he was in the city. He had his letters directed to the theater, and that was the cause of his frequent visits there, as I thought then. The last time I saw Booth was some two or three weeks before the assassination. The last appearance of John McCullough at my theater in Washington was on the 18th of March, the night, I believe, when the "Apostate" was played. Mr. McCullough always appears with Mr. Forrest, and he has since appeared in New York.

Cross-examined by ASSISTANT JUDGE ADVOCATE BINGHAM. I can not state positively that the private boxes are locked when not in actual use; that is our custom in Baltimore. Mr. Gifford, who had control of the whole theater, is the responsible party whom I should blame for any thing wrong about the boxes. We keep the boxes locked, and the keys in the box-office; here, I understand, the custom is for the ushers to keep the keys. James O'Brien was the usher of the dress-circle, and James R. Ford and Henry Clay Ford were the parties authorized to sell tickets for those boxes that day.

Q. Do you know as a fact that none of the boxes were occupied that night, except that occupied by the President? ***A.*** I have only heard so.

Q. Is the play of the "American Cousin" a popular one? Does it attract considerable audiences? ***A.*** It was, when originally produced, an exceedingly attractive play; of late years it has not been a strong card, but a fair attraction.

Q. Is it not a very unusual thing, when such plays are produced, for your private boxes to be entirely empty? ***A.*** Washington is a very good place for selling boxes usually. They are generally in demand, and nearly always two or three boxes are sold.

Q. Can you recall any occasion on which a play, so popular and attractive as that was, presented when none of your private boxes, save the one occupied by the President was used? ***A.*** I remember occasions when we sold no boxes at all, and had quite a full house—a good audience; but those occasions were rare. My reason for constructing so many boxes to this theater was, that usually private boxes were in demand in Washington— more so than in almost any other city. It is not a favorable place to see a performance, but it is a fashionable place here to which to take company.

Recalled for the Defense.—June 9. By Mr. EWING. I have known Edward Spangler for nearly four years. He has been in my employ most of that time. He was always regarded as a very good-natured, kind, willing man. His only fault was in occasionally drinking more liquor than he should have done, not so as to make him vicious, but more to unfit him to work. Since he has been in my employ I never knew him to be in but one quarrel and that was through drink. He was always willing to do any thing, and was a very good, efficient drudge. He was considered a very harmless man by the company around the t heater, and was often the subject of sport and fun. I do not think he was intrusted with the confidence of others to any extent. He had not many associates. He had no self-respect, and was a man that rarely slept in a bed; he usually slept in the theater. I never knew any thing of his political sentiments in this city; never heard from him an expression of partisan or political feeling. In Baltimore he was known to be a member of the American Order.

By Mr. CLAMPITT. I never met J. Z. Jenkins except in Carroll Prison.

JOSEPH J. SESSFORD. ***For the Defense.—June 3.*** I was a seller of tickets at Ford's Theater. My business commenced about half-past 6 in the evening. None of the private boxes, except that occupied by the party of the President, were applied for on the evening of the assassination, nor had any been sold during the day that I know of.

WILLIAM WITHERS, JR. ***Recalled for the Defense.—May 31.*** *By* Mr. EWING. The door leading into the alley from the stage was shut when Booth rushed out. After he made the spring from the box, and ran across the stage, he made a cut at me, and knocked me down to the first entrance; then I got a side view of him. The door was shut, but it opened very easily; I saw that distinctly. He made a plunge right at the knob of the door, and out he went, and pulled the door after him. He swung it as he went out. I did not see Booth during the day.

HENRY M. JAMES. ***For the Defense.—May 31.*** *By* Mr. EWING. I was at Ford's Theater on the night of the assassination. When the shot was fired, I Was standing ready to draw off the flat, and Mr. Spangler was standing right opposite to me on the stage, on the same side as the President's box, about ten feet from me. From his position he could not see the box, nor the side of the stage on which Booth jumped. I had frequently during the play seen Spangler at his post. I saw no one with him. The passageway was clear at the time; it was our business to keep it clear; it was more Spangler's business than mine. I saw Spangler when the President entered the theater. When the people applauded on the President's entry, he applauded with them, with hands and feet. He clapped his hands, and stamped his feet, and seemed as pleased as anybody to see the President come in. I did not see Jacob Ritterspaugh near Spangler that evening. He might have been there behind the scenes, but I did not see him. I can not say how long I staid in my position after the shot was fired; it might have been a minute. I did not see Spangler at all after that happened. *By* ASSISTANT JUDGE ADVOCATE BINGHAM. Jacob Ritterspaugh was employed there, and it was his business to be there behind the scenes, though I did not see him.

J. L. DEBONAY. ***For the Defense.—May 31.*** *By* Mr. EWING. I was playing what is called "responsible utility" at Ford's Theater at the time of the a ssassination. On the evening of the assassination, Booth came up to the alley door and said to me, "Tell Spangler to come to the door and hold my horse." He then went to the door and went outside, and was there about a minute, when Mr. Booth came in. Booth asked me if he could get across the stage. I told him no, the dairy scene was on, and he would have to go under the stage and come up on the other side. About the time that he got upon the other side, Spangler called to me, "Tell Peanut John to come here and hold this horse; I have not time. Mr. Gifford is out in the front of the theater, and all the responsibility of the scene lies upon me." I went on the other side and called John, and John went there and held the horse, when Spangler came in and returned to his post. I saw Spangler there or four times that evening on the stage in his proper position. I saw him about two minutes before the shot was fired. He was on the same side I was on—the same side as the President's box. About five minutes after the shot was fired, I again saw Spangler standing on the stage, with a crowd of people who had collected there. I saw Booth when he made his exit. I was standing in the first entrance on the left-hand side. When he came to the center of the stage, I saw that he had a long knife in his hand. It seemed to me to be a doubled-edged knife, and looked like a new one. He paused about a second, I should think, and then went off at the first entrance to the right-hand side. I think he had time to get out of the back door before any person was on the stage. It was, perhaps, two or three seconds after he made his exit before I saw any person on the stage in pursuit. The first person I noticed was a tall, stout gentleman, with gray clothes on, I think, and I believe a moustache. Booth did not seem to run very fast across the stage; he seemed to be stooping a little when he ran off. The distance he ran would be about thirty-five or forty feet; but he was off the stage two or three seconds before this gentleman was on, and of the two, I think Booth was running the fastest.

By Mr. AIKEN.I was at the theater at 12 o'clock that day. I did not see Booth there. *Recalled for the Prosecution.—June 13.* When the shot was fired on the night of the assassination, I was standing on the left-hand side of the first entrance, the side the President's box was on. About a minute and a half or two minutes after Mr. Stewart left the stage, or about time to allow of his getting to the back door, I saw Spangler shove the scene back to give the whole stage to the people who came on. I do not know who assisted him. then came to the front of the stage with the rest of the people. There was then a cry for water. I started to the green-room, and he came the same way. About a half dozen of us went to get some water to carry it to the private box. When Booth wanted Spangler to hold his horse, and I went over to tell him, Spangler and Sleichman were standing close to each other on the opposite side of the stage, the side of the President's box. Spangler then left; I saw him go out to Booth, and in about a minute or a minute and a half Booth came in. I heard no conversation between Spangler and Booth. Booth met Spangler at the door, and was standing at the door on the outside; the door was about half open when Spangler went out. If any person had followed Spangler I should have seen him. I was half-way between the back door and the green-room, about eighteen or twenty feet distant, I suppose. Booth, when he came in, went under the stage to the opposite side, and went out of the side door; I went under the stage and crossed with him. I did not see him speak to any one. I was in front of the theater about five minutes before the assassination; I did not see Spangler there. I have known Spangler for about six months. I have never seen him wear a moustache. He is a man that has been a little dissipated a considerable portion of his time—fond of spreeing round. He is free in conversation, especially when in liquor.

Cross-examined by the JUDGE ADVOCATE. When Booth passed under the stage, he went through the little side passage, level with the lower floor of the theater, that leads out into Tenth Street; that side passage also leads up to Mr. Ford's room. I went out through that passage to the front of the theater, and returned by the same way, and had taken my place on the stage when the pistol was fired. I was not doing any thing, but was leaning up against the corner of the scene at the time. We were waiting for the curtain to drop. Mr. Harry Hawk was on the stage at the moment, playing in a scene.

.**WILLIAM R. SMITH.** ***For the Defense.—June 2.*** *By* Mr. EWING. I played in the piece, taking the part of ***John Wigger***, the gardener I saw the gentleman who first got upon the stage after Booth got off. He was a large man, dressed in light clothes, with a moustache. This gentleman was the first that got upon the stage, and I suppose it was probably two or three minutes—about that long—after Booth went off the stage that this man went out of the entrance. I saw no one else run out of the entrance except Hawk,, the young man who on the stage at the time Booth jumped from the box. If any one had run out of the entrance following Booth, I should probably have seen him, because I thought it was very singular that those who were near the stage did not try to get on it. *Cross-examined by* ASSISTANT JUDGE ADVOCATE BINGHAM. I sat in the dress-circle on the north side, the same side as the entrance through which Booth passed. From the place where I sat I could not distinctly see the mouth of the entrance.

JAMES LAMB. ***For the Defense.—June 2.*** *By* Mr. EWING. For over a year I have been employed at Ford's Theater as an artist and scene-painter. [The rope found in Spangler's bag exhibited to the witness.] I have seen ropes like this at the theater. There are probably forty or fifty of such ropes in use there. They are called border-ropes and are about seventy or eighty feet in length, used for suspending the borders that hang across the stage. The borders are long strips of canvas, painted to represent some exteriors, others interiors, and as they are required to be changed for the scene that is on, they are raised or lowered by means of such ropes as these. This rope has the appearance of having been chafed; a new rope would be a little stiffer in its texture than this. I should say this a new rope, but has been in use, though I can not detect any thing that would lead to say it has been in use as a border-rope; if it had been, there would been a knot fastening at the end, or have the appearance of having been tied. *Cross-examined by* ASSISTANT JUDGE ADVOCATE BINGHAM. I think it is a rope very similar to the ones used at the theater, but I should be very sorry to swear that it was one of them. I should say the material was manilla. I know John Wilkes Booth by sight. I never spoke a word to him in my life. I did not hear him say any thing in March or April last about the President. I never was in his company.

By Mr. EWING. From an examination of the rope, I have no reason to believe that it was used as a border rope. I was in the theater the whole of Saturday, the day after the President was assassinated, from 10 o'clock until the military guard took possession, and I saw Spangler there several times during the day. *By* ASSISTANT JUDGE ADVOCATE BINGHAM. I saw him on the stage. Maddox, Jake, Mr. Gifford, and Mr. Wright, the stage-manager, were in and out occasionally. Carland was also there with Spangler, Maddox, and myself, in the forenoon, loitering and walking about, sometimes sitting down; there was no companionship particularly. I have not seen Spangler since this morning.

JACOB RITTERSPAUGH. ***Recalled for the Defense.—June 2.*** *By* Mr. EWING. When I was in the theater with Mr. Lamb, the next day after the assassination, I told him about Spangler slapping me and saying, "Shut up; don't say which way he went;" and on the night of the assassination, when Carland came up to Mr. Gifford's room, he woke me up and asked where Ned was. I told him I did not know, and then I told him that Ned had slapped me in the mouth, and said, "Don't say which way he went." As I was on the stage with Spangler on the day of the assassination, we saw a man in The dress-circle smoking a cigar. I asked Spangler who it was, but he did not know; and I said we ought to tell him to go out; but Spangler said he had no charge on that side of the theater, and had no right to do so. I took no more notice of him, and went to my work again. After awhile I saw him sitting in the lower private box, on the right-hand side of the stage. He was looking at us. I told Ned, and he spoke to him, and then the man went out. That was about six o'clock on the evening of the day on which the President was assassinated. That was about 6 o'clock in the evening. *Cross-examined by* ASSISTANT JUDGE ADVOCATE BINGHAM. I never saw the man before. He wore a moustache. I saw him first in the dress-circle, then in the lower private box on the right-hand side of the stage, the left-hand when you come in from the front of the theater.

JAMES LAMB. ***Recalled for the Defense.—June 2.*** I saw Ritterspaugh on the stage on Saturday, the day following the President's assassination. Ritterspaugh was grumbling, and saying that it was well for Ned that he hadn't something in his hand at the time. I asked him why. He replied, "He struck me last night a very hard blow, and he said at the same time, 'Shut up; you know nothing about it.'" This was said in connection with Ritterspaugh having said it was Booth that ran across the stage. Ritterspaugh said he called out, "I know him; I know who it was; it was Booth," or something of that kind, and then Ned struck him and said "Hush up; be quiet. What do you know about it?" That was while Mr. Booth, or whoever it was, was leaving the stage. It was when he was making his escape that this man Jake said he was rushing up and made this exclamation, "That was Booth; I know him; I know him; I will swear that was Booth;" when Ned turned round and struck him in the face with his hand. Ritterspaugh said, "It is well for him I had not something in my hand to return the blow." Then he represented Spangler as saying, when he slapped him "Hush up; hush up; you know nothing about it. What do you know about it? Keep quiet;" hushing him up. Ritterspaugh did not say to me that when Spangler hit him on the face he said, "Don't say which way he went." I am certain Ritterspaugh did not say that to me, or words to that effect.

Cross-examined by ASSISTANT JUDGE ADVOCATE BINGHAM.

Q. Can you tell just exactly the words he did say, that you have sworn to already? ***A.*** Yes, sir.

Q. State them. ***A.*** "Shut up; what do you know about? Hold your tongue."

Q. That is what Jake said? ***A.*** That is what Spangler said to Jake.

Q. Are you now reporting what Jake said, or reporting what Spangler said? ***A.*** I am reporting what Spangler said and what Jake said.

Q. We are not asking you for what Spangler said; we are asking you what Jake said. State, if you please, what Jake said on that occasion, and exactly what you have sworn he said, and all he said. ***A.*** I will, as near as I can recollect. As e told me, he said, "I followed out the party, was close at his heels, or near to him, and I said that is Booth. I know him; I know him;" or words to that effect, as near as can be.

Q. Jake said he followed out the party, close to his heels? ***A.*** Near to him.

Q. And that he knew who that was? ***A.*** He did not say that he followed the party.

Q. I am asking you what he said. Did you not swear just now that he said he followed the party close to his heels? ***A.*** He was near to him.

Q. Did you or did you not swear that he said he followed the party close to his heels? ***A.*** You know whether I swore it or not.

Q. I ask you whether you did swear to it or not? ***A.*** I say he did.

Q. Very well, then, stick to it. Then Jake said he followed the party close to his heels? ***A.*** Yes, sir.

Q. And he knew who he was? ***A.*** Yes, sir.

Q. What more did Jake say? Did he say he came back after following him close to his heels? *A*. No; he received a blow from Spangler, and that shut him up.
Q. Do you swear now that Spangler followed the man close to his heels? *A*. No, sir.
Q. Then how did they fix it? *A*. Spangler was standing in the way.
Q. While Jake was following the man close to his heels? *A*. No, not at all.
Q. How was that? *A*. Spangler, I suppose—
Q. You need not state what you suppose. State what Jake said. That is the only question before the Court. *A*. That is what I have stated.

LOUIS J. CARLAND. ***For the Defense.—June 12. By*** Mr. EWING. I am acquainted with Jacob Ritterspaugh. On the night of the assassination I went to Mr. Gifford's room, and Ritterspaugh was there asleep. I woke him up, and asked him where Spangler was. He seemed frightened, and thought I was Mr. Booth. I asked him where Mr. Spangler was. He told me he did not know where he was now; the last he had seen of Mr. Spangler was when he was standing behind the scenes, and that he did not know where he had gone; that when the man was running past he had said that was Mr. Booth, and Spangler had slapped him in the mouth, and said to him, "You don't know who it is; it may be Mr. Booth, or it may be somebody else." He did not say that Spangler slapped him on the face with the back of his hand and said, "Don't say which way he went," nor any thing to that effect. I did not see Spangler until the next day; then I saw him in the theater, on the stage. When he went up stairs to bed on the Saturday night after the assassination, he said There some talk that the people were going to burn the theater, and as he slept very heavily, he was afraid to sleep up there, so I took him into my room, and he was there all night. He was put under arrest that night in my room. At half-past 9 o'clock Sunday morning the guard came and relieved him, and when I was discharged we both went into the street. I went to church, and in the afternoon saw Spangler again in the street near the theater. We walked round that afternoon, and to Mr. Gurly's on C street. Some one came there and told he was going to be arrested, and I advised him at once to go and see the detectives, and not have them come after him when he was asleep and take him out of his bed. I went to Mr. Barry, one of the detectives, and asked him if there was any such report at the police head-quarters, and he said no. I know that Spangler had very little money those two days, for he wanted to see Mr. Gifford to get some. Booth frequented the theater very familiarly before the assassination. He was there a great deal, and was very intimate with all the employees, and called them by name. He was a gentleman who would soon get acquainted, and get familiar with people on a very short acquaintance. [Exhibiting to the witness the rope found in Spangler's bag.] We use just such rope as that in the theater to pull up the borders and scenes, and for bringing up lumber to the top dressing-rooms, because the stairs are too narrow. About two weeks before the assassination, we used such a rope as that to haul up some shelving for my wardrobe, through the window, to the fourth story; Spangler and Ritterspaugh brought it up. I do not know that the rope we used was an extra one; there were a great many ropes around the theater. I am not qualified to judge about how much the rope has been used; this one does not look like an entirely new rope; it is not such as I would buy for a new one; it looks as if it had been exposed out of doors, or in the rain. *Cross-examined by* ASSISTANT JUDGE ADVOCATE BINGHAM. Spangler used to sleep in the theater before the assassination, and he slept there on that night, but not in the room he usually slept in. On that night he slept in the carpenter's shop attached to the theater. I do not know where he slept on Sunday night. It was about 12 o'clock on Friday night when I woke Ritterspaugh up; there was no one with me, but a policeman stood in the manager's office, on the first floor of the green room; that is where I found Ritterspaugh. He was frightened when I woke him up, and thought it was Booth. He did not say any thing to me about Booth drawing a knife on him. When I asked, "Where is Ned?" he said he did not know where he was; that he supposed he was up. I made no reply, and he went on and said that when Booth ran out through the passage-way, while he and Ned were standing behind the scenes, he made the remark, "That is Mr. Booth," and Ned slapped him in the mouth and said "You don't know whether it is Mr. Booth, or who it is." That is all that I remember he said. I never told it to any one but Mr. William Withers, jr. I dined with him on the Sunday after the assassination, and told him then.

By Mr. EWING. The carpenter-shop is attached to the theater just the same way as my wardrobe is. It is not in the theater building, but it is included in the theater. You do not have into the street to get to it. You leave the theater, and there is a passage-way to go up, the same as we have to go to the green-room and the dressing-rooms. Ritterspaugh had fully waked up when he told me that; he stood up and recognized me. He knew who it was before he began to speak. The theater was guarded on Sunday night, but any of the employees who slept there could get in. Mr. Spangler had a pass from the captain or officer of the guard to go in and out when he liked, and on Saturday I had a pass for that purpose.

JAMES J. GIFFORD. ***Recalled for the Defense.—May 30. By*** Mr. EWING. On Monday evening of the week previous to the assassination, I heard Booth tell Spangler to take his horse and buggy down to Tattersall's, the horse-market, and sell it. I presume Spangler sold it. He brought the man up with him, and asked me to count the money and give him a receipt. I took the money and handed it over to Booth.
Q. State whether or not, since the assassination, and previous to his release from Carroll Prison, Ritterspaugh told you at the prison that the prisoner, Edward Spangler, directly after the assassination of the President in the theater, hit him in the face with the back of his hand and said, "Don't say which way he went." *A*. To the best of my knowledge, I never heard him say so. He asked me if he could amend the statement that he had made. He asked me if he could amend it. I told him certainly, but he ought to be particular and state the truth of what he knew. That is all the conversation we ever had regarding it. He told me he had made a misstatement, and had not told all he knew. He did not say what he had omitted; if he had, I should surely have remembered it, for I have had nothing but this case to think about since I have been in the Old Capitol Prison. If any thing was wrong about the locks on the private boxes at the theater, it was the duty of the usher to inform me, and for me to have them repaired. No repairing was done to any door leading to the President's box since August or September of last year. I have frequently heard of Spangler going crab-fishing, but I never saw him. He has told me of going down to the Neck on the Saturday night, and staying till Monday morning; and I have heard others say that they had gone crabbing with him. [Exhibiting to the witness the rope found in Spangler's bag.] They use a line of that sort, with small lines tied to it, about three feet apart, and pieces of meat attached as bait. The line is trailed along, and as the crabs seize the bait they are dragged along and taken. I have seen ropes similar to this used, and sometimes a little longer. As there is but little strain upon the rope, it is not particular about the size.

By Mr. AIKEN. I saw J. Wilkes Booth, about half-past 11 or 12 o'clock on the 14th, pass the stage entrance and go to the front door. He bowed to me, but we had no conversation. *Cross-examined by* ASSISTANT JUDGE ADVOCATE BINGHAM.It is fully three weeks ago that Ritterspaugh said he was scared, and that he could not tell what he was doing; but I do not remember his precise words. He seemed to be troubled about it, and asked me if he could not make a correct statement, and I told him certainly he could.

THOMAS J. RAYBOLD. ***For the Defense.—June 2. By*** Mr. EWING. I have been engaged at Ford's Theater since the first Monday of December a year ago. I was employed to take charge of the house; to see to the purchasing of every thing required in the house, and if any repairs were needed, they were done through my order. In the absence of the Messrs. Ford, I was in the box-office and sold the tickets. I know of the lock on the door of box 8, the President's box, as it is called, being burst open during Mrs. Bower's engagement in March. On the 7th of March, Mr. Merrick, of the National Hotel, asked me, while at dinner, to reserve some seats in the orchestra for some company, which I did. It is customary, after the first act is over, for reserved seats, which have not been occupied, to be taken by any person wanting seats. Mr. Merrick did not come by the end of the first act, and the seats were occupied. Shortly afterward word was sent to me in the front office, saying that Mr. Merrick and his friends were there, and inquiring for the seats. I took them up stairs to a private box, No. 6, but it was locked, and I could not get in; I went then to boxes 7 and 8, generally termed the President's box, and they were also locked. I could not find the keys, and I supposed the usher had them; but he had left the theater, as he frequently does, when the first act is over; so I put my shoulder against the door of No. 8, the box nearest the stage, to force it open, but it did not give way to that, and I stood from it with my back and put my foot against it close to the lock, and with two or three kicks it came open. There is another lock in the house to which I did the same thing when I could not find the key. When the President came to the theater, boxes 7 and 8 were thrown into one by the removal of the partition between them. The door to No. 8—the one I burst open—was the one always used, and was the door used on the night of the assassination. The other door could not be used. I do not know whether the lock was ever repaired after I burst it open. It was my place to report it to Mr. Gifford and have it repaired, but I never thought of it from that time. I frequently entered the box afterward, and always passed in without a key. I never said a word to Mr. Gifford about repairing the lock, and never thought even of reexamining it to see what condition it was in. The locks were only used to keep persons out when the boxes were not engaged. I have frequently had to order persons out when the boxes were left open. About two weeks prior to the 14th of April, J. Wilkes Booth engaged a private box, No.4, at Ford's Theater, and in the afternoon he came again to the office and asked for exchange of the box, and I believe it was made to box 7. I can not be positive whether it was box 7 or 8, that he occupied that night, but I think it was 7. It is the door leading into box 7 that has the hole bored in it. To the best of my knowledge, there were no tickets sold up to the time of the opening of the theater on the night of the assassination; I can not say positively, for I had been sick with neuralgia for several days, and was not in the office the whole of the day. I was there in the morning, between 10 and 11, when the messenger obtained tickets for the President, and again in the afternoon, but do not know of any applications, and if there had been, I should have seen when I counted the house at night, which I did on the night of the assassination, at 10 o'clock, as usual. I saw Booth on the morning of the 14th at the office; I do not know whether before or after the box was engaged for the President. I know he got a letter from the office that morning. Booth's letters were directed to Mr. Ford's box at the post-office, and he generally came every morning for them. Mr. Ford would get the letters as he came from breakfast in the morning, and bring them to the office, when the letters that belonged to the stage would be sent there, and those belonging to Booth would be called for by him. The rocking-chair was placed in the position in occupied in the President's box simply because, in any other position, the rockers would have been in the way. When the partition was taken down, it left a triangular corner, and the rockers went into the corner at the left of the balustrade of the box; they were there out of the way. That was the only reason why I put it there. I had it so placed on two occasions before; last winter a year ago, when Mr. Hackett was playing, when the President was there. The sofa and other parts of the furniture had been used this last season, but up to that night the chair had not. [Exhibiting to the witness the coil of rope found in Spangler's carpet-bag.] I can not swear that this rope has been used at the theater, but we used such ropes as this at the time of the Treasury Guard's ball, from the lobby to the wings, to hang the colors of different nations on. It is like the kind of rope we use in the flies for drawing up the different borders that go across from one wing to the other. From its appearance, I judge this rope has been used. It would be lighter in color if it had not been.

Cross-examined by ASSISTANT JUDGE ADVOCATE BINGHAM. Any rope that was used about the theater, I should judge, ought to stay there; I do Not think its proper place would be in a carpet-sack a half mile off. We use a great many such ropes; and sometimes when they are taken down, they lie upon the scene-loft until we need them again. The outer door, or door of the passage to the President's box, never had a lock on; I do not think it has even a latch on. I do not know whether the force I employed against the door burst the lock or the keeper of; I supposed at the time that it started the keeper. The fastening on the door is of pine I believe; I do not know whether it was split or not; I did not examine it. I did not touch box 7. The last time I was in the President's box was on the morning after the assassination. I went in with some gentlemen to look at the hole in the door. I did not see the mortise in the wall, nor any piece of wood to fasten the door with, nor did I see the mortise the previous afternoon. I was there but for about five minutes, while the flags were being put up. The chair was in the box when I went in to help put up the flags; it was placed behind the door of box No. 7, with the rockers in the corner toward the audience. I did not see him in the box, but my opinion is that the way the chair was placed, the audience was rather behind the President as he sat in the chair. I can not say the precise day on which Booth occupied box No. 7. Mr. Ford was the one who sold him the box and exchanged it. There were ladies and men with Booth, I think.

By Mr. EWING. I can not state whether it was after Booth played *Pescara* that he occupied that box. To the best of my recollection, it was about two weeks before the assassination; it might have been more. He had the box on two occasions. Once when he engaged it, he did not use it; he told me that the ladies at the National Hotel had disappointed him. I do not know any thing at all as to whether Spangler got that rope from the theater rightfully or not.

Recalled for the Defense.—June 2. By Mr. EWING. Since I was upon the stand, I have visited Ford's Theater, and examined the keepers of The locks of boxes Nos. 7 and 8. The lock of box 8 is in the condition that I stated this morning. It has been forced, and the wood has been split by forcing the lock. The screw in the keeper is tight, and the keeper has been forced aside. The lock on the door of box 7 has been forced, which I was not aware of until I saw it just now. You can take the upper screw out with your finger, and put it in and out; you can put your thumb against it, and put it in to the full extent of the screw. I can not say as it its having been done with an instrument. It must have been done by force; I know that No. 8 was done by force Applied to the outside of the door; the other has a similar appearance. *Cross-examined by* ASSISTANT JUDGE ADVOCATE BINGHAM. The wood in box 7 is not split a particle. The reason why I think force has been used with that lock is, that if the screw was drawn by a screw-driver, when it went back again it would have to be put back by the driver, but when force has been used, it would make the hole larger, and you could put the screw in and out just as you can the screw in the door of box 7.

By Mr. AIKEN. I do not know John H. Surratt. I do not know any of the prisoners except Spangler. He is the only one I ever saw with the exception of one, [Herold,] whom I knew when he was quite a boy.

HENRY E. MERRICK. ***For the Defense.—June 2. By*** Mr. EWING. I am a clerk at the National Hotel, Washington. On the evening of the 7th of March, in company with my wife, Mr. Marcus P. Norton of Troy, N. Y., Miss Engels, and Mrs. Bunker, I went to Ford's Theater. Mr. Raybold took us to a private box. We passed down the dress-circle on the right- hand side, and entered the first box; there was a partition up at the time between the two boxes. Mr. Raybold went to the office for the key, but could not find it. He then placed his shoulder, I think, against the door and burst it open. The keeper was burst off I think; at least the screw that held the upper part of the keeper came out, and it whirled around, and hung by the lower screw. Our books show that John McCullough, the actor, left the National Hotel on the 26th of March; since then I have not seen him. I have never known him to stop at any other hotel than the National. *Cross-examined by* ASSISTANT JUDGE ADVOCATE BINGHAM. Mr. McCullough may have called on some friend in the house, and I not see him. I have not seen him since the 26th of March. It was the very first box that we went into on visiting the theater on the 7th of March; the partition was between the box we occupied and the one to our right, further on toward the stage. The box nearest the stage we did not enter at all. It was the very first box we came to that we entered, and it was the door of this box that was burst open. The upper screw came out entirely, and the keeper swung round on the lower screw, and left the lock without any fastening at all.

JAMES O'BRIEN. ***For the Defense.—June 3.*** I have been employed as clerk in the Quarter-master General's office. I also had an engagement at night as usher at Ford's Theater. Some time before the assassination I noticed that the keeper of box 8 had been wrenched off. I was absent one evening, at home sick, and when I came next I found that the keeper was broken off; but, as the door shut pretty tight, I never thought of speaking about it. You might lock the door, but if you were to shove it, it would come open. The keeper on box No. 7 appeared to be all right; I always locked that box. The door of No. 8 was used when the Presidential party occupied the box; when the party occupying the Presidential box entered, the door was always left open. The door of the passage leading to the two boxes had no lock on it, or fastening of any kind.

JOSEPH T. K. PLANT. ***For the Defense.—June 2. By*** Mr. EWING. My occupation at present is that of a dealer in furniture; ever since I was fourteen Years old I have been, more or less, engaged in cabinet work. I have visited Ford's Theater today and have examined the keepers on boxes No. 7 and No. 8. To all appearances they have been forced. The wood-work in box 8 is shivered and splintered by the screws. In box 7, I could pull the screw with my thumb and finger; the tap was gone clear to the point. I could force it back with my thumb. In box 4, which is directly under box 8, the keeper is gone entirely. I should judge that the keepers in boxes 7 and 8 were made loose by force; I could not see any evidence of an instrument having been used to draw the screws in either of them. I noticed a hole in the wall of the passage behind the boxes; it had the appearance of having been covered with something; I could not see what, as no remnant of it was left, in size about five by seven and half or eight inches. I noticed also a hole, a little more than one-fourth of an inch in diameter, in the door of box 7. It is larger on the outside than it is on the inside. The left side of the hole feels rough, as if cut by a gimlet, while the lower part of the right-hand side appears to have been trimmed with a penknife or some sharp instrument. The hole might, I think, have been made by a penknife, and the roughness might have been caused by the back of the knife.

G. W. BUNKER. *For the Defense.—June 2.* I am clerk at the National Hotel. The day after the assassination I packed Booth's effects at the National, and had his trunk removed into our baggage-room. In his trunk I found a gimlet with an iron handle.* I carried it to my room, and afterward gave it to Mr. Hall, who was attending to Mr. Ford's business.* The gimlet would bore a hole three-sixteenths of an inch in diameter. John McCullough, who always made his home at the National, I find he registered his name the last time on March 11; he left on the 26th of March.

JOHN GOENTHER. *For the Defense.—June 2. By* Mr. EWING. I boarded in the same house with the accused, Edward Spangler, previous to his arrest. He boarded there on and off for six or seven months, perhaps longer. I have lived there off and on for the last three years. To my certain knowledge, I saw Spangler about the house for two or three days before the assassination; I never saw him wear a moustache.

Cross-examined by ASSISTANT JUDGE ADVOCATE BINGHAM. I am not certain what days it was that I saw Spangler at the house. He did not sleep there. I used to see him in the morning, and of evenings when I came from my work. I work in the arsenal, and generally take my dinner with me.

The names have not been changed, to implicate the facts.

Appendix II

THE HANGING OF MARY SURRATT

Part 1 of 4

Mike Scruggs

For The Tribune Papers

On July 7, 1865, forty-two-year-old Mary Surratt, an attractive, dark-haired widow, was hanged on the gallows at the Old Arsenal Penitentiary in Washington along with three others convicted of complicity in the assassination of Abraham Lincoln by a military court. Mary Surratt was the only woman of the four. She was, in fact, the first woman ever executed by the government of the United States. The execution of Mary Surratt was not a triumph of justice. It was a disgraceful political atrocity that still stains the national conscience and mars the American ideal of justice.

Americans have a strong tendency to whitewash history. It is more pleasant for us to believe and easier to teach our children that all our great leaders have been virtuous, that all our causes have been noble, and that all our courts have been just. No nation can long endure without a strong sense of patriotism. But genuine patriotism, a love of one's country and people that endures over many generations, is undermined when truth is mangled in the service of propaganda or political ambitions. Truth and love are inseparable. Patriotism without truth is a monstrous impostor.

The Lincoln assassination conspiracy trial was marked by judicial despotism, perjury, bribery, and even intimidation and torture of witnesses and defendants. The investigation, prosecution, trial, and sentences were all managed by the War Department under its ambitious Secretary, Edwin Stanton. Four of the eight defendants were hanged and the others sentenced to life imprisonment on an isolated island.

A principal objective of the conspiracy trial, conducted by nine high-ranking officers handpicked by Stanton, was the implication of Confederate President Jefferson Davis in Lincoln's assassination. But Stanton, like many of his Radical Republican allies in Congress and government, was also motivated by a consuming hatred for the South. Furthermore, he hoped to be elected President of the United States in 1868. According to the diary of Secretary of the Navy Gideon Welles and biographical statements by many other Union political and military leaders, Stanton was noted for his manipulative, and often treacherous, political dealings. He had often manipulated Lincoln and other Cabinet Members, and for a short time, he was very successful in persuading or manipulating President Andrew Johnson into supporting his schemes for vengeance on the South.

Mary Surratt, the devout Catholic mother of three children ranging in age from twenty to twenty-four, was the owner of a boarding house in Washington. She also owned her former residence, the Surratt House and Tavern, and some farmland in the tiny community of Surrattsville (now Clinton), Maryland, southeast of Washington. But when her husband, John Surratt, Sr., died in 1862, she was unable to manage the facilities and rented them to John Lloyd, a Southern sympathizer with a problematic drinking habit. The Surratts were Southern sympathizers. They came from the strongly pro-Southern agricultural area of southern Maryland, where in better times they had owned several hundred acres of land and as many as twelve slaves. Her 24-year-old son, Isaac, was a sergeant in the 33rd Texas Cavalry, and her 20-year-old son, John, had become a Confederate courier. Both John and her attractive 22-year-old daughter, Anna, lived at the boarding house in Washington. Although Mary Surratt was definitely pro-Southern, she was not very political. Especially by late 1864, she only wanted her two sons home and safe. For that reason she was not comfortable with John's courier trips and intrigues.

In December 1864, John ran into Dr. Samuel Mudd, who was visiting from southern Maryland. Dr. Mudd introduced him to John Wilkes Booth, one of America's most famous actors. John became good friends with the 26-year-old actor and soon became involved in Booth's plot to kidnap Abraham Lincoln in order to force a prisoner of war exchange or even end the war. The Confederate Government had considered such a plan in 1863 but rejected it. Jefferson Davis, in particular, was strongly opposed to such intrigues on both practical and philosophical grounds.

The wealthy and charismatic Booth generally stayed at the most expensive hotels in Washington, but he became a frequent visitor to the Surratt boarding house, where he befriended both the Surratts and their 20-year-old boarder, Louis Weichmann, a clerk at the Prisoner of War Commissariat. His planning and recruitment for his kidnapping plot were, however, mostly done at hotels and taverns. Booth managed to recruit six men for his daring abduction plot.

Before the fall of Richmond early in April, John Surratt left Washington carrying important financial instructions to Confederate Commissioners in Montreal, Canada. From there he went to Elmira, New York, to investigate the possibility of rescuing Confederate POWs there. When he heard of the assassination, he fled to Canada and then Europe.

Once on an early visit to the Surratt home, Lewis Powell had inadvertently blurted out something about the abduction plot. John Surratt firmly berated him, saying that neither his mother nor his sister knew anything about such plans and emphatically stressed that he did not want them to know anything. Lewis Powell later proclaimed to the military court, his religious and legal counsellors, and to his executioners that Mary Surratt was completely innocent of the charges against her or any wrongdoing. No one in the War Department or political chain of authority would listen. Every effort was made to isolate and silence the accused conspirators.

The government's case against Mary Surratt was weak and largely circumstantial, but for some reason they made every effort not only to convict her of complicity in the assassination of Lincoln, but to make sure she received the death penalty. To make their case, they bribed, threatened, and even tortured witnesses and defendants. They suppressed critical evidence and used completely unrelated emotional issues, such as "starving Union prisoners or war," to inflame the military court and the public against the defendants. There is substantial evidence that Secretary of War Stanton, Army Judge Advocate General Joseph Holt, and several Stanton and Holt associates deliberately deceived President Andrew Johnson in respect to a clemency plea for Mary Surratt, which had been urged by a majority of the officers on the military court. To be continued.

Appendix III

References & Bibliography:

Arnold. I.N. 1866. History of Abraham Lincoln and the Overthrow of Slavery.
Arnold. R.E. M.D. Paper Contradictions Concerning the Death and Autopsy of John Wilkes Booth. ARAR839572@aol.com
Baker, L.B. 1868. The United States Secret Service.
Booth-Clarke, A. 1938. The Unlocked Book. (With a Forward by Eleanor Farjeon). Faber & Faber. London.
Bancroft, F. 1900. Life of William H. Seward. 2 vols. Barton.
Barton, W. E. 1920.The Soul of Abraham Lincoln.
Botts, J. M. 1866. The Great Rebellion.
Brooks, N. 1895. Washington in Lincoln's Time.
Carpenter, F. B. 1866. Six Months at the White House with Abraham Lincoln.
Chapman, E. 1917. Latest Light on Abraham Lincoln. The Charleston Mercury.
Chittenden, L. 1891. Recollections of President Lincoln and His Administration.
Crawford, S.W. 1887. The Genesis of the Civil War.
C. W. Report of the Joint Committee on the Conduct of the War. 1863. Dabney, D.D. 1876. Memoir of a Narrative Received from Colonel John B. Baldwin, of Staunton, touching the Origin of the War.
Davis, J. 1881.Rise and Fall of the Confederate Government. 2 Vols.
Dunning, A. 1898. Essays on the Civil War and Reconstruction and Related Topics.
Durand, G.L. America's Ceaser.
Eisenschiml. O. 1937. Why Was Lincoln Murdered.
Field, H.M. 1898. Life of David Dudley Field.
Flower, F.A. 1902. Edwin McMasters Stanton.
Forrester, I.L. 1938. This One Mad Act.
Gilmore, J. R. 1899. Personal Recollections of Abraham Lincoln and the Civil War.
Gore, J. R. 1921. The Boyhood of Abraham Lincoln.
Gorham, C. 1899. Life and Public Services of Edwin M. Stanton. 2 vols.
Grant, U.S. 1886. Personal Memoirs.
Greeley, H. 1864-67.The American Conflict. 2 Vols.
Gutteridge, L. & Neff, R. 2003. Dark Union. John Wiley & Sons
Hanchett, W. 1983. The Lincoln Conspiracy Murders.
Hay, J. 1890. Century. Life in the White House in the Time of Lincoln. Century Magazine. The New York Herald.
Hill, F. T. 1906.Lincoln the Lawyer.
Kelley, W.D. 1885. Lincoln and Stanton.
Lamon, W.H. 1872. The Life of Abraham Lincoln.
Lincoln, A. Complete Works of Abraham Lincoln. Edited by John G. Nicolay and John Hay. 2 vols. New and enlarged edition. 12 volumes. 1905. Colter edition.
McCarthy, C.M. 1901. Lincoln's Plan of Reconstruction.
McClure, A.K. 1892. Abraham Lincoln and Men of War Times.
Munford, B.B. 1910. Virginia's Attitude toward Slavery and Secession.
Neff, R. History Archives at Indiana State University.
Newton, J.F. 1910. Lincoln and Herndon.
Nicolay, J.G. 1902. A Short Life of Abraham Lincoln.
N. and H. Abraham Lincoln: A History. By John G. Nicolay and John Hay. Scott, Lt. General. 1864. Memoirs of Lieutenant General Scott, LL.D. 2 vols.
Seward, W.H. 1884. Works of William H. Seward. 5 vols.
Stoddard, W.O. 1890. Inside the White House in War Times.
Taft, H.N. Diary kept in the Library of Congress and on the 'Webb.'
Tarbell, I.M. 1917. The Life of Abraham Lincoln. New edition. 2 vols.
Tidewell, W., Hall, J. & Gaddy, D. 1988. Come Retribution. Jackson University Press Of Mississippi.
Turner, T.R. 1999. The Assassination of Abraham Lincoln.
Welles, G . Diary. Library of Congress

Acknowledgements

McFarland Press
Ron Williams
History Buff
Michael Goad
Mike Scruggs. Tribune News
Art Library and Building Conservation Directory London. 2005
Bert Bacharach & Hal David: 'Trains and Boats and Planes'
Kent Lavoie: 'Me and You and a Dog named Boo'
R. Dean Taylor: 'Indiana Wants Me'
Bob Marley and Curtis Mayfield: 'One Love, One Heart'
Bob Marley: 'I Shot the Sheriff'
Frank Sinatra: 'Strangers in the Night'
Google Earth

If I have purloined any site be it in a small way, without knowing it, please accept my sincere apologies, be it an illustration, a map, a photograph or a saying to which I am indebted and can only give my special thanks. Though indeed I believe there are few if any that I have not already gratefully acknowledged. In regards to historians, due notes have been made in the relative passages regarding their contributions and natural disputes of knowledge and interplay.

My special thanks to my son John, for his advice and help on technical elements on the computer and IT. And to my printers Paul and Peter and Graeme at Advek and Henry Mills of Aston. And to my solicitor J. Smitheman.

Jack K. Ronayne.

About the Author:

The Author's real name is Michael Seamus O'Geraghty - O'Rielly and was born near Tamworth, England and has a Bachelor's degree in Science, majoring in Astro-Physics and Cosmology at the Open University. He has spent 38 years in Industry as a Chemist and is a Member of the Institute of Corrosion. Later in his Industrial career he worked 13 years for Lucas Advanced Engineering, specialising in Corrosion, Materials and Surface Technology having engineered many projects in various fields, particularly in Automotive and Aerospace.

He was a member of the successful Gouffre Berger Expedition in 1962 the second team to achieve, the then world depth record at -3760 feet. This British team led by Frank Salt from Birmingham, bottomed the Gouffre Berger in the French Alps near Engine, following the Isere underground river, that exits into the labrynth of the Vats of Sassanage. He also made another successful world second, leading the first Anglo-German ascent of Hydraungi in 1967, a remote 3000 foot pinnacle peak on the Arctic circle in Iceland. He has been a member of many caving expeditions around the world, in the 60's, 70's and 90's and 2000. He has explored extensively around the world climbing, caving and diving, including France, Spain, Mexico, Andorra, Morocco , Tunisia, Algeria, Libya, Egypt, The Lebanon, Jordan, Syria, Turkey, Greece, Albania, Yugoslavia, Trieste, Italy, Austria, Liechtenstein, Switzerland, Luxembourg, Belgium and Ireland making the first circumnavigation of the Mediterranean to include cave exploration; the 'Dirty Seven' in a long wheeled based land rover led by Barry Twist, caving in most of these countries. He has pioneered many first time descents in the Pecos de Europia, the Austrian Tenneberger and French Alps in the 60's and has caved in all areas of England, Wales and Ireland.

He was a paratrooper trained in operations intelligence, signals, ciphers and covert operations, carrying out NATO exercises in Germany, Holland, Denmark, Belgium and the U.S He worked for 7 years in the US and Canada as an oil construction engineer, building giant oil storage tanks in very many States and worked on remote Canadian railways in winter, and in the fishing camps of the Westmann Islands and fishing and logging camps of British Columbia, and fought forest fires.

At present he does some Consultancy work in Industrial Corrosion and is the captain of a chess team and a stamp collector, since a lad. He still maintains his interest in Astronomy and has built his own 6" reflecting telescope. He is a Christian but respects the values of all moral beliefs and philosophies. He teaches English and poetry by text to young people in Africa and takes a keen interest in Jazz musicians being an agent for an Internationally famous Jazz Composer and Sax player. He has a son who is a computer expert and a keen writer of rock ballads, a fine singer and keyboard player. And he has a beautiful step-daughter, who has three beautiful daughters. And a beautiful niece, who has two beautiful daughters and also a nephew and another beautiful and talented niece.

End